# Biological Applications *of* Freezing and Drying

# Biological Applications *of* Freezing and Drying

*Edited by*

R. J. C. HARRIS

*Research Fellow*
*British Empire Cancer Campaign*
*Institute of Cancer Research*
*London, England*

ACADEMIC PRESS INC., PUBLISHERS
NEW YORK, 1954

ACADEMIC PRESS INC.

125 EAST 23RD STREET
NEW YORK 10, N. Y.



*Library of Congress Catalog Card Number:* 54-7614

# Contributors

L. G. Beckett, *Research Laboratories, W. Edwards and Co., Ltd., Crawley, Sussex, England.*

R. E. Billingham, *Department of Zoology, University College, London, England.*

E. W. Flosdorf, *Research and Development Division, F. J. Stokes Machine Co., Philadelphia, Pennsylvania.*

R. M. Fry, *Public Health Laboratory, Cambridge, England.*

R. Gane, *Low Temperature Station for Research in Biochemistry and Biophysics, University of Cambridge, Cambridge, England.*

Isidore Gersh, *Department of Anatomy, University of Chicago, Chicago, Illinois.*

R. I. N. Greaves, *Department of Pathology, University of Cambridge, Cambridge, England.*

R. J. C. Harris, *Institute of Cancer Research, London, England.*

Duncan C. Hetherington, *Duke University Medical School, Durham, North Carolina.*

G. G. A. Mastenbroek, *Netherlands Red Cross, Amsterdam, The Netherlands.*

J. H. Singer, *Glaxo Laboratories Ltd., Greenford, England.*

Audrey U. Smith, *National Institute for Medical Research, Mill Hill, London, England.*

John L. Stephenson, *Department of Anatomy, University of Chicago, Chicago, Illinois.*

Max M. Strumia, *Graduate School of Medicine, University of Pennsylvania, Philadelphia, Pennsylvania.*

Robley C. Williams, *Virus Laboratory, University of California, Berkeley, California.*

# Foreword

A method for drying frozen biological material by sublimation of the ice *in vacuo* has been known for more than fifty years, but the advantages of the process were not fully appreciated until just before the outbreak of the second World War when apparatus for laboratory and small-scale commercial use was first becoming available. Enormous quantities of blood plasma and penicillin were required during this war. Freeze-drying was found to be an excellent method of preservation, and the procedure emerged in 1946 as a fully tested technique. Since that time, too, there has been rapid progress in work on the effects of low temperatures on cells and tissues with important practical applications for the long-term storage, for example, of spermatozoa for artificial insemination, of red blood cells for transfusion, and even of tissue "spare parts" for surgical purposes. At the present time, freeze-drying is used for the preservation not only of blood products and antibiotics but also of human milk, bacteria, tissue-culture media, and viruses, and for the preparation and preservation of tissues for morphological and histochemical studies, and of specimens for electron microscopy.

The authors of many of these chapters need no introduction, for they are the pioneers in their particular fields; the techniques which they have devised are being used and will be used increasingly in laboratories throughout the world, and apparatus similar to that which they first described is now being manufactured in many lands.

The aim of this volume is to provide for the first time a comprehensive and authoritative treatise on such aspects of freezing and of freeze-drying. It is intended to serve as a work of reference for all those already using such techniques and as a guide to those who may wish to employ them.

I should like to express my thanks to the publishers for their cooperation in, indeed for their toleration of, the editorial whims, and especially to Miss Christine Kilburn for her invaluable help in the preparation of typescripts.

The pleasure which I have found in the editing of this book has been marred by the tragic death of Joseph Singer, the author of Chapter 5, in an air accident in the summer of 1953.

R. J. C. HARRIS

*March, 1954*

# Contents

### Chapter 10



### Chapter 11



### Chapter 12



### Chapter 13

## Chapter 14

CHAPTER 1

# Effects of Low Temperatures on Living Cells and Tissues

AUDREY U. SMITH

*National Institute for Medical Research, Mill Hill, London, England*



## I. INTRODUCTION

Accurate thermometers were invented by Fahrenheit in 1714 and by Réaumur in 1731, and were rapidly taken into use by biologists. Réaumur himself was one of the first to study the action of cold on insects (1736). Forty years later Spallanzani recorded observations on the effects of low temperatures on animalcules, insects, fish, amphibia, reptiles, birds, mammals, and man, as well as the results of cooling spermatozoa and eggs of several species (Spallanzani, 1787). Spallanzani, who referred to the Réaumur and to the Fahrenheit thermometers, succeeded in producing a temperature of 24 degrees below zero by adding spirits of niter to a mixture of ice and rock salt. He found that butterfly and silkworm eggs survived exposure to 17 degrees below zero under outdoor conditions.

and to 24 degrees below zero in the laboratory, and that spermatozoa survived 15 degrees below zero although the animals from which the gametes were derived were killed at about 7 degrees below zero.* He showed that, when the medium was supercooled, animalcules survived lower temperatures than when ice formation had occurred. Spallanzani was aware that temperatures 30 degrees below zero were common in Quebec and St. Petersburg, and as low as 70 degrees below zero in Siberia where various plants and animals, including man, survived either by withstanding freezing of the tissues or by mechanisms which maintained body temperature despite intense environmental cold.

In the late eighteenth and early nineteenth centuries much further information was gathered about the effects of chilling on plants and animals. It became evident that there was remarkable species variation in sensitivity, some organisms having a capacity for withstanding extreme cold whereas others were killed or damaged at temperatures little below or even above the freezing point of water (Luyet and Gehenio, 1940).

During the latter half of the nineteenth century the stage was set for spectacular advances in the field of low-temperature biology by fundamental discoveries in new sciences as well as by developments in physics and chemistry. Thus, Pasteur's work on fermentation was the starting point of bacteriology and microbiology, and Claude Bernard's research laid the foundations of modern physiology. In the same period, Liebig and Fischer applied organic chemistry to the study of the products and components of animal and plant tissues, and Buchner demonstrated enzyme activity in cell-free extracts of yeasts. Biophysics stemmed from the work of Graham, who studied the properties of colloidal solutions and the phenomenon of diffusion. Raoult investigated the effect of organic substances on freezing points of solutions, and Pfeffer and van't Hoff developed the modern theories of osmosis. Notable progress was also made in pure physics. For instance, oxygen was liquefied in 1877 by Cailletet and by Pictet, liquid air was produced in quantity by Linde in 1895, and three years later, in 1898, Dewar succeeded in liquefying hydrogen. Great strides had meanwhile been made in thermometry, so that very low temperatures could be measured and recorded.

Biologists were quick to take advantage of the new knowledge and facilities. Brown and Escombe (1897), working in Dewar's laboratory, found that the germinative power of seeds was not affected by slow cooling to and storage for 11 hours at −182° to −192°C. in liquid air, and Thiselton-Dyer (1899) obtained similar results with seeds exposed to liquid hydrogen. Soon after, Macfadyen and Rowland (1900a, b) showed

* It is not clear to which scale Spallanzani is referring at this point, but severe cold is clearly indicated.

that bacteria retained unimpaired vitality and enzymes unaltered activity after exposure to or storage in liquid air and liquid hydrogen. Other methods of cooling and higher storage temperatures, on the other hand, proved effective in killing or checking the growth of microorganisms (Hilliard and Davis, 1918; Haines, 1934).

During the same era new feats of engineering had produced steamships with screw propellers and steel hulls capable of carrying refrigerating plants, so that in 1879 the first consignment of frozen meat was brought to England from Australia (Williams, 1933). Popular interest in the biological effects of low temperature was aroused on the one hand by the need for more food for the growing industrial populations of Europe, and on the other by the exploits of Nansen and other scientific explorers in the Arctic who drew attention to the paucity of medical knowledge about frostbite and other pathological effects of cold.

The stimulus of the varied discoveries and inventions and the potentialities of their practical application resulted in investigation from many angles of the action of low temperatures on living cells. Between 1890 and 1940 a vast literature grew up. Viruses, bacteria, yeasts, microorganisms of many kinds, plants, flowers, fruits, invertebrate animals, amphibia, reptiles, birds, and mammals of many species were exposed to low temperatures and studied during and after cooling and rewarming. Parts of whole animals and limbs, organs, tissues, and cells isolated from many species were similarly examined. The chemical components of cells and tissues, including proteins, lipids, carbohydrates, water, and solutions of electrolytes and non-electrolytes have all been cooled to different extents and under different conditions. The properties of colloidal solutions and gels and the activity of vitamins, hormones, and enzymes subjected to similar treatment have been investigated. The reports of results have been scattered throughout journals of every branch of academic and applied science, including medicine, agriculture, engineering, and food science. Much of the work up to 1940 has been summarized in classic monographs by Bělehrádek (1935) and by Luyet and Gehenio (1940).

Since 1940 there has been a further spate of work, so that the field is now too wide to be reviewed in a single article. The action of frost on plants and plant products was reviewed by Kidd (1929), Modlibowska and Field (1942), Rogers (1952), and at the 8th International Congress of Refrigeration (1951), and is outside the scope of this article. Extensive reviews on freezing meat and other foods have been published by Bate-Smith (1944), Callow (1952), and Reay (1951). The effect of low temperatures on tumor tissues was recently summarized by Passey and Dmochowski (1950), and physiological and medical aspects of cold have been dealt with exhaustively by Edholm (1953). No attempt will therefore be made to review these topics again or to deal in a comprehensive manner with every aspect of the action of cold on living things. Attention will, instead, be directed to certain fundamental aspects of the subject, particularly in the light of work done between 1940 and 1952 on isolated cells and tissues of animal origin. It has been possible to make reference to only a few of the many relevant papers published in 1953.

Even with this restriction, terminological difficulties arise. For instance, there is no agreement on the meaning of the expression "low temperature." Thus, to clinicians, 15°C. is a very low temperature. To inhabitants of the Tropics, ice and snow at 0°C. represent severe cold. To refrigeration engineers −20°C. is low, and −40°C. a very low temperature. Some physicists, on the other hand, regard temperatures as low only when close to the absolute zero, −273°C. (de Klerk, 1952). In this article the following classification will be adopted:

| Temperature Range | Description |
|---|---|
| +20° to 0°C. | Subnormal |
| 0° to −70°C. | Low |
| −71° to −273°C. | Very low |

Differences of outlook have similarly led to confusion over rates of cooling. Meteorologists consider a fall in the air temperature of 50°F. (28°C.) in 8 hours as rapid (Hawke, 1944; Manley, 1952) (Fig. 1a). In the meat industry a change in temperature from +5° to −5°C. in 30 minutes is regarded as quick (Bate-Smith, 1944; Callow, 1952; Moran, 1935). By contrast, biophysicists of Luyet's school would call the rate of fall rapid only if the temperature changed from 0° to −190°C. in a matter of seconds (Fig. 1b.)

We shall arbitrarily adopt the following classification:

| Temperature Range | Time | Description | Reference |
|---|---|---|---|
| 0° to −190°C. | 2 sec. or less | Ultrarapid | Luyet |
| 0° to −79°C. | 2 sec. to 5 min. | Rapid | Smith and Polge |
| 0° to −79°C. | 10 min. or more | Slow | Smith and Polge; Polge and Lovelock |
| 20°C., any range | 1 hr. or more | Very slow | |

Another problem is raised by the loss of meaning of the term "living" (Pirie, 1937). Animals used to be regarded as dead when the circulation and respiration had ceased. Andjus (1951) has shown, however, that this is not necessarily the case. In dealing with isolated cells, irritability, motion, metabolism, growth, and reproduction were at one time regarded as criteria of life. During the last fifty years it has become increasingly clear that these criteria are no longer infallible. In the present state of knowledge it is impossible to say whether, at very low tempera-

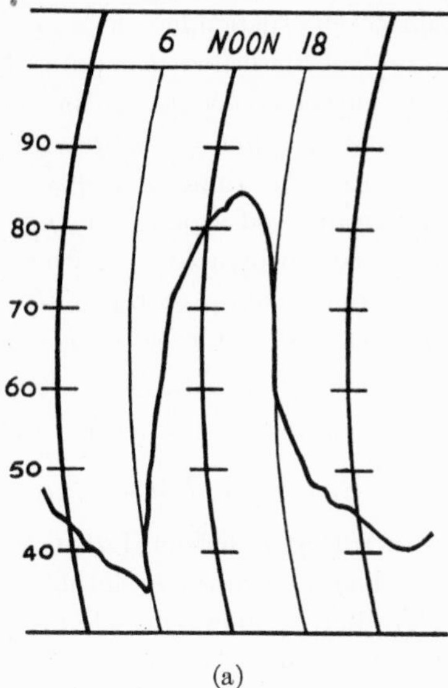


(a)

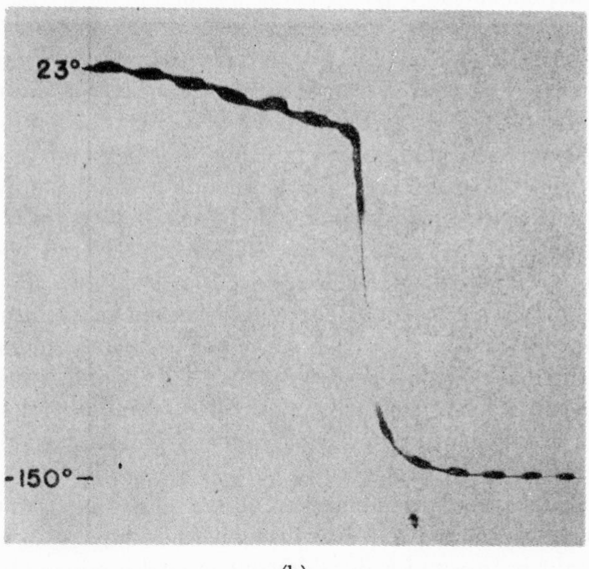


(b)

FIG. 1. Contrast in cooling rates. (a) Extreme temperature gradients in a Hertfordshire frost hollow. (Fig. 55 from Manley, 1952.) (b) Ultrarapid cooling in *iso*pentane at −150°C. (Abscissa: time; each dash corresponds to 1/2000 second.) (Fig. 9 from Luyet, 1951.)

tures, animation is completely suspended or very greatly slowed. Cells and tissues will, therefore, be described as living when they retain the capacity to exhibit metabolic activity and to perform specific functions under suitable conditions at a normal environmental temperature.

Finally, it may be pointed out that the study of biological effects of low temperatures has again entered a phase of very active growth, since the discovery of the protective properties of glycerol (Polge *et al.*, 1949), and that, although facts in the sense of reproducible observations will remain as such, interpretations and conclusions must be regarded as tentative.

## II. THERMAL SHOCK

### 1. *At Subnormal Temperatures*

It has long been known that a sudden fall in temperature to a subnormal level above 0°C. has a harmful or lethal effect on a variety of living cells to which a gradual temperature change over the same range or a steady subnormal temperature is innocuous. The phenomenon which has come to be known as temperature shock, but which will be referred to here as thermal shock, is particularly common in higher plants (Kidd, 1929; Modlibowska, 1951). It occurs also in simple organisms such as algae and was noted, for instance, by Kylin (1917) with *Nitella clavata* in which complete cessation of plasma streaming occurs after sudden but not after gradual cooling between +20° and +3°C. Certain bacteria are extremely sensitive to sudden cooling. Thus, Hegarty and Weeks (1940) found that cultures of *B. coli* during their logarithmic growth phase showed great sensitivity to rapid cooling from +37° to 0°C. Sherman and Cameron (1934) found that 95% of *B. coli* in very young cultures were killed by sudden transfer from +45° to 0°C., whereas gradual cooling, taking 30 minutes to make the same temperature change, caused no injury. It has even been suggested that bacteriophage is susceptible to thermal shock between +60° and +2°C. (Smith and Krueger, 1952). Among protozoa slow cooling to 0°C. often permits adaptive changes. For example, *Stentor coeruleus*, which is killed by sudden cooling to 0°C., undergoes encystment during slow cooling and resumes an active form when its temperature is raised to normal after many hours at 0°C. (Greely, 1901). A gradual fall in environmental temperature is particularly important in insects for development of cold hardiness, an adaptation which depends partly on decreased water content (Payne, 1926; Salt, 1936, 1950; George, 1953). With higher animals a gradual fall in environmental temperature induces hibernation in some species and in others promotes increased growth of hair and laying down of fat to improve insulation.

Among isolated mammalian cells and tissues the deleterious effects of sudden temperature change between +40° and 0°C. are best known with spermatozoa. The term "temperature shock" originating from Milovanov in 1934 (Anderson, 1945) was first and is still widely used to describe the irreversible decrease in motility of bull and ram semen which occurs on sudden cooling, particularly between +15° and 0°C. Thermal shock can be avoided by gradual cooling over the same range (Chang and Walton, 1940). Sensitivity to thermal shock is decreased by the use of egg yolk diluent, so that the rate of cooling can be increased (Phillips

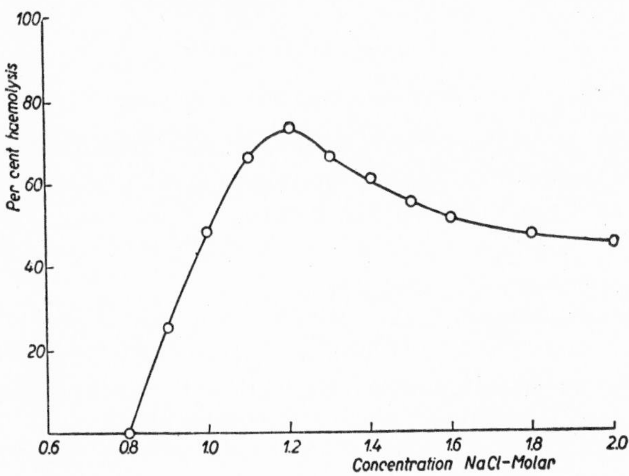


FIG. 2. The hemolysis which occurs when red blood cells suspended in sodium chloride solutions of various strengths are suddenly cooled from 30° to 5°C. (Fig. 7 from Lovelock, 1953a.)

and Lardy, 1940), but even so the change should not exceed 5°C. in 20 minutes (Salisbury *et al.*, 1941).

Until quite recently it was not realized that the majority of mammalian cells are, to some extent, subject to thermal shock and that their susceptibility to it can be increased or decreased by altering the composition of their medium. Red blood cells, for example, are not normally affected by sudden chilling; in the presence of sodium chloride solutions stronger than 0.8 *M*, however, they hemolyze readily when cooled suddenly from +30° to +5°C. (Lovelock, 1953a) (Figs. 2 and 3).

The mechanism of thermal shock to bull spermatozoa at subnormal temperatures has not so far been explained. The nature of the palliative action of egg yolk is also obscure, although lecithin is thought to be the active agent (Tosic and Walton, 1947). Luyet and Gehenio (1940) thought that abrupt cooling might cause gelation of protoplasmic sols, followed immediately by contraction of the gel and spontaneous expulsion of fluid,

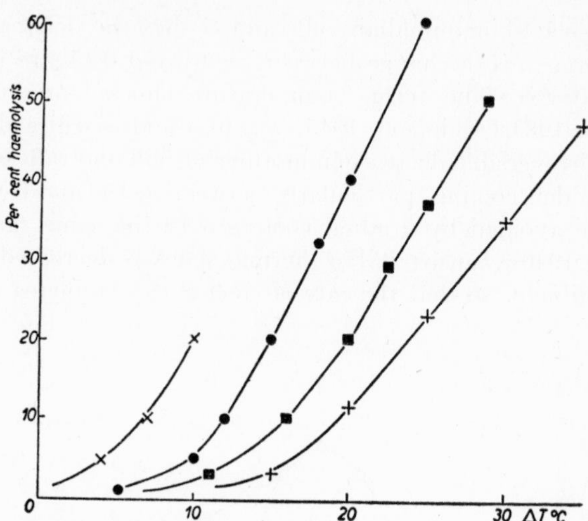


FIG. 3. The hemolysis which occurs when red blood cells suspended in 1.0 *M* NaCl are suddenly cooled through various temperature intervals ($\Delta T$), and from different initial temperatures. Initial temperature 0°, x — x; +20°, ● — ●; +30°, ■ — ■; +45°, + — +. (Fig. 8 from Lovelock, 1953a.)

and that such syneresis would cause death. This hypothesis has not so far been proved.

### 2. *At Low Temperatures*

In spite of various earlier observations, it was only recently recognized that thermal shock, or something superficially similar, could occur in ranges far below 0°C. Rahm, for instance, had shown in 1922 that certain rotifers, nematodes, and tardigrades in the wet state survived exposure to low temperatures only if cooled slowly. Some years later Breedis and his colleagues found that mouse leukemia cells survived and retained their ability to transmit the disease after freezing to −70°C. only if cooled slowly (Breedis *et al.*, 1937; Breedis, 1942). Slow cooling also permitted better survival of various pathogenic protozoa than was obtained with rapid freezing (Weinman and McAllister, 1947). Parkes (1945) demonstrated that human spermatozoa survived exposure to and storage at −79° or −196°C. when frozen in bulk, but not when frozen at the maximum rate in microscopic films or capillary tubes by the technique of Hoagland and Pincus (1942). Nevertheless, rapid or ultrarapid freezing of living cells was, until a few years ago, still advocated and widely practiced to reduce or avoid damage by ice crystals (*v. infra*, and Sections IV and V of this chapter).

The occurrence of thermal shock between 0° and −79°C. and its avoidance by slow cooling were conclusively demonstrated with glycerol-treated bull spermatozoa (Smith and Polge, 1950a, b; Polge and Rowson, 1952a, b; Polge and Lovelock, 1952).

Grafting experiments have shown that skin survives exposure to very low temperatures better after slow than after rapid cooling, the epidermal melanoblasts being particularly sensitive to thermal shock (Medawar and Billingham, 1951; Billingham and Medawar, 1952; also Chapter 11). Similarly, ovarian tissue maintains viability, as judged by *in vitro* growth or by regeneration of functionally active grafts, only after slow cooling (Smith, 1952a; Smith and Parkes, 1951, 1953; Parkes and Smith, 1953). It is now established that many other cells and tissues, including pathogenic amoebae (Fulton and Smith, 1953), mammalian eggs (Smith, 1952b; 1953a), pituitary and adrenal tissue (Smith, S. E., 1953), testicular tissue (Deanesly, 1953), and certain tumor cells (Lépine *et al.*, 1951) survive slow but not rapid or ultrarapid freezing to low temperatures. The optimum rate of cooling and the role of glycerol will be discussed in subsequent sections.

The mechanism of thermal shock at low temperatures as at subnormal temperatures is obscure. It is not even clear whether with isolated mammalian cells and tissues the mechanism is the same in both cases. However, on the whole it seems likely that one phenomenon is an extension of the other, and certain basic ideas are beginning to emerge.

The complex biochemical and biophysical reactions of living cells inevitably change in balance and pattern when the temperature is altered because of their different temperature coefficients (Kidd and West, 1924; Callow, 1951). Thus, when cells are cooled below their normal environmental temperature, enzyme activities are progressively but differentially slowed (Joslyn, 1949, 1951), whereas diffusion continues at a rate which, by comparison, is little altered until much lower temperatures. The dynamic equilibrium of cells, internally and externally, is thus upset. This change, occurring suddenly, might be harmful, whereas occurring slowly it might evoke adaptation. It could be argued equally well, however, that rapid freezing would reduce the amount and duration of disorganization and that ultrarapid cooling to very low temperatures would instantly arrest all physicochemical processes, so that after ultrarapid rewarming they would be returned without disturbance to the normal balance. The mode of action of egg yolk and of lecithin in diminishing thermal shock and of certain toxins in increasing it both at low and at subnormal temperatures is receiving particular attention. Preliminary evidence suggests that sudden falls in temperature may alter the arrangement of lipoid constituents in the red blood cell, thereby affecting its permeability and other properties, and that this effect is reduced in the presence of a high lecithin content in the medium and enhanced by the lyotropic action of high concentrations of salt or by various chemicals and toxins which alter surface tension or dissolve liqids (Lovelock, 1953a, b, c, d).

At low temperatures, when water separates as ice, additional factors probably contribute to thermal shock. In the past, much emphasis has been placed on the formation of ice crystals. Moran (1926), working with disks of gelatin gel of different strengths, found that the rate of cooling as well as the gelatin concentration affected the microstructure produced by freezing and the amount of ice which separated. Thus, 12% gels cooled slowly at −3°C. froze only on the surface, where a thick shell of ice formed enclosing a core of dehydrated gel, whereas when cooled rapidly in liquid air no detectable quantity of ice formed on the surface and discrete centers of crystallization formed throughout. By contrast, when strong gels containing 65.5% gelatin were immersed in liquid air, they remained clear and transparent as though no ice had been formed. Moran thought that with weaker gels the slower rates of cooling were required to suppress internal centers of crystallization. He also thought that the water in gels existed partly in a free form which could be frozen out, and partly as bound water, amounting to approximately 35% of the gel, which was not freezable.

Breedis (1942) wondered whether the superiority of slow over rapid cooling of leukemia cells might be explained along the lines suggested by Moran. Thus, the initial freezing of water in extracellular fluids might result in concentration of osmotically active material outside the cell so that water would diffuse out of the cell to restore equilibrium until a stage was reached when no further water could escape from the protoplasmic gel and intracellular ice crystallization could not occur. Such transfer of water would require an appreciable time and could only occur during relatively slow cooling, whereas rapid cooling might cause intracellular crystallization.

Microscopic studies of animal cells during slow cooling leave little doubt that the cell membrane acts as a barrier to intracellular crystallization which occurs at lower temperatures than extracellular ice formation (Chambers and Hale, 1932; Smith *et al.*, 1951). Cells suspended in saline or surrounded by paraffin or silicone can generally be supercooled to −8° to −12°C. before intracellular crystallization occurs. When suspended in or previously exposed to glycerol-containing media, however, they have been cooled to −60°C. without visible internal crystallization (Smith and Smiles, 1953). There is, however, no proof that intracellular crystals form within cells which experience thermal shock at low temperatures, or that the prevention of intracellular crystallization would prevent thermal shock. It is not even certain that intracellular ice crystals would, in themselves, be damaging (*v.* Section V).

The question of whether a proportion of the protoplasmic water content is bound in such a way as to resist freezing has been much disputed. The evidence now available suggests that none of the techniques used to demonstrate or to estimate bound water is reliable (Blanchard, 1940). It is therefore unlikely that avoidance of thermal shock depends on gradual dehydration until the cell contains only bound water. On the other hand, intracellular colloids and gels may interfere with the attainment of ice-water equilibrium and enhance the well-known tendency of water to supercool (Hardy, 1926; Blanchard, 1940), particularly in capillary systems (Fisher, 1924) and during slow cooling. The value of slow cooling might, therefore, be to promote supercooling.

One definite cause of thermal shock at low temperatures has recently been established. Spermatozoa, red blood corpuscles, and other cells are highly susceptible to the salt concentration of their environment (Milovanov, 1934—*v.* Anderson, 1945; Emmens, 1948; Ponder, 1948; Lovelock, 1953a). A sudden change beyond narrow limits of osmotic pressure at any temperature will cause osmotic shock manifested by irreversible loss of sperm motility and hemolysis of red cells. When ice separates from a saline solution, cells suspended in it are subjected to an osmotic shock. Slow cooling reduces osmotic shock at low temperatures, particularly in the presence of glycerol which causes a gradual separation of ice down to −50°C. (Lovelock, 1953b). Prolonged exposure to hypertonic salt solutions, however, causes other harmful effects distinct from osmotic shock. These effects are also counteracted by glycerol and are discussed in Sections III.2 and VI.

## III. REMOVAL OF WATER

### 1. *At Normal and Subnormal Temperatures*

Loss of a high proportion of their water content is a normal event in the life cycle of many organisms. Thus, spores of bacteria and protozoa as well as seeds of plants contain considerably less water than the vegetative forms of these species, and eggs of locusts and other insects remain dormant for long periods in a desiccated state. Moreover, reduction of water content at normal and subnormal temperatures occurs during the natural development of frost hardiness in plants and insects (Wilson and Miles, 1946; Wigglesworth, 1947; Modlibowska, 1951; Kidd, 1929; Nilsson-Leissner, 1929; Payne, 1926; Salt, 1936).

Organisms which withstand complete desiccation at normal temperatures will also withstand exposure to extreme degrees of cold approaching the absolute zero. This has been demonstrated by Becquerel in a series of researches extending over the years 1905 to 1951. He dried cells over barium oxide *in vacuo*, sealed them under high vacuum at a pressure of the order of $10^{-5}$ mm. mercury, and then exposed them to liquid helium at $-269°C$. The cells so treated included tardigrades, rotifers, spores of bacteria and fungi, non-sporing bacteria, algae, lichens, mosses, and also seeds of higher plants. When rewarmed and moistened, specimens of all these species resumed active forms and multiplied normally. Becquerel postulates that preservation of life under these rigorous conditions depends on inducing a reversible state of dehydration so that the protein components of the protoplasmic colloidal system are capable of reimbibing water. According to Becquerel, death is a structural disorganization identical with that occurring when inanimate gels break down during and after expulsion of water (syneresis) and is due to coagulation of proteins so that subsequent rehydration is impossible.

These observations and results and the popular notion that ice crystallization was the major damaging factor at low temperatures (*v.* Sections III.2 and V) encouraged many attempts to induce cold hardiness in otherwise susceptible living cells by dehydration at normal and subnormal temperatures. The basic theory was that desiccation before cooling would diminish the amount of water which could form ice and would also favor gelation of protoplasm (Heilbrunn, 1943). Sufficient drying might even suppress ice formation altogether as in concentrated gelatin gels (Moran, 1926). Dehydration has often been carried out by the osmotic action of strong sugar solutions, and a variety of cells partially dehydrated in this way have been exposed to low temperatures. The survival rates have usually been disappointing, especially after slow cooling, but positive results have been obtained with cells from a few species. For instance, about 30% of fowl spermatozoa previously treated with concentrated levulose solutions revived after rapid cooling to and thawing from $-76°C$. (Shaffner *et al.*, 1941). Similarly about 20% of frog spermatozoa survived ultrarapid cooling in liquid air after preliminary treatment with 40 to 50% sucrose solutions (Luyet and Hodapp, 1938). Spermatozoa of other species, however, have not survived such experiences (Polge *et al.*, 1949; Polge and Parkes, 1952). Luyet and his colleagues have shown that, after soaking in 30% ethylene glycol, vinegar eels, and hearts and other tissues of embryonic chicks, survive ultrarapid freezing and thawing (Luyet, 1941b; 1944; Luyet and Gehenio, 1940; Luyet and Hartung, 1941a, b; Gehenio and Luyet, 1947, 1951; Gonzales and Luyet, 1950; Luyet and Gonzales, 1951b). They stated that the ethylene glycol acted as a dehydrating agent and that the reduced water content decreased the possibility of ice crystallization and favored vitrification. The dehydrating action of ethylene glycol, if any, and the occurrence of vitrification in living cells will be discussed in Sections V and VI.

So far there is no decisive evidence that the resistance to low temperatures of the majority of living cells can be improved by dehydration above 0°C. On the other hand, there is much evidence that partial dehydration at normal and subnormal temperatures is harmful to most cells, particularly those of vertebrate origin (Jensen, 1943), and that, depending on type and species, they will tolerate removal of not more than 20 to 80% of their original water content. Thus, mammalian ovaries which had lost 60% of their original weight during drying *in vitro* never "took" as grafts, whereas loss of 56% of their weight was compatible with a high proportion of functional "takes" (Lipschütz, 1929). Moran (1929) showed that frog muscle fibers from which not more than 40% of their moisture had been removed recovered completely when water was restored to them; after water losses of 40 to 77.5%, physiological activity progressively diminished, whereas beyond 78% dehydration the muscle died immediately.

### 2. *At Low Temperatures*

The most striking effect of cooling to low temperatures is the separation of ice from solutions and suspensions within and around the cell. When plant tissues are cooled slowly below 0°C., ice crystals form in the intercellular spaces and grow by withdrawing water from within the cells. This has been known for many years, and as long ago as 1860 Sachs propounded the theory that the death of plant cells at low temperatures was caused by dehydration due to the removal of water in the form of ice. Extracellular freezing has also been demonstrated in animal tissues (Chambers and Hale, 1932; Koonz and Ramsbottom, 1939; Moulton and Lewis, 1940), and death of isolated animal cells below freezing point has also been attributed to dehydration. Even when intracellular freezing was known to have occurred as the result of more rapid freezing or other conditions, it was thought that separation of ice caused dehydration of the protoplasm so that the ordered structural arrangement of the cell was disturbed. For instance, Maximov (1938) thought that withdrawal of water during freezing would cause cell death by altering protoplasmic colloids and by increasing cellular permeability. Luyet (1939c) postulated that water existed in living tissue in five forms; that, whereas "excess" and "metabolic" water could be removed with impunity, the separation of "vital" water was lethal; and that "remnant freezable" water froze after death, whereas "unfreezable" water never froze at any temperature.

The fact that cells which resist desiccation (*v.* Section III.1) are also resistant to low and very low temperatures lent support to the theory that dehydration is the fundamental cause of death by freezing. Nevertheless, the theory did not fit all the observed facts and was widely criticized (*v.* Luyet and Gehenio, 1940). Moreover, it is now evident that other changes concomitant with crystallization of ice could be lethal, and probably the most important of these is the increase in concentration of electrolytes. Thus, Gorke (1907) showed that the proteins in plant saps were precipitated by increasing the salt concentration either at normal temperatures or by removal of water as ice during freezing. Gorke showed that the precipitates became permanent and irreversible after different times of exposure and at different temperatures according to whether the sap originated from a frost-hardy or a frost-sensitive plant.

Much evidence was obtained at the Cambridge low temperature station showing that with muscle fibers the harmful effect of removing water by freezing was due to the strong salt solutions so produced (*v.* Moran, 1929). One action of strong salt solutions is to denature proteins. In muscle juice the denaturation during freezing and thawing depends both on pH and on salt concentration. Thus, at pH 5.2 maximum denaturation is caused by 0.8 *M* NaCl solutions. This is the salt concentration reached when the muscle juice is frozen to between −2° and −3°C., which was the temperature range already known to be critical for living muscle fibers (Finn, 1932).

Another effect of strong salt solutions is to dissolve lipoproteins which can then be precipitated by dilution. For instance, the complex lecithovitellins of egg yolk are soluble in 10% NaCl between 0° and −10°C. but are thrown out of solution by addition of water. The freezing point of egg yolk is −0.58°C., and at temperatures below this the salt concentration rises. Egg yolk which has been cooled to and kept frozen below a critical temperature of −6°C. fails to regain its normal fluidity when thawed. At −6°C. there is a concentration in the unfrozen part of the yolk of at least 10% NaCl which would dissolve the lipoproteins; when subsequently rewarmed, sufficient water would be added from the melting ice to precipitate them so that the original colloidal solution would not be reformed. The embryos in fertilized eggs are immediately killed at −6°C., whereas after 47 hours at −4.6°C. a small proportion resume development and hatch normally in the incubator (Moran, 1925).

The harmful effects on red blood corpuscles of strong solutions of electrolytes have been emphasized by Lovelock (1953a, b). He has shown that the damage suffered by erythrocytes when frozen and thawed from a given temperature can be reproduced quantitatively by exposing the cells to a solution of sodium chloride which freezes at the same temperature and returning them to isotonic saline (Table 1). Lovelock has shown that there is a critical region of temperature in which the cells are irreversibly damaged if they remain longer than a few seconds. The upper limit of this region is −3°C. and is the freezing point of 0.8 *M* NaCl (= 4.68%); its lower limit of −40°C. is the eutectic temperature for the mixture of salts and other substances present within the red blood cell.

The damaging action of strong solutions of electrolytes on red blood cells is of several kinds (Lovelock, 1953a, c). In the first place, in sodium chloride solutions stronger than 0.8 *M* the cells appear to become permeable to sodium ions so that the internal concentration of $Na^+$ rises.

TABLE 1

A COMPARISON OF THE EFFECTS OF FREEZING AND THAWING WITH THOSE OF TRANSFER FROM ISOTONIC NACL TO STRONG NACL AND BACK AGAIN

| Temperature °C. | Molarity of NaCl solution with this freezing point | Hemolysis, %* | | | |
|---|---|---|---|---|---|
| | | 1 | 2 | 3 | 4 |
| −2 | 0.6 | 0 | 0 | 0 | 0 |
| −3 | 0.86 | 1.4 | 0 | 0 | 0 |
| −4 | 1.15 | 6.0 | 0 | 3.3 | 3.3 |
| −5 | 1.43 | 13 | 0 | 11.3 | 11.3 |
| −6 | 1.7 | 26 | 0 | 25 | 25 |
| −7 | 2.0 | 40 | 0 | 38 | 38 |
| −8 | 2.2 | 57 | 0 | 56 | 56 |
| −9 | 2.4 | 76 | 2 | 74 | 76 |
| −10 | 2.6 | 96 | 11 | 78 | 89 |
| −12 | 3.0 | 100 | 13 | 80 | 93 |
| −15 | 3.6 | 100 | 23 | 80 | 103 |

* Column 1 gives the hemolysis which occurs when red blood cells in 0.15 *M* NaCl are frozen at the stated temperatures for 5 minutes; column 2 that which occurs when the cells are exposed to the stated NaCl concentration; column 3 that which occurs when the cells are transferred to 0.15 *M* NaCl after exposure to the strong NaCl; column 4 the addition of columns 2 and 3.

When resuspended in physiological saline (0.15 *M* NaCl), the cells tend to hemolyze as a result of the excessive internal osmotic pressure. During freezing and thawing the cells pass through a similar cycle of alternate exposure to strong and to weak sodium chloride solution. A second consequence of exposing red blood cells to salt solutions stronger than 0.8 *M* is the development of sensitivity to thermal shock (*v.* Section II). Lovelock has also shown that cells suspended in strong salt solutions become susceptible to mechanical shocks such as centrifuging so that on resuspension in 0.15 *M* NaCl they hemolyze. He suggests that mechanical shocks might occur during sudden formation of ice crystals. A third way in which sodium chloride solutions are damaging appears at concentrations greater than 3.0 *M* (17.55%). Exposure of the cells to solutions of this strength causes complete destruction of the cell as a whole. This process appears to be connected with the lyotropic properties of sodium chloride solutions and is shown by lower concentrations of salts such as LiI and KSCN which are more lyotropic than sodium chloride (Lovelock, 1953a).

The protective action of glycerol during freezing and thawing can, in part, be explained by counteracting the rise of sodium chloride concentration during freezing (Lovelock, 1953b). This will be discussed in detail in Section VI.

The survival of red blood cells when rapidly frozen and thawed (Strumia, 1949a, b; Luyet, 1949, 1951) depends on the relative slowness with which the destructive action of strong solutions of electrolytes occurs (Lovelock, 1953a, b). The revival of other cells such as human spermatozoa (Parkes, 1945), skin (Medawar and Billingham, 1951; Billingham and Medawar, 1952) and tumor cells (Passey and Dmochowski, 1950) may be due to differences in permeability and resistance to strong salts and to osmotic shocks. The destruction during freezing and thawing of various cells, for instance rabbit spermatozoa, may be allied to their extreme sensitivity to changes in the osmotic pressure of their environment (Emmens, 1948; Lovelock, 1953c).

Cells which survive removal of water as ice, and the resultant concentration of electrolytes in their environment, should, theoretically, suffer no further damage if the ice is subsequently removed completely by high-vacuum distillation at low temperatures. Medawar and Billingham (1951; also Billingham and Medawar, 1952) have shown, however, that skin will survive removal of not more than 75% of its water content when dried from the frozen state after preliminary soaking either in Ringer's solution or in media containing glycerol (*v.* Chapter 11). The skin grafts in question were dehydrated for varying lengths of time at −22.5° to −32°C. This might well be a highly critical temperature range giving maximum damage from concentration of salts or from other effects, and dehydration to completion might be possible if drying from lower temperatures could be achieved. Alternatively, damage might occur during rehydration which is often carried out rapidly by pouring on an excess of an isotonic medium at room temperature. Death during freeze-drying may, however, be due to irreversible changes of the kind suggested by Becquerel (1938; 1951) depending perhaps on excessive concentration of electrolytes and nonelectrolytes within the cells. Nevertheless, the possibility of reviving a variety of living cells other than bacteria after desiccation by high-vacuum distillation at low temperatures cannot be discounted entirely in our present state of knowledge.

## IV. TEMPERATURE GRADIENTS

### 1. *With Falling Temperatures*

There is much evidence to suggest that many organic and biochemical materials may be unaltered by freezing if the rate of cooling is rapid or ultrarapid and the storage temperature low. Thus, disks of concentrated gelatin gel frozen rapidly in liquid air are found, when subsequently thawed, to have been unaltered by crystallization of ice or by any other effect (Moran, 1926). Egg yolk, which loses its normal fluid consistency after freezing at −6°C., is not so affected when frozen rapidly in liquid air at −190°C. and thawed in warm mercury (Moran, 1925). The solubility and other properties of purified lecithovitellin are less changed by rapid freezing to and from −65° or −183°C. than by slow cooling (Lea and Hawke, 1952). Chlorophyll solutions which flocculate when cooled slowly are unaltered by rapid freezing (Stiles, 1922). The stability of colloidal silicic acid sols is not upset by rapid freezing at temperatures below −55°C., whereas slower cooling causes coagulation (Fig. 4). The sharpening of absorption bands which occurs at very low temperatures has made rapid cooling a useful addition to the technique of spectroscopic examination of biological material (Keilin and Hartree, 1949).

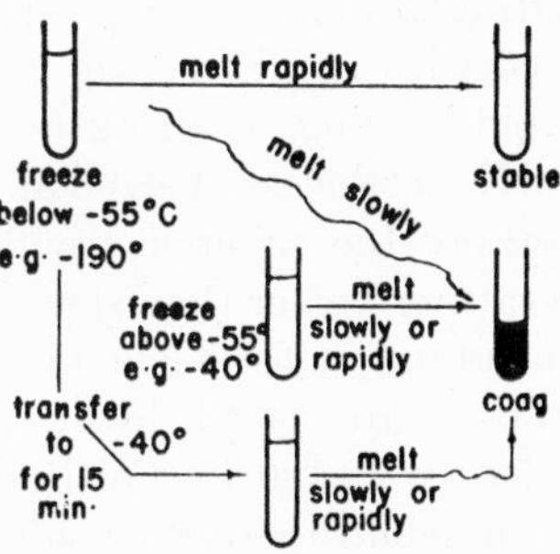


FIG. 4. Effect of rate of freezing and thawing on coagulation of silica sols. (Fig. 6 from Hazel and Schipper, 1950.)

Enzymes retain their activity and may even show enhanced activity after freezing quickly to very low temperatures (Hepburn, 1915; Nord and Lange, 1935). Mixtures of enzymes and their substrates also resist rapid cooling and may in some cases benefit from it. For example, when the reaction catalyzed is a simple endothermic one, the products are isolated in better yield if cooling from the reaction temperature is rapid. When a complex chain or cycle of reactions is involved, as in living cells, undesirable catabolic reactions leading to formation of toxic products occur (Callow, 1951) and might be prevented by sudden chilling to a very low temperature. Similarly, loss by diffusion of substances required for metabolism at normal temperatures might be minimized. Another advantage of rapid cooling is that, after separation of ice, less time is allowed for the action on proteins and lipoproteins of concentrated salt solutions before their eutectic temperature is reached (*v.* Section III).

The biochemical evidence in favor of rapid cooling has been supported by microscopists who find that fragments of tissue cooled to very low temperatures at the maximum rate show superb cytological and histological preservation (Gersh, 1932, 1951; Hoerr, 1936; Mendelow and Hamilton, 1950; Flosdorf, 1950; Bell, 1952). The remarkable revivals of vinegar eels (Luyet and Hartung, 1941a, b, c), spermatozoa (Luyet and Hodapp, 1938) and muscle fibers of frogs (Thoennes, 1940), and hearts and other tissues of embryonic chicks, obtained by Luyet and his colleagues after ultrarapid freezing and thawing, lent further support to the theory that rapid cooling is less injurious to living cells than slow cooling. It became widely accepted that the large crystals of ice formed during gradual cooling were more harmful than the small crystals associated with rapid freezing, and that avoidance of crystallization by ultrarapid freezing, resulting in vitrification, was the ideal (*v.* Section V).

Nevertheless, discrepancies were numerous. Although certain bacteria, notably the tubercle bacillus, survive rapid freezing to very low temperatures better than slow cooling (Kyes and Potter, 1939), the majority, including coliform bacilli, show little difference in mortality rates when cultures are cooled slowly to −15° or −30°C. and when frozen rapidly to −78° or −190°C. (Weiser and Osterud, 1945). Attempts to preserve mammalian tissues for subsequent *in vivo* grafting or *in vitro* cultivation by rapid freezing to very low temperatures give disappointing results. Survival and multiplication of cells under such conditions have been conclusively demonstrated only with certain tumors (Passey and Dmochowski, 1950; Walsh *et al.*, 1949; Warner *et al.*, 1950), with skin (Briggs and Jund, 1944; Medawar and Billingham, 1951; Billingham and Medawar, 1952), and with thyroid and parathyroid tissue (Blumenthal and Walsh, 1950). The majority of mammalian cells, however, show no signs of viability when cultured *in vitro* or implanted *in vivo* after rapid freezing to and storage at low temperatures (*v.* Parkes and Smith, 1953, for references). By contrast, ovarian, testicular, pituitary, and adrenal tissues have all given functional grafts or growths in tissue culture after slow cooling to and storage at −79° and −190°C, particularly in the presence of glycerol (Smith, 1952a; Parkes and Smith, 1953; Deanesly, 1953; Smith, S. E., 1953).

The explanation appears to be that a wide variety of living cells is susceptible to thermal shock (*v.* Section II). It therefore follows that the optimum rate of cooling for preserving the viability of any cell or tissue depends on conflicting factors. The occurrence of thermal shock must be avoided without cooling so slowly as to prolong the harmful action of concentrated salt solutions during separation of ice, or to allow the coagulation and loss of solubility of colloidal substances, or any other form of intracellular disorganization.

Fundamental work along these lines has recently been carried out with red blood cells by Lovelock (1953c, d) and on bull spermatozoa by Polge (Polge, 1953, Polge and Rowson, 1952a, b). Optimum low-temperature preservation of bull semen has been obtained by dilution with an equal part of egg yolk citrate buffer at +37°C., and by addition of glycerol to a final concentration of 10% 6 hours later, after the diluted semen has cooled to +5°C. The semen is then allowed to equilibrate with the glycerol for 20 hours at +5°C. before further cooling. The use of sodium citrate is important and appears to be less damaging at low temperatures than that

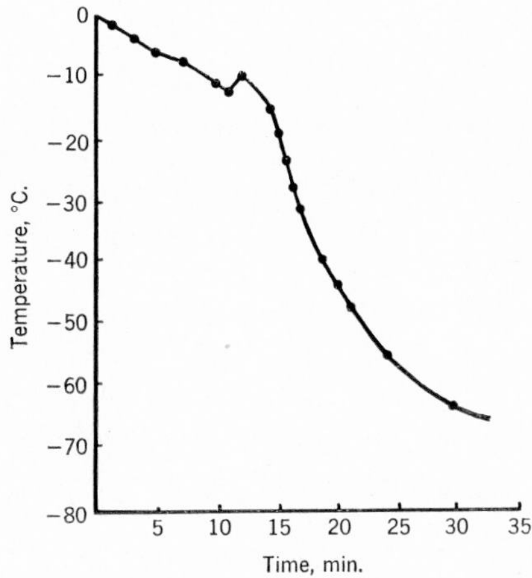


FIG. 5. Freezing of 1.0 ml. of a 15% glycerol solution contained in a 1-cm. diameter ampoule, by immersion of the ampoule, contained in an insulated cooling vessel, in a bath at −79°C.

of phosphate buffers, physiological saline, or Ringer's solution. The value of egg yolk is to combat temperature shock. The fact that 10% is the optimum concentration of glycerol for bull spermatozoa is interesting and, together with the protective action of glycerol at low temperatures, will be discussed further in Section VI. The semen so diluted can be cooled from +5° to −15°C. at the rate of about 1 degree per minute. A critical temperature range between −15° and −25°C. must then be passed through in 2 minutes or less to avoid damage to the spermatozoa. Cooling from −25° to −79°C. can be accomplished in a further 10 to 20 minutes. The complete cooling curve from 0° to −79°C. is shown in Fig. 5 and can readily be obtained in the apparatus described by Polge and Lovelock (1952). Bull semen so treated has been stored for many months without loss of fertilizing capacity (Polge and Rowson, 1952a, b; Polge, 1953).

Spermatozoa of other species and cells of other kinds do not necessarily survive this exact procedure and may require different media, different final concentrations and methods of adding glycerol, as well as modification of the rate of cooling in order to obtain the best survivals after freezing to, and storage at low temperatures and thawing (Smith and Polge, 1950a; Polge and Parkes, 1952; Smith, 1952a, b; Parkes and Smith, 1953; Smith, S. E., 1953; Fulton and Smith, 1953). Much further work is needed to determine the critical salt concentrations and the critical temperature range for cells and tissues as well as their permeability to water and glycerol and the amount of glycerol required for protection during freezing and thawing.

### 2. *With Rising Temperatures*

A great deal of attention has been devoted to the study of cooling velocities, and many authors have drawn curves to show the rates of cooling in their experiments on living and dead tissues and with suspensions, solutions, and gels of different kinds. By contrast, relatively little attention has been paid to rates of thawing (Luyet and Gehenio, 1940).

A certain amount of evidence is forthcoming to suggest that thawing too rapidly may be a cause of injury and death to plant cells. Thus, Iljin (1934) showed that, when red cabbage leaves were frozen, water was extruded from the cell vacuoles so that the protoplast contracted while ice formed in the interstitial spaces. Rapid thawing was fatal to the cells, because water invaded the contracted protoplast and tore it open. By contrast, the cells survived when thawed slowly and rehydrated gradually by slow addition of cold hypertonic solutions of sugar and glycerol of progressively decreasing concentration.

With bacteria and animal cells, on the other hand, the consensus of opinion is that rapid thawing at their optimum metabolic temperature is preferable to slow thawing. Turner and Brayton (1939) found that spirochaetes of relapsing fever could be cooled from 0° to −78°C. either in 30 seconds or in 2 to 6 hours with little damage; rewarming over the same range in 2 to 6 hours killed most of the organisms, whereas thawing rapidly in a water bath at +37°C. permitted their survival. Luyet and his coworkers found that the revival of vinegar eels, frog spermatozoa, and muscle fibers after vitrification by ultrarapid cooling was prevented if the specimens were rewarmed slowly. They ascribed this result to devitrification and crystallization, in the course of the slow thawing (Luyet and Hartung, 1941b, c; Luyet and Gehenio, 1940).

Rapid thawing also gives the best results with mammalian tissues. Thus, skin grafts frozen in Ringer's solution and kept at −150° or −79°C.

contain no viable epithelial cells or melanoblasts after slow thawing and even in the presence of 15% glycerol melanoblasts do not survive unless rewarmed rapidly (Billingham and Medawar, 1952; *v.* Chapter 11). It is at first consideration remarkable that cells such as bull spermatozoa which are sensitive to rapid cooling require to be thawed by transfer from −79°C. to a bath at +40°C. and deteriorate when rewarmed more gradually. It appears that living cells are not susceptible to thermal shock

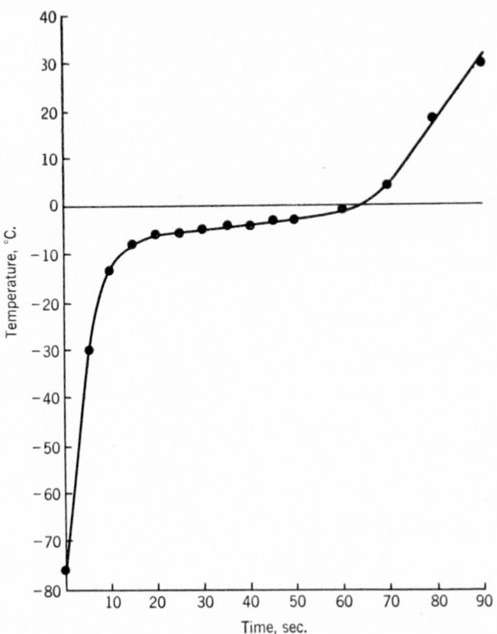


Fig. 6. Thawing of 1.0 ml. of a 15% glycerol solution contained in a 1-cm. diameter ampoule, by immersion in a bath at +40°C. (From Lovelock, 1953c.)

during warming. The essential features of a thawing curve are shown in Fig. 6. During rewarming an ampoule containing 1 ml. of semen by transfer from a freezing mixture at −76°C. to a bath at +42°C., 90 seconds was taken to pass from −76° to +30°C. Fifty seconds was spent in the range between −25° and 0°C., which is not an excessive time for the cells to be exposed to concentrated salt solutions. When thawing takes place at temperatures lower than +40°C., the period spent in the range of critical temperatures and critical salt concentrations is prolonged because of the absence of anything analogous to supercooling. Delay at this stage is just as harmful as delay after the beginning of ice formation during cooling (Lovelock, 1953d).

## V. EXTRA- AND INTRACELLULAR CHANGES: CRYSTALLIZATION AND VITRIFICATION

The theory that ice crystals are the major source of damage to living cells during freezing is accepted widely and quoted repeatedly. Furthermore, slow cooling with formation of large ice crystals is generally supposed to be more damaging than rapid cooling resulting in small crystals, or than ultrarapid cooling when crystallization may even be suppressed (Moran, 1929; Moulton and Lewis, 1940; Luyet and Gehenio, 1940; Rahn, 1945; Luyet, 1941b, 1944, 1949; Strumia and Hodge, 1945; Strumia, 1949a, b; Ferrer, 1951; Flosdorf, 1950; Greaves, 1944; Fry and Greaves, 1951; Gersh, 1951; Bell, 1952; Fidler, 1952).

The acceptance of these ideas is in large measure due to the experimental work and publications of Luyet and his school (1937–1952) and to the authoritative monograph by Luyet and Gehenio (1940) which has for many years dominated all thought and work on low-temperature biology. The time has now come to review in a critical way these theories, the physical principles on which they are based, and the experiments on living cells which appear to support or to conflict with them.

### 1. *The Effects of Extracellular Crystallization*

The suggestion has frequently been made that sharp crystals of ice forming in the surrounding medium might pierce the cell wall and thus cause death (Proom and Hemmons, 1949; Rahn, 1945; Schumacker, 1951). This has not been confirmed by microscopic studies of living cells during freezing. Instead, the cell membranes, when intact, appear to act as a barrier to the passage of ice crystals. For instance, the protoplasm of frog muscle fibers could be supercooled to $-10°$C. although the surrounding medium had frozen at $-1.2°$C. and intracellular crystallization was induced only when the cell wall was punctured by a micropipette tipped with ice (Chambers and Hale, 1932). The cell membrane also checked the growth of ice crystals around amoebae in which intracellular crystallization could be induced by inoculation with ice, or occurred spontaneously after an interval of supercooling to lower temperatures (Chambers and Hale, 1932; Smith *et al.*, 1951). Similar observations have also been made with plant cells (Rogers and Modlibowska, 1953). Moreover, artificial membranes of various kinds, particularly those less permeable to water, can arrest the passage of ice crystals (Cook and Lusena, 1951).

Another theory was that cells were damaged by the pressure of the surrounding ice or by crushing between adjacent crystals. Most cells, tissues, and organisms, however, survive exposure to hydrostatic pressures of great magnitude (Cattell, 1936; Luyet, 1937; Luyet and Gehenio, 1940; Marsland, 1950). It is therefore unlikely that pressure by extracellular ice would cause damage to individual cells unless they were crushed or distorted, or separated irreparably from their blood supply and innervation in tissues and organisms. Furthermore, it is probable that, before spearing or crushing by ice crystals could occur, the cells would have succumbed to the action of concentrated salt solutions (*v.* Section II). Lovelock (1953c) has shown that, when an isotonic saline solution in a test tube is frozen by immersion in a low-temperature bath, ice separates as a pure substance. The inward moving shell of apparently solid ice consists, in fact, of a meshwork of crystals with concentrated saline in the interstices. These interstices must form continuous channels because there is no change in the conductivity of the system until the eutectic temperature is reached, when the entire solution solidifies. The continuity of channels of this kind was also demonstrated by Sloviter (1951c) in suspensions of red blood cells in 15% glycerol in 0.85% NaCl frozen at −20°C. The preparations appeared at first as solid frozen masses, pink in color throughout. During one week at −20°C., however, the cells passed through microscopical channels to form a dark-red sediment beneath a pure white supernatant mass of ice. The cells were protected from hemolysis by the presence of glycerol (*v.* Section VI).

During microscopic observations of freezing and thawing in the presence of glycerol the channels containing freely moving blood corpuscles were particularly conspicuous. In the absence of glycerol the crystals grew slowly between −10° and −40°C., encroaching on the interstices, and a proportion of the red blood cells gradually faded away as though dissolving. Other corpuscles remained intact, lying between adjacent crystalline plates, and lysed only during thawing when any crushing effect would have been reduced (Smith *et al.*, 1951). Crushing was not observed when the brine shrimp, *Artemia salina,* was cooled under the microscope to −20°C. This remarkable organism, which withstands either distilled water or saturated saline at normal or low temperatures, continued to move while almost surrounded by ice and even after complete encasement resumed full activity when the medium thawed (Lovelock, 1953d).

### 2. *Intracellular Freezing*

The theory that intracellular freezing causes damage and death is founded on much better evidence. Chambers and Hale (1932) observed that intracellular crystallization induced in frog muscle fibers or occurring spontaneously in amoebae always caused death and that the cells disintegrated on thawing. Smith *et al.* (1951) showed that amoebae suspended in 5% glycerol did not survive intracellular freezing, although the

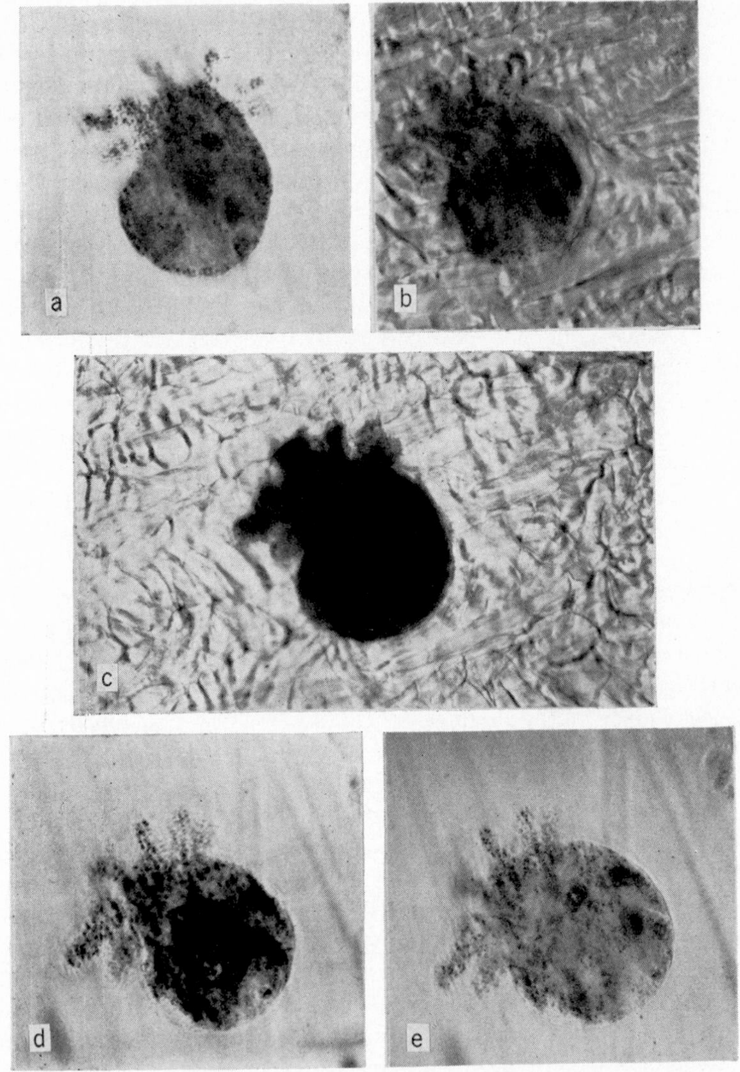


FIG. 7. Amoebae suspended in 5% glycerol in rain water. (a) At 5°C. when protoplasmic streaming had ceased (175×; exposure 1/50 second). (b) Medium crystallized at −10°C. (175×; exposure 1/25 second). (c) Intracellular crystallization at −15°C. (175×; exposure 1/5 second). (d) Medium thawed; intracellular crystals receding at 50°C. (175×; exposure 1/125 second). (e) Rewarmed to 20°C. (175×; exposure 1/50 second). (From Smith *et al.*, 1951.)

cells were morphologically normal (Fig. 7a, b, c, d, e). Internal crystallization was not seen in fowl spermatozoa, which resumed full motility after exposure to −45°C. in the presence of 15% glycerol or in red blood cells similarly treated, although in each case ice formed in the surrounding medium. In these experiments the small size of the cells, the density of the frozen medium, and the limitations of the methods of observation precluded certainty as to the presence of intracellular ice.

Recently, Smith and Smiles (1953) have improved the method for direct microscopic observation of living cells during freezing to and thawing from temperatures of the order of −60° to −80°C. They have found that, after treatment with 15% glycerol, a proportion of the giant multinucleated spermatids do not "black out" or show any other visible changes indicative of internal crystallization during cooling to −80°C., in spite of the presence of crystals in the surrounding medium (Fig. 8a, b). On rewarming the cells are morphologically unchanged and the spermatid tails resume motility. In the absence of glycerol the cells freeze internally after super-cooling to a variable degree (−5° to −20°C.), and on thawing they are disorganized and dead.

Lovelock (1953d) found that the brine shrimp, *Artemia salina*, recovered after the surrounding medium, whether distilled water or saline, had frozen completely, but not after intracellular crystallization had occurred. Siminovitch and Scarth (1938) and Rogers and Modlibowska (1953) have shown that internal freezing can kill plant cells. So far, survival of animal cells subjected to intracellular ice for an appreciable time has not been shown conclusively, although the possibility was admitted by Pütter (1927), by Stiles (1930), and by Bělehrádek (1935), and even now cannot be ruled out.

The fundamental nature of the damage caused by intracellular freezing is still not clear. There is little evidence that expansion during crystallization of ice causes cells to burst, although the suggestion has recently again been made (*v.* Luyet and Gehenio, 1940; Schumacker, 1951). According to Stiles (1930) the formation of intracellular ice might cause a mechanical disturbance leading to breakdown of the protoplasmic colloidal system. He postulated that the formation of ice crystals in protoplasm would disturb the relations between the disperse phase and the dispersion medium in protoplasmic sols and gels (Stiles, 1922, 1930). Another suggestion is that on thawing there is agglutination or precipitation with destruction of surface charges so that the colloids of cells and tissues break down (Sible, *v.* Schumacker, 1951). Luyet and Gehenio (1940) postulated that the processes of crystallization require the change from a random to an ordered arrangement of molecules, and that this

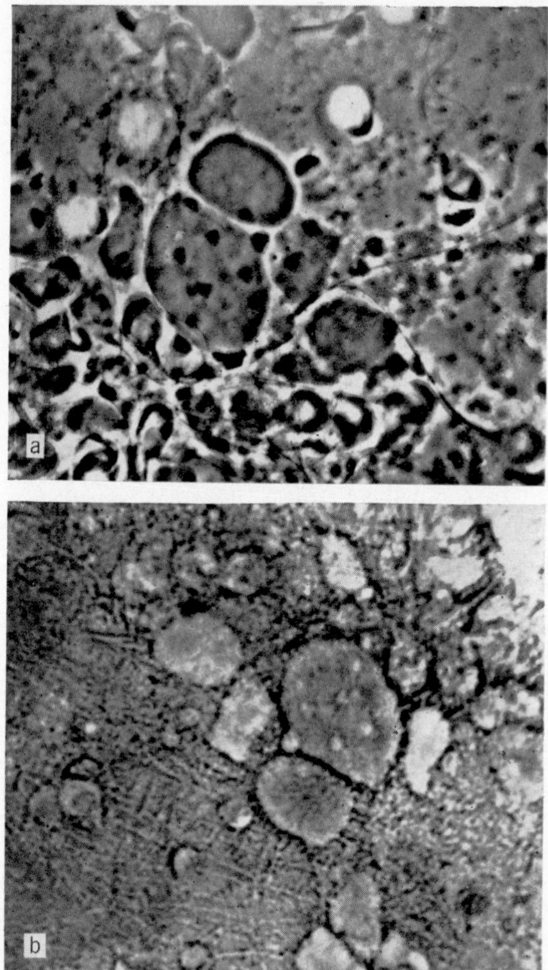

FIG. 8. Fresh preparation of guinea pig testis treated with 15% glycerol in Ringer's solution. (a) At +20°C. (phase contrast, 850×). A multinucleated spermatid. (b) At −60°C. (direct illumination, 850×). The same field showing extracellular but no intracellular ice crystals. (Unpublished photomicrographs by Mr. J. Smiles, National Institute for Medical Research.)

molecular reshuffling could ruin the delicate structure of protoplasm and so cause death (*v.* Luyet, 1941b, 1949, 1951).

The effects of intracellular crystallization in cells of various kinds have been discussed by Lovelock (1953c). He suggests that cells such as the fresh-water amoeba are relatively impermeable to water and salts. So long as the cells supercool, their internal medium remains unchanged despite freezing of the surrounding medium. As soon as intracellular crystallization takes place, however, the proteins and lipids will be exposed to increasing concentrations of the salts normally present within the cell, and when a critical salt concentration is reached they will be denatured, dissolved, or precipitated. This theory may require modification, in view of studies on active transport of water by fresh-water organisms (Robinson, 1953). Most mammalian cells, on the other hand, like red blood corpuscles, are highly permeable to water. They must, therefore, remain in osmotic equilibrium with their suspending medium as freezing progresses in it. They lose water during freezing at a rate which maintains the freezing point of their inner contents a little below that of the surrounding fluid medium. By the time the medium has concentrated to saturation at its eutectic, the cell contents are too dry to freeze. The majority of cells are, however, irreversibly damaged by the concentrated salt solution without and within, long before saturation is reached (*v.* Section III). In glycerol-containing media, on the other hand, cells permeable to this substance are protected from the full effect of the salts and have a chance of survival (*v.* Section VI). The absence of internal crystallization in glycerol-treated mammalian testicular cells at −80°C. might support Lovelock's thesis that insufficient water remained to freeze (*v.* Fig. 8a, b, above, and Smith and Smiles, 1953).

The deleterious effects of strong salt solutions at low temperatures has now been proved beyond doubt (Gorke, 1907; Moran, 1929; Lovelock, 1953a, b, c), and their action could plausibly explain damage done during extra- and intracellular ice formation. Nevertheless, effects suggested by Moran, Becquerel, Heilbrunn, and others, such as disturbance of colloidal solutions or sol-gel equilibria, and disorganization of the relations between enzymes and their substrates, have not been ruled out and might occur in addition.

We come now to a consideration of the theory and practice of vitrification and its application by Luyet to the preservation of living cells at very low temperatures. Stiles, and subsequently Luyet, based his ideas on Tamman's theory (1898a, b) that it should be possible by suitable treatment to convert any fluid into a glassy state. Tamman postulated that crystallization could occur only at or near the freezing point of a solution. At temperatures below this relatively narrow range crystallization would be impossible because the molecules would have insufficient mobility to assume the new positions required to build up a crystalline structure. Tamman thought that, instead, they would be immobilized in their original random positions so that the solid would be amorphous and vitreous. Both Stiles and Luyet believed that death during exposure to low temperatures would be avoided if the protoplasm could be converted to and from the vitreous state without intracellular crystal formation. Luyet states that the critical range of temperatures in which death occurs, 0° to −40°C., is identical with the range in which crystallization of ice takes place. He has found that, when thin films of strong solutions of proteins, sugars, polyhydric alcohols, gums, and other substances are cooled at an ultrarapid rate by plunging into fluid at the temperature of liquefied atmospheric gases (−150° to −196°C.), they are converted into transparent glasses (Luyet, 1939a, 1941a, b). When slowly rewarmed they devitrify and become opaque because of crystallization. On rapid rewarming, however, the glasses melt without intervening crystallization. Luyet's practical demonstrations of vitrification, devitrification with crystallization, and vitrofusion without crystallization are most convincing (Luyet, 1951), but they depend on the doubtful assumption that transparency is a criterion of the vitreous state. The difficulty, noted by Luyet (1939a, 1941a), of vitrifying pure water has been emphasized vigorously by Pryde and Jones (1952). Luyet says that the cooling velocity required for vitrification of material which, like protoplasm, contains 70 to 80% of water is of the order of several hundred degrees per second. This can be achieved only in minute preparations a fraction of a millimeter in thickness. Luyet and his colleagues think that, in some instances, partial dehydration of the cytoplasm increases the chance of vitrification during subsequent ultrarapid cooling and of revival after ultrarapid thawing. Thus, in early experiments on frog spermatozoa, 50% sucrose was used as a dehydrating agent. In later experiments on vinegar eels and on chick embryonic tissue they preferred 30% ethylene glycol (Luyet and Gehenio, 1940; Luyet and Hartung, 1941a, b, c; Luyet and Gonzales, 1950; Gonzales and Luyet, 1950, 1951; Gehenio and Luyet, 1947, 1951; Luyet, 1941b, 1944, 1951), which they supposed to cause cellular dehydration by osmotic action. The question arises, however, whether ethylene glycol could act in this way. A substance in solution which withdraws water from cells by osmosis must remain outside the cell. If it diffuses into or is taken up by the cell, it will exert no osmotic effect. Thus, urea, which freely penetrates into red blood cells until equilibrium is established, does not act as an osmotic dehydrating agent, however high the concentration in the plasma or other suspending medium. There is evidence that ethylene glycol penetrates readily into certain cells. For instance, its toxic actions on living animals (Smyth *et al.*, 1950) and its conversion into oxalic acid by tissue slices (Carr and Kranz, 1945) suggest that many cells are, in fact, highly permeable to it. The configuration and relatively small size of its molecule as well as quantitative studies also indicate that ethylene glycol penetrates into a variety of cells (Heilbrunn, 1943). Furthermore, the beneficial effects of ethylene glycol in facilitating the revival of living cells after ultrarapid freezing and thawing can be explained in other ways (*v.* Section VI).

It remains a fundamental problem as to whether complete suppression of intracellular crystallization is, in fact, ever achieved by Luyet's technique (Luyet, 1944). The discussion after Schumacker's paper (1951) at a recent Macy Foundation Symposium on Cold Injury indicates that this is still open to doubt. Unless the material had been examined by x-ray diffraction, by electron microscopy, or even by high powers of phase contrast microscopy, the existence of minute crystals could not be ruled out. The process of devitrification might, in fact, be due to growth of submicroscopic or microscopic crystals into larger ones. This was recognized by Luyet and Gehenio (1940) and is discussed by Pryde and Jones (1952). Nevertheless, Luyet has often assumed on biophysical grounds, without any definite proof, that vitrification does actually occur in living cells cooled and rewarmed at an ultrarapid rate. He postulated that the revival of a cell after freezing and thawing could be used as a criterion of whether vitrification had occurred. The actual words used by Luyet and Gehenio (1940) are as follows: "The vitality of living matter treated by vitrification methods is taken as indicative that the material was actually vitrified." Further on they write: "Studies on the duration of immersion in liquid air which the spermatozoa can support have shown that the number of survivors and their activity are the same after 5 days as after 5 seconds. This finding is in good agreement with the assumption that the material is vitrified and stays unaltered at low temperatures." This surely is an outstanding example of the classic fallacy of *petitio principii*, or begging the question, especially as Luyet (1951) admits that a small proportion of vinegar eels survived slow cooling when vitrification could not have taken place.

The discovery that a variety of living cells can, in the presence of glycerol, survive slow cooling to and storage at −79° or −190°C., in spite of crystallization in the medium, proves that ultrarapid cooling to prevent ice formation is not the only or even the most important method for protecting cells against the effects of extreme cold (Polge *et al.*, 1949; Smith and Polge, 1950a, b; Sloviter, 1951a, b; Parkes and Smith, 1953; Lovelock, 1953a, b, c). Certain cells, notably human spermatozoa (Parkes, 1945) and mammalian skin (Billingham and Medawar, 1952), will also survive cooling in the absence of glycerol. It remains to be seen whether such cells survive in spite of intracellular crystallization. Lovelock's suggestion is that they would be completely dehydrated by osmotic withdrawal of water which would augment the extracellular ice until insufficient water remained to crystallize within (*v.s.*, and Section VI).

It does not seem possible that the water contained in cytoplasm could be vitrified during slow cooling. Pryde and Jones (1952) have shown that only under most stringent experimental conditions will water form a glass and that the transformation temperature lies between −150° and −125°C. Specimens of vitreous water which contain crystalline ice at −190°C. complete their crystallization precipitately when the temperature is raised to −129°C. Lovelock (1953d) points out that it would therefore be impossible for vitreous intracellular water to exist at all and certainly not to coexist with crystalline extracellular water at any temperature above −129°C. According to him the presence of solutes might well depress rather than raise the vitrification temperature. Rapid cooling can undoubtedly be used to preserve cells which are not sensitive to thermal shock. Thus red blood cells cooled rapidly to −60° or to −50°C. in less than 1 second can be kept at that temperature for several hours without hemolysis. When rewarmed from −50° to +20°C. in less than 2 seconds they are recovered without loss (Strumia, 1949a, b; Lovelock, 1953a, b). Their survival of this treatment cannot be connected with intracellular vitrification, because uncrystallized intracellular water would rapidly distill over onto ice crystals in the external medium. Ice at −50°C. is almost as potent a drying agent as phosphorus pentoxide. The prevention of hemolysis could, on the other hand, be explained by avoidance of prolonged exposure to strong salt solutions during rapid cooling (Lovelock, 1953d).

Furthermore, Lovelock (1953a, b, c) has shown that the degree of damage sustained by red blood cells and by spermatozoa of rabbit, bull, and fowl during freezing can be quantitatively accounted for, at any temperature, by the concentration of the suspending medium due to the amount of water converted to ice. The critical salt concentration and the critical range of temperature in which maximum damage occurs differ for each type of cell. For instance, with red blood cells the peak of damage is at −35°C. in a critical range −3° to −40°C. Bull spermatozoa, on the other hand, suffer most at −17°C., and the critical range is −1.5° to −30°C. It is quite impossible to explain this in terms of a change in the physical state of water occurring at −35°C. in red blood cells and at −17°C. in bull spermatozoa. It is, by contrast, easy to explain in terms of concentration of the medium.

To conclude, it would appear that the survival of cells after ultrarapid cooling and rewarming can be explained without evoking intracellular vitrification. There is no definite evidence that protoplasm has survived after intracellular crystallization or that it has ever been vitrified. To prove the existence of the vitreous state, the absence of crystals must be demonstrated by x-ray studies and electron microscopy, and definite changes in physical properties such as specific heat must be determined. Until these proofs are forthcoming, Luyet's theory, attractive though it is, must be treated with reserve.

## VI. THE ACTION OF GLYCEROL AND RELATED SUBSTANCES

### 1. *Evidence of Protection against Freezing*

It has been known for many years that sugar solutions can, to some extent, protect living cells against the effects of exposure to low temperatures. Thus, development of frost hardiness in plants is often associated with the breakdown of starch into simple sugars. This change may facilitate supercooling and also lower the freezing point of sap and cells. Factors other than a high extra- and intracellular content of mono- and disaccharides and pentoses must, however, be involved, since sugar cane and sugar beet, in spite of a high content of sucrose and other sugars, are very susceptible to frost damage (Lidforss, 1907; Kidd, 1929; Modlibowska, 1951).

Sugar solutions have also been found to exert a slight though limited effect in protecting animal cells and products during freezing. Thus, the use of 40 to 50% sucrose made possible the revival of about 20% of frog spermatozoa after immersion in liquid air (Luyet and Hodapp, 1938), and addition of levulose enabled about 30% of fowl spermatozoa to resist freezing at −79°C. (Shaffner *et al.*, 1941; Shaffner, 1942). Five per cent glucose has also been used in the preservation at low temperatures of tumor cells (Craigie, 1949). The sugars were thought to act as dehydrating agents, and, according to Luyet and his colleagues, this not only reduced the amount of intracellular water available for freezing but also increased the chances of vitrification during ultrarapid freezing (Luyet, 1941a, b, 1944, 1951; Luyet and Gehenio, 1940).

The great majority of cells and tissues, however, are afforded little or no protection against the damaging effects of freezing and thawing by media containing sugars, and Luyet and his coworkers were led to use media containing 30% ethylene glycol, also ostensibly as a dehydrating agent, for vinegar eels and embryonic chick tissues subjected to ultrarapid cooling and thawing (Luyet and Hartung, 1941a, b, c; Gonzales and Luyet, 1950; Luyet and Gonzales, 1951b).

In general, it may be said that little progress was made in the freezing and thawing of normal vertebrate cells until the chance discovery that glycerol had the remarkable property of protecting fowl spermatozoa against the damaging effects of freezing to −79°C. and thawing (Polge *et al.*, 1949). Prior to this, glycerol had been used without notable effect by Luyet and Hartung (1941a) to protect vinegar eels against exposure to liquid air. Twenty per cent glycerol had also been used by Rostand (1946) to preserve frog spermatozoa for limited periods at −6°C., a temperature at which the material did not solidify. With these exceptions it seems that up till 1949 glycerol had been used, not to preserve animal cells exposed to low temperatures, but to kill them, particularly when it was hoped to preserve viruses (Gye *et al.*, 1949; Craigie, 1949; Mann, 1949).

The action of glycerol and related substances was then tested on mammalian spermatozoa at normal temperatures and during and after cooling to very low temperatures (Smith and Polge, 1950a, b). Bull and goat spermatozoa which are highly active in 10 to 20% glycerol at body temperatures survived exposure to −79° and −190°C., provided that they were cooled slowly. The protective action on spermatozoa of other species including horse and rabbit was less efficient. This was apparently due to damage before cooling and could be reduced by altering the medium and the method of adding glycerol (Smith and Polge, 1950a; Parkes, 1951; Polge and Parkes, 1952).

Among a large number of polyhydric alcohols and their derivatives which were tested, only propylene and ethylene glycols exerted effects comparable with those of glycerol in protecting avian and mammalian spermatozoa against damage at low temperatures (Smith and Polge, 1950a). Some of the early results, which were entirely concerned with the motility of spermatozoa after freezing, were confirmed by Emmens and Blackshaw (1950).

Preliminary results on the fertilizing capacity of spermatozoa were not altogether encouraging. For instance, the addition of glycerol to fowl semen with or without freezing caused a serious reduction in fertilizing capacity, and no fertile eggs were obtained from hens inseminated with semen containing more than 2% glycerol. Semen frozen and thawed in this low concentration of glycerol contained few motile spermatozoa; nevertheless, when inseminated it led to the fertilization of a small number of eggs from which normal chicks were hatched (Smith and Polge, 1950a; Polge and Parkes, 1952). Later on, studies with mammalian red blood cells suggested that the reduced fertility of the highly motile glycerol-containing fowl semen might be due to excessively rapid loss of glycerol in the hen's oviduct. The glycerol was therefore removed by dialysis before insemination, with the result that the fertilizing power of both unfrozen and frozen samples was retained unimpaired, and large numbers of healthy chicks which developed normally were obtained (Polge, 1951a, b).

By contrast, bull semen diluted to contain 15% glycerol and inseminated without dialysis or any other treatment had normal fertilizing capacity. After freezing and thawing, however, only one cow out of five inseminated in the first trial became pregnant (Stewart, 1951), and a larger-scale trial the following year was entirely negative (Polge and Rowson, 1952a). The value of egg yolk in protecting bull semen against thermal shock, as well as the importance of the temperature at which glycerol was added and the time allowed for equilibration with it, was then considered. The technique finally adopted as far as glycerol was concerned, was to dilute the semen immediately after collection with yolk citrate buffer at +28°C. and cool it to +5°C. during 4 hours in the refrigerator before adding an equal volume of cold yolk citrate buffer containing 20% glycerol. After a period of 8 to 20 hours at +5°C. the semen containing a final concentration of 10% glycerol was cooled slowly to −79°C., as described in Section IV. Samples thus treated have been stored at −79°C. for periods varying from 2 hours to one year. When thawed at +40°C. and inseminated into cows, the pregnancy rate obtained with this material has ranged from 56 to 80% and has been of the same order as that obtained with unfrozen control samples, even in dilutions as high as 1 in 40 and 1 in 100 (Polge and Rowson, 1952a, b, c; Polge and Lovelock, 1952; Polge, 1953a, b). The practical applications and fundamental implications of the experiments with glycerol-treated frozen bull semen will be discussed later. So far little progress has been made in reviving semen of laboratory rodents or other farm animals after storage in the frozen state.

The effect of glycerol on the viability of many other cells and tissues at normal temperatures and after exposure to low temperatures has been tested. Like urea, glycerol rapidly penetrates mammalian red blood cells and therefore fails to exert an osmotic effect. Exposure of the cells to isoosmotic solutions of glycerol in distilled water is, from the osmotic standpoint, practically equivalent to treatment with pure water and causes almost as rapid hemolysis (Jacobs *et al.*, 1950). Concentrations as high as 50%, in isotonic saline are, on the other hand, harmless (Johnson *et al.*, 1933). Sudden dilution or transfer of the corpuscles to glycerol-free solutions, however, causes hemolysis. In the presence of 15 to 30% glycerol red blood cells can be cooled to, stored at, and thawed from −79°C. with little or no hemolysis (Smith, 1950). Provided that the glycerol is removed slowly, for instance by dialysis, the previously frozen cells can be resuspended in saline or plasma and after transfusion survive normally in the blood stream of animals and man (Sloviter, 1951a, b; Mollison and Sloviter, 1951; Sloviter, 1952; Mollison *et al.*, 1952). The glycerol can be removed more rapidly and easily either by displacement with strong sodium citrate solutions (Lovelock, 1952) or by continuous washing (Chaplin and Veall, 1953).

Mammalian skin is unusually resistant to freezing and thawing (Mider and Morton, 1939; Webster, 1944; Briggs and Jund, 1944; Strumia and Hodge, 1945). A pronounced protective action of glycerol has, nevertheless, been demonstrated (*v.* Chapter 11).

With the exception of the thyroid and parathyroid glands, untreated endocrine tissue does not survive exposure to low temperatures (Blumenthal and Walsh, 1950; Lipschütz, 1928, 1929; Payne and Meyer, 1942). By contrast, glycerol-treated ovarian tissue which had been cooled to and kept for long periods at −79° and −190°C. rapidly gave functional grafts when thawed and implanted into spayed animals (Parkes and Smith, 1953). Equally good results were obtained with testicular tissue (Deanesly, 1953). Less regular "takes" were obtained with adrenal tissue cooled to −79° or −190°C. in presence of glycerol, although like similarly treated pituitary tissue it grew in tissue culture (Parkes, 1953; Smith and Parkes, 1953; Smith, S. E., 1953).

Unlike the surrounding ovarian granulosa cells, isolated mammalian eggs proved exceptionally sensitive to sudden addition of 15% glycerol and survived only when it was gradually added and removed at +37°C. After cooling to −79° or −190°C. in the presence of glycerol, only about 1% of recently fertilized rabbit eggs resumed normal development after thawing and cultivation. This result, though slight in itself, shows that exposure to low temperatures is not necessarily lethal to rabbit eggs even in their highly active and unstable state between syngamy and segmentation (Smith, 1952a, b; 1953a). The suggestion that the survival of tumor tissues at low temperature may be dependent on the presence of dormant cells (Craigie *et al.*, 1951) cannot, therefore, be of general application.

The protective action of glycerol is not restricted to the cells and tissues of higher animals. For instance, *Entamoeba histolytica*, which had not hitherto survived exposure to low temperatures, resumed normal activity and reproduction when cultured after cooling to and storage at −79°C. in media containing 5% and 10% glycerol (Fulton and Smith, 1953). Yeasts of various species, which are hardy in comparison with amoebae, show quantitatively better survival rates when cooled rapidly in the presence of glycerol, the protective action being particularly well marked between −20° and −79°C. (Smith, 1953b).

### 2. *Method of Protection against Freezing*

Ethers and other derivatives of glycerol, ethylene glycol, propylene glycol, as well as a variety of neutral solutes, have been tested on red blood cells, spermatozoa, eggs, and other cells, organisms, and tissues. So far none has excelled glycerol in protecting them against damage at low temperatures, and the majority have in themselves proved toxic. Attention has therefore been focused on the mode of action of glycerol.

Chemically, glycerol is the simplest trihydric alcohol with an empirical formula $C_3H_8O_3$ and a structural formula:

$$\begin{array}{ccccccc} & & H & & H & & H & \\ & & | & & | & & | & \\ H & - & C & - & C & - & C & - & H \\ & & | & & | & & | & \\ & & O & & O & & O & \\ & & | & & | & & | & \\ & & H & & H & & H & \end{array}$$

Because of its multiple hydroxyl groups it possesses an unusual range of reactions and derivatives. Although easily oxidized, reduced, and dehydrated by suitable agents, it is remarkably stable under ordinary atmospheric conditions. It occurs in plants and animals in the form of natural fats and oils and is produced in the course of carbohydrate metabolism and fermentation (Godfrey, 1953a, b; Segur, 1953a; Werkman, 1953; Carr and Krantz, 1945). Glycerol has no adverse effect on enzymes of many kinds and has been widely used in their isolation and storage (Waldschmidt-Leitz, 1929; Sumner and Somers, 1943). It has been used to study the absorption spectra at low temperatures of pepsin (Lavin and Northrop, 1935) and of hemoproteins (Keilin and Hartree, 1949). Fifty per cent glycerol at $-20°C$. is used to preserve myosin and the contractile properties of muscle fibers (Szent-Györgyi, 1949, 1951). At normal and at low temperatures it is a valuable preservative for egg yolk (MacFarlane and Hall, 1943; Godston, 1934). Glycerol can be used as a food by many organisms and animals (Johnson *et al.*, 1933). Even in high concentrations it is non-toxic, so that its valuable lubricant, solvent, and humectant powers and its sweet taste are employed in the production of a variety of medicaments for external and internal use (Hanke, 1953; Segur, 1953b).

By contrast, ethylene and propylene glycols are not normal anabolites or catabolites and are toxic to many cells and organisms. They have been little used for the storage and study of biochemical or food products or in pharmaceutical preparations (Carr and Krantz, 1945).

Glycerol is characterized by remarkable physical properties. For instance, of all substances, glycerol is one of the least compressible. It is soluble in water and alcohols in all proportions besides blending with oily and lipoid substances. Furthermore, it possesses considerable solvent powers for electrolytes and other inorganic and organic compounds. There seems to be no component of living cells with which it would not mix. In spite of the high viscosity of glycerol, water and electrolytes diffuse into it rapidly and it diffuses rapidly into other solutions and gels.

Its presence has little effect on the dissociation constant of water, or on the hydrogen ion concentration of buffered and non-buffered solutions (Segur, 1953c).

Glycerol has a strong tendency to supercool, and although the melting point is +18.0°C. it is seldom seen in the crystalline state. Furthermore, it is exceedingly hygroscopic, and small amounts of water have a pronounced effect in depressing its freezing point. Conversely, it depresses

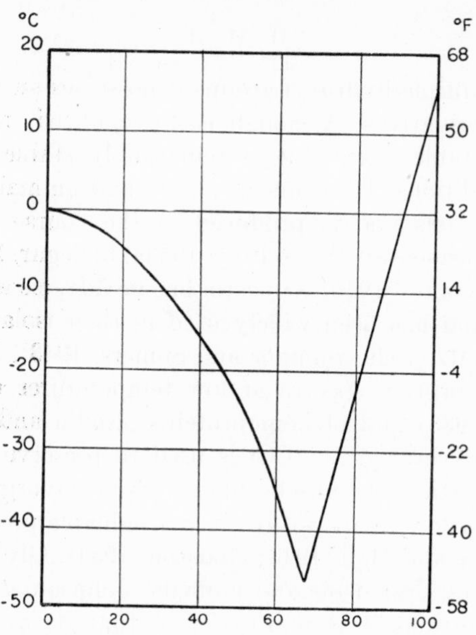


FIG. 9. Freezing points of glycerol-water solutions. Abscissas represent per cent of glycerol by weight. (From Segur, 1953.)

the freezing point of aqueous solutions and in moderate concentrations forms a valuable antifreeze agent (Fig. 9). Aqueous solutions of glycerol have a higher specific heat than the pure substance and are useful thermal buffers at low temperatures. When glycerol solutions are cooled, ice and salts eventually crystallize out at well-recognized temperatures, depending on the respective concentrations of the solutes (Segur, 1953c). Pure glycerol, on the other hand, supercools to very low temperatures and increases in viscosity until, in the range between −70° and −110°C. it becomes vitreous. Vitrification is characterized by an abrupt change in specific heat, thermal expansion coefficient, and other properties (Kauzmann, 1948). It is not known whether vitrification of glycerol could occur in the presence of ice and salts in complex systems such as living cells.

The varied chemical and physical properties of glycerol may all, to some extent, be responsible for its value in preserving the viability of living cells during exposure to low temperatures. Attention was first directed to its effect on extra- and intracellular crystallization (Smith *et al.*, 1951). Microscopic studies during freezing and thawing revealed that 15 to 20% glycerol promoted supercooling so that ice formation in the medium was postponed till the temperature had reached −10° to −20°C. In Ringer's solution the spears and plates of ice increased in size, until at −25°C. the clefts between them were almost obliterated. There was no evidence that red blood cells were pierced or compressed by crystals, and much hemolysis occurred during thawing. During freezing and thawing spermatozoa were distorted, disrupted, and killed. In the presence of glycerol the ice crystals grew in fern-like forms, leaving relatively spacious channels in which the spermatozoa or red blood cells lodged. Thawing was a more gradual and less violent process than in glycerol-free media and left the red blood cells intact and the spermatozoa with unimpaired motility.

More recently an improved type of freezing slide and a more accurate temperature recording system have been devised. Giant multinucleated spermatids and other cells from the guinea pig testis have been studied during freezing and thawing. The untreated cells crystallized internally between 0° and −10°C. and on thawing were disrupted. Many of the glycerol-treated cells, on the other hand, contained no visible intracellular crystals at temperatures as low as −80°C. and on thawing were morphologically unaltered (*v.* Fig. 8a, b). Similar observations were made with glycerol-free and glycerol-treated corneal epithelial cells (Smith and Smiles, 1953).

Working on model systems, Lusena and Cook (1953) find that glycerol modifies the rate of crystal growth, membrane permeability, and related phenomena and partially controls the real rate of freezing.

Luyet and Gehenio (1952) have studied the action of glycerol in preventing injury during freezing of chick embryonic tissues. They say that glycerol, besides dehydrating the tissues, lowers their freezing point, delays the initiation of crystallization, retards the advance of the ice front, and reduces the amount of ice formed at a given temperature. They think that the protective action of glycerol may be associated with its water-binding properties.

There is, however, some doubt whether crystallization is a crucial factor in causing death. Evidence has accumulated to show that, in many cells, death occurs before intracellular crystallization has taken place. With other cells the lethal effect of both extra- and intracellular ice formation can be explained by the associated rise in the concentration

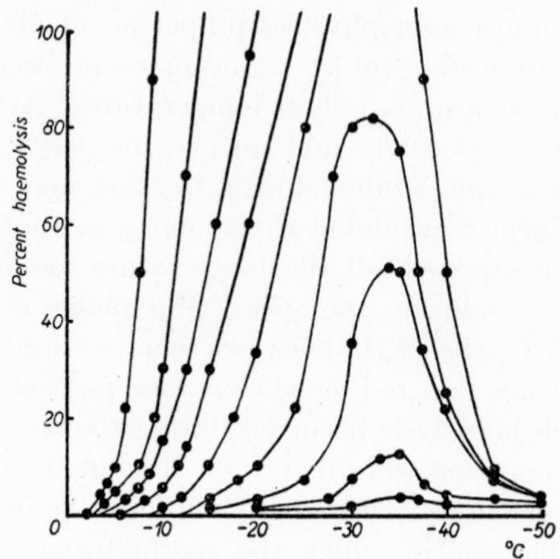


FIG. 10. The hemolysis when red blood cells in suspension in 0.16 *M* NaCl containing various concentrations of glycerol are frozen. The curves shown are, from left to right, those corresponding to glycerol concentrations of 0.0, 0.15, 0.3, 0.5, 0.75, 1.0, 1.5, 2.0, and 2.5 *M*. In all experiments the cells were frozen for 10 minutes at the temperatures indicated. (From Lovelock, 1953b.)

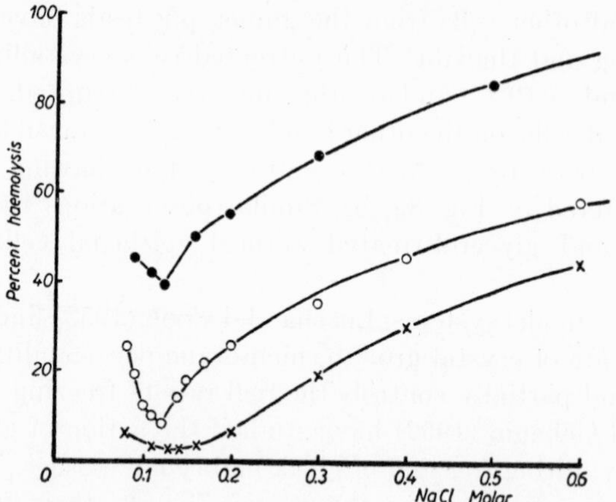


FIG. 11. The effect of the initial sodium chloride concentration of the suspending medium on the hemolysis of red blood cells. The glycerol concentrations were (x) 2.0, (○) 1.5, and (●) 1.0 *M*, respectively. The cells were frozen to −30°C. for 10 minutes. (From Lovelock, 1953b.)

of electrolytes. For instance, Lovelock (1953a, b) has shown that the hemolysis of red blood cells during freezing can be attributed chiefly to the concentration of salts in the suspending medium and within the cells. The critical temperature range in which damage occurs is −3° to −40°C. and coincides with the region in which the cell is exposed to concentrated salt. The nature of damage by strong salts has been discussed above (*v.* Section III). Lovelock (1953b) has shown that the extent of the critical temperature range decreases with increasing concentration of glycerol up to 2.5 *M* (23% by weight), as shown in Fig. 10. When the initial sodium chloride concentration of the medium is increased from 0.11 *M* to 0.6 *M* the hemolysis during freezing to and thawing from −30°C. is progressively increased, but it is diminished at all sodium chloride

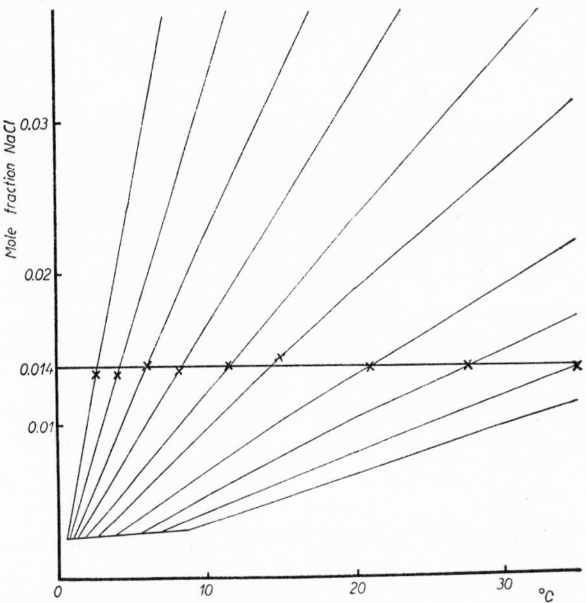


FIG. 12. The sodium chloride concentration of the liquid phase when 0.16 *M* NaCl, with various initial concentrations of glycerol also present, is frozen. The lines shown are, from left to right, those for solutions containing initially 0.0, 0.15, 0.3, 0.5, 0.75, 1.0, 1.5, 2.0, 2.5, and 3.0 *M* glycerol. The point marked "X" on each line is the observed temperature at which hemolysis first occurs with cells suspended in a medium whose initial glycerol concentration is the same as that of the line. The intersecting horizontal line lies at sodium chloride concentration mole fraction 0.014, i.e., 0.8 *M* in water. (From Lovelock, 1953b.)

levels by raising the glycerol concentration from 1.0 *M* to 2.0 *M* (Fig. 11).

According to Lovelock, it follows from the colligative properties of solutions that the mere addition of a neutral solute to a solution of an electrolyte will lower the concentration of salt in equilibrium with ice at any temperature during freezing. The concentration of salt which occurs when a solution of sodium chloride is frozen is thus greatly reduced by addition of glycerol. The sodium chloride content of the liquid phase in equilibrium with ice at various temperatures in the presence of different concentrations of glycerol is shown in Fig. 12. The temperature and corresponding sodium chloride level at which hemolysis starts is also shown. It is of particular interest that hemolysis always begins when the mole fraction of sodium chloride reaches 0.014 (0.8 *M* in water). The higher the glycerol content, the lower is the temperature at which the salt concentration rises to the critical level. When the initial concentration of glycerol exceeds 2.5 *M* (25%) the critical sodium chloride level is not reached in the temperature range 0° to −40°C. (Lovelock, 1953b, c).

When glycerol was prevented by the action of copper ions from entering the cell it failed to exert any protective action. This indicates that the internal potassium chloride concentration is at least as important as the external sodium chloride in causing damage. The suggestion that glycerol protects by dehydrating the cells before exposure to low temperatures is not applicable to red blood cells. Lovelock (1953b, c) has also shown that the dehydration is normally only transient and that as glycerol permeates the corpuscles they are rapidly restored to their original degree of hydration. They remain dehydrated in the presence of glycerol only if it is prevented from permeating them as by treatment with copper. Cells so dehydrated did not survive freezing.

Lovelock (1953c) has worked out a formula for testing the theory that cells are protected by glycerol against the increase in salt concentration during freezing. He explains it as follows:

"The depression ($T$) of the freezing point of an aqueous solution of sodium chloride and glycerol, the concentrations of which are $X$ and $Y$ respectively, is given by the relationship

$$T = K(2X + Y)$$

where $K$ is the freezing point depression of water produced by unit concentration of solute.

"If the critical salt concentration above which a cell is irreversibly damaged is given by ($nX$) then the temperature ($T_D$) below 0°C. at which irreversible damage will first occur is given by

$$T_D = Kn(2X + Y)$$

"This equation can be transposed to give the glycerol concentration ($Y$) required to prevent irreversible damage at a given temperature

$$Y = \frac{T_D - 2KnX}{Kn}$$

This relationship can be used to test the validity of the hypothesis that glycerol prevents damage during freezing and thawing by functioning as a salt buffer."

The concentration of glycerol required in practice to prevent damage has been compared with that required by theory. Figure 13 shows lines plotted according to the equation above and the experimentally observed concentrations of glycerol needed to prevent damage.

The cells tested in these experiments were rabbit and bull spermatozoa and human red blood cells, respectively. The close correspondence

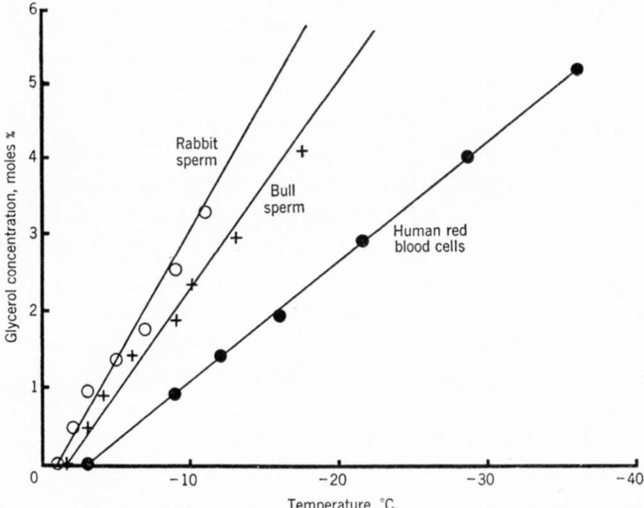


FIG. 13. The concentration of glycerol required to protect rabbit spermatozoa, bull spermatozoa, and human red blood cells when frozen at various temperatures for 10 minutes. The lines are derived theoretically, and the points are experimental observations. (From Lovelock, 1953c.)

between the theoretical predictions and the practical findings offers strong support for the view that glycerol protects living cells against low temperature damage by virtue of its salt buffering potentiality. The superiority of glycerol over analogous substances and other possible salt buffers probably lies in its relatively low molecular weight, its ability to permeate freely into cells, its miscibility with salt solutions, and, even in high concentrations, its lack of toxicity.

There seems little reason to postulate that ethylene glycol, for instance, protects cells from damage by cold in some way totally different from that of glycerol. The dominant lethal factor during freezing and thawing appears, at the present time, to be the increasing concentration of electrolytes. The dominant mode of protection, therefore, is likely to be the buffering of salts. Additional protective effects of glycerol and related substances may, however, emerge and prove equally important after further consideration of their behavior and other properties at low temperatures.

## VII. DURATION OF SURVIVAL AT LOW TEMPERATURES: METABOLIC AND PHYSICAL FACTORS

It was at one time supposed that at temperatures not far below 0°C. biochemical and biophysical changes in living cells would be arrested or slowed to a negligible rate. Abundant evidence is now forthcoming to contradict this view. For instance, twenty-one species of bacteria, yeasts, and molds survived and actually multiplied during one year at 16°F. (−8.9°C.), although the culture medium had frozen (Smart, 1935). Fruit, vegetables, milk, eggs, meat, and fish all alter in flavor or appearance during cold storage, even when microbial activity cannot be implicated (Joslyn, 1949; Sizer 1943; Sizer, and Josephson, 1942).

One reason for these phenomena is that enzyme activity continues, although at a much decreased rate, even when the medium has frozen. The decrease in velocity with falling temperature varies for different enzymes (Joslyn, 1951) and this variation causes an imbalance in the chains and cycles of interconnected reactions in living cells and may result in accumulation of toxic products (Joslyn, 1949). It seems likely that unless the temperature is lowered sufficiently to inhibit all enzymic action, the life span of living cells may be reduced by autointoxication rather than prolonged by an overall reduction in metabolic rate. Even if the imbalance were harmless, the cells would age and their survival time would be limited by the continuation of metabolism.

Sizer and Josephson (1942) found that lipase was active at −24.5°C. Tryptic digestion proceeded at −15°C., and invertase hydrolyzed sucrose at −18°C. From experimental results between 0° and −25°C. they calculated the activation energies of these enzymes in the range 0° to −70°C. They state clearly, however, that during several weeks at −70°C. no hydrolysis was detected in any of the systems tested. The calculated values must also be regarded with reserve in view of work by Gibson (1953) on methods of deducing activation energies. Nevertheless, the work of Sizer and Josephson suggests that foodstuffs can be stored at −25°C. for many weeks without serious change, and this has been confirmed in practice (*v.* Section VIII). It is still not known whether biochemical reactions catalyzed by enzymes cease, or whether they continue at an infinitesimal rate at very low temperatures.

Many vital processes depend on diffusion as well as on enzyme action. During refrigeration of living cells, diffusion, which is slowed relatively little, is of great importance and may cause damage. For example, essential intermediate metabolites and cell components may be lost. Other substances such as water normally excreted or excluded by active means may accumulate within the cells. The selective permeability of the cell membrane is probably modified when chilled because of the importance of active transport mechanisms. As a result of altered permeability and continued diffusion the normal dynamic equilibrium of cells with their environment may be chemically and physically altered in a variety of other ways. The new equilibrium is unlikely to become static until very low temperatures are reached. These considerations may explain in part why certain bacteria succumb rapidly during storage close to 0°C. (Haines, 1937) and why temperatures between 0° and −40°C. are unfavorable for the preservation of glycerol-treated red blood cells, spermatozoa, and eggs of mammals.

The concentration of electrolytes, which increases during separation of ice until their respective eutectics are reached, is known to constitute a serious source of damage during cold storage. The action of hypertonic salts on living cells, which includes denaturation of proteins and solution of lipoproteins and mucoproteins, has been discussed in Section III. Even in the presence of glycerol, which acts as a salt buffer, their damaging effect continues and is apparent after time intervals and at critical temperatures which vary according to the cell (*v.* Section VI). The harmful effects of concentrated salts can be avoided only by storing at temperatures below −40°C. when they are no longer in solution.

Water, the major component of living cells, undergoes physical transformations down to and below −40°C. Supercooling, which may occur in pure water as low as −40°C. (Cwilong, 1945, 1947; Owston, 1951; Pound *et al.*, 1953), is facilitated by the presence of solutes and by dispersion of fluid in capillary or colloidal systems such as occur in living cells (Fisher, 1924; Blanchard, 1940). Even after crystallization as ice a stable state is not immediately attained. The small crystals formed during rapid cooling or after supercooling tend to grow and become converted into larger crystals (Moran and Hale, 1932). When ice has formed in one part of a system subdivided by membranes, continuous freezing may occur rapidly throughout, or individual cells may freeze independently, depending on the permeability of the membranes (Cook and Lusena, 1951). Free supercooled water cannot coexist with ice in different parts of such a system for any great length of time. The low vapor pressure of ice necessitates the transfer of molecules of unfrozen water to the surface of the ice until the concentration of solutes has reduced the vapor pressure of the solution to equal that of ice at the same temperature (Lovelock, 1953c, d). These relationships have important consequences for refrigeration in the food industry (*v.* Section VIII). They may contribute to the gradual loss of viability of glycerol-treated fowl spermatozoa and ovarian tissue in the eourse of storage for days or weeks at temperatures as low as −79°C. (Polge and Parkes, 1952; Parkes and Smith, 1953). The unimpaired vitality of these cells kept in the presence of glycerol for as long as one year at −190°C. may be due to the diminished energy and greater stability of water molecules at that temperature. It may also be

TABLE 2
LONG-TERM STORAGE OF BULL SEMEN AT −79°C. (FROM POLGE, 1953)
(1 year)

| Age of semen, weeks | No. of cows | Conception rate, % |
|---|---|---|
| 1–4 | 16 | 63 |
| 5–8 | 16 | 69 |
| 9–12 | 16 | 81 |
| 13–16 | 16 | 63 |
| 17–20 | 16 | 50 |
| 21–24 | 16 | 75 |
| 25–28 | 16 | 38 |
| 29–32 | 16 | 56 |
| 33–36 | 16 | 69 |
| 37–40 | 16 | 69 |
| 41–44 | 16 | 56 |
| 45–48 | 16 | 75 |
| 49–52 | 16 | 88 |
| 1–52 | 208 | 65 |

*Notes:* Normal conception rate in A.I. = 68%.
Semen diluted 1:4.
Concentration of glycerol in semen = 10%.

connected with the conversion of glycerol at about −83°C. from a viscous supercooled fluid to a rigid glass (Kauzmann, 1948; Segur, 1953c). The results already obtained with glycerol-treated bull semen kept at −79°C. and ovarian tissue kept at −190°C. show that deterioration does not occur during one year's storage at these temperatures (Tables 2 and 3). Becquerel (1951) has calculated that, if chemical changes continue and still obey van't Hoff's law, the metabolic rate of spores normally living one year between +10° and +20°C. would be slowed 85,300 times at −100°C. and the reduction in rate would be $7.13 \times 10^{13}$ times at −270°C. These figures indicate the life spans to be anticipated if biochemical changes continue at very low temperatures. The operation of certain physical factors, such as increased viscosity, should still further retard chemical activity and postpone chemical aging. Other physical factors may, however, be harmful, even at very low temperatures. If all chemical reactions and physical processes were arrested or controlled, living cells could presumably be preserved for infinite periods in a state of suspended animation.

TABLE 3
RETENTION OF VIABILITY IN LONG-FROZEN OVARIAN TISSUE
(FROM PARKES, 1953)

| Duration of freezing of tissue, days | No. of implantations | No. of active grafts obtained | Average time taken for reappearance of cycle, days |
|---|---|---|---|
| 1/24 | 5 | 5 | 15.4 |
| 9 | 5 | 5 | 14.4 |
| 83 | 5 | 5 | 18.8 |
| 117 | 8 | 8 | 15.1 |
| 235 | 9 | 9 | 16.0 |
| 367 | 12 | 12 | 16.3 |

## VIII. EFFECTS OF COLD ON THE WHOLE ANIMAL

It is clear from clinical and experimental studies that local injury can result from cooling exposed parts of intact animals and man in ways which do not cause the death of the whole organism. Prolonged exposure to damp at temperatures not far below that of the normal environment may lead to peripheral damage. The mildest manifestation of such an effect is the chilblain which occurs on fingers, toes, and ears of well-housed people living in temperate climates and never exposed to severe degrees of cold (Ingram, 1949; Wheatley, 1950). More serious syndromes, such as trench foot and immersion foot, are caused by exposure to wet and cold for hours or days at temperatures between +10° and 0°C. In the most severe cases the condition culminates in gangrene and necessitates amputation (Ungley, 1949; White, 1943; Greene, 1941).

The first effect of subnormal temperatures on exposed parts is local vasodilatation, which maintains their temperature for a time. This is followed by vascular stasis resulting in edema and accompanied by a fall in metabolic rate of the tissues. Finally the parts become ischemic and cool to a temperature close to that of their surroundings. On returning to normal temperature and humidity, reactions set in of which the most noticeable are hyperemia with increased edema, paraesthesia or anesthesia, and loss of fine movements (Greene, 1943; Edholm, 1953; Kreyberg, 1949).

The most severe form of local injury is frostbite. The duration of exposure and other factors besides the degree of cold are determining factors. The highest temperature at which frostbite has been recorded is in the neighborhood of −4.4°C. when there was an accompanying wind (Greene, 1941, 1942; Lake, 1917). There are numerous reports, however, that ears, noses, and fingers, which blanched and hardened after a few seconds' exposure to severe atmospheric cold between −20° and −70°C., recovered completely from their incipient frostbite when rapidly re-warmed to their normal temperature (Schumacker, 1951; Greene, 1941). More prolonged exposure over minutes or hours results, on the other hand, in the full syndrome culminating in gangrene and loss of the part. Under certain circumstances the severity of the condition can be reduced by rapid reheating, although other clinicians favor gradual warming (Edholm, 1952, 1953).

There is still much doubt as to whether ice forms within the tissues and in so doing constitutes a major source of damage, or whether the severe cold causes injury independent of freezing. There is little doubt, on the other hand, that the serious reactions which set in after rewarming are responsible to some degree, if not entirely, for the ultimate death of cells and tissues. Of these, vascular reactions are probably the most important. Vasodilatation is followed by stasis and intravascular clotting and by local edema. The blood supply to an entire extremity may thus be cut off. Unless adequately counteracted these changes lead to death of all cells and tissues in the part, including those which were unharmed by exposure to the low temperature (Kreyberg, 1949; Crismon, 1951a, b; Edholm, 1953).

The sensitivity to mild and moderate cold of the tissues of tropical and laboratory animals and man contrasts with the resistance to severe cold of species which hibernate, and of arctic creatures. With arctic mammals this is in part due to the superb insulation afforded by the fur, and also to the characteristically low critical atmospheric temperature below which body temperature is maintained by increasing the metabolic rate (Scholander *et al.*, 1950a, b, c). The white fox, for instance, sleeps on snow or at atmospheric temperatures as low as −50°C. without experiencing frostbite or even shivering (Scholander *et al.*, 1950a, b, c). Smaller animals, less well insulated, burrow underground or into the snow for protection, and arctic birds depend partly on insulation by their feathers. It has been recorded that pigeons survived 144 hours at −40°C. but died within 20 minutes if exposed to the same temperature after plucking (Streicher *et al.*, 1950). Insulation and increased metabolic rate, however, are not the only factors involved. The legs and feet of birds, for instance, have no special insulation, yet ducks and gulls walk on ice and snow at low temperatures and the tissues of their feet persistently remain without ill effect at temperatures which are far below that which is normal for the internal organs and which would be lethal for the animal as a whole. The skin and peripheral parts of arctic mammals also remain for long periods at temperatures which would be harmful to human tissues. For instance, the subcutaneous temperatures of the muzzle and footpads of arctic sleigh dogs were often found to be +10°C. when the air temperature ranged from −30° to −45°C. Temperatures below +10°C. were recorded within the hooves and lower limbs of caribou deer. There is some evidence of biochemical adaptation of the fats and other components of the tissues in the exposed parts of these animals (Irving, 1951).

In arctic mammals and birds the rigid maintenance of an internal temperature 100°C. above that of their environment for weeks on end is a remarkable achievement. All warm-blooded animals, with the exception of those adapted to hibernation, maintain an internal temperature between +37 and +40°C. whatever their habitat. When the body temperature falls below +20°C. life is endangered, and the lowest rectal temperature which the non-hibernating mammals until recently were known to have survived was +14°C. in guinea pigs and cats (Britton, 1923; Gagge and Herrington, 1947; Edholm, 1953). Survival with body temperatures at or below +10°C. was supposed to be possible only for the marmot and other hibernating animals. Rats, however, have been fully revived after the rectal temperature had reached 1°C., and after cessation of respiration and heart beat, for 1 hour (Andjus, 1951).

It is of great interest that, after death of the whole animal from cold or other causes, skin, ovaries, and other tissues and organs contain living cells. Thus, mitosis may continue for some hours after death of the animal (Bullough, 1950a, b). Ovaries from corpses of rats which had been kept at +4°C. for 2 days "took" and functioned normally when homografted into spayed animals. Ovarian tissue from stored corpses also contained viable cells after exposure to low temperatures in glycerol-containing media (Smith and Parkes, 1953). The largest entire animal so far successfully frozen and thawed is the vinegar eel (Luyet and Hartung, 1941a, b, c; Gehenio and Luyet, 1947, 1951). No doubt conditions appropriate to larger entire organisms will in time be determined, but it is difficult to imagine that there are early prospects of storing whole animals in solid carbon dioxide or in liquid air. There is, in fact, a formidable gap between our knowledge of the effects of cooling the whole animal and our knowledge of the preservation of isolated cells and tissues at low temperatures, and no one can tell when it will be bridged.

## IX. PRACTICAL APPLICATIONS

The aim of food refrigeration is palatability and not viability of the tissues to be eaten at a future date. Nevertheless, many of the fundamental principles and experimental results already described have had important applications in this industry. Thus, an understanding of the physical effects of different rates of cooling and of different storage temperatures has led to methods which reduce excessive "drip" from meat. Similarly, the occurrence of "freezer-burn" due to sublimation of moisture from the surface of foodstuffs onto the refrigerating pipes has been diminished (Birdseye and Fitzgerald, 1932; Bate-Smith, 1944; Callow, 1925, 1952).

Biochemical changes cause deterioration of meat, fish, eggs, milk, fruit, and vegetables during storage in the chilled or frozen state. They can to some extent be prevented by appreciating the importance of pH, salt effects, oxidation, and continued action of enzymes at low temperatures (Sair and Cook, 1938; Empey, 1933; Moran, 1935; Reay, 1933, 1935; Pearce and Lavers, 1949; Joslyn, 1949; Proc. 8th International Congress of Refrigeration, 1951). The prevention of spoilage by microorganisms depends not only on hygienic measures but also on a knowledge of the minimum temperature at which they multiply or survive, and on the use of supplementary procedures to destroy them (Haines, 1937; Hampil, 1932; Rahn, 1945; Smart, 1935; Tanner and Williamson, 1927).

In departments of pathology and microbiology, on the other hand, there is a considerable demand for methods of preserving the viability of microorganisms. This is frequently achieved by freeze-drying pure cultures of bacteria (*v.* Chapter 10 ). It is possible that in certain cases the yield of viable organisms in the final product could be improved by modifying the method of cooling prior to high-vacuum distillation. For instance snapfreezing might cause thermal shock and give worse results than slow cooling. Furthermore, the salt content of ordinary media may, when concentrated by freezing, prove harmful whereas reduction of the initial electrolytes or introduction of salt buffers might be beneficial. Each species may have a different critical temperature at which maximum damage occurs during freezing, and this should be determined and avoided when selecting the temperature to be held during dehydration. Pathogenic protozoa, which have not hitherto survived drying from normal or low temperatures, are likely to be preserved with or without glycerol at very low temperatures in an increasing number of laboratories. This would abolish the labor and dangers of repeated subcultivation or animal inoculation (Coggeshall, 1939; Manwell and Edgett, 1943; Weinman and McAllister, 1947; Levaditi, 1952; Fulton and Smith, 1953).

The survival of glycerol-treated living cells during exposure to and storage at very low temperatures promises important applications to clinical as well as to scientific medicine. Thus, red blood cells, which hitherto could not be kept *in vitro* for more than 3 weeks at +5° to +10°C., can be stored in bulk in the presence of 15 to 30% glycerol for many months at −79°C. After treatment to remove the glycerol, they can be transfused and, in the blood stream of suitable recipients, have a normal survival time (Smith, 1950; Sloviter, 1951a, b; Mollison and Sloviter, 1951; Sloviter, 1952; Mollison *et al.*, 1952; Lovelock, 1952, 1953b; Chaplin and Veall, 1953). Other methods of preventing the hemolysis which normally occurs during freezing and thawing, such as those suggested by Luyet (1949; 1951) and by Strumia (1949a, b), are of great academic interest. They are not, however, readily applicable to the needs of blood banks, either because of the difficulty of ultrarapid freezing when dealing with large volumes or because of the impracticability of maintaining the temperature rigidly at −3°C.

The possibility of preserving glycerol-treated blood corpuscles at low temperatures which can be maintained by ordinary refrigeration, e.g., −20°C., has not been overlooked (Chaplin and Mollison, 1953). The high degree of hemolysis during long-term storage at this temperature suggests that it would not prove an economic proposition even if the cells which survived storage had a normal life span *in vivo*. Blood storage at −79°C. or possibly between −79° and −40°C., which is the lower level of the critical temperature range of red blood cells, should, on the other hand, prove most valuable in keeping erythrocytes belonging to rare groups for immunological tests as well as for transfusion. The high cost of building and maintaining the necessary refrigerators would no doubt be overcome if there were sufficient demand for storage at very low temperatures.

The value of frozen skin for surgical grafting in humans may be outweighed by the immunological problems of homografting (*v.* Chapter 11). Endocrine tissue, on the other hand, has frequently been grafted from one individual to another without such complications and with functional results (Gaillard, 1948, 1953; Jones, 1953; Smith and Parkes, 1953). The difficulty of providing suitable human material for grafting at the time when it is needed has so far limited the clinical applications of this practice. The demonstration that glycerol-treated ovarian, testicular, and adrenal tissue regenerates when grafted after storage at −79° or −190°C. opens the possibility of banking endocrinological spare parts for future surgical use (Parkes, 1951; Smith and Parkes, 1951, 1953; Parkes and Smith, 1953; Deanesly, 1953). Although the best results have so far been obtained by storage at −190°C., further research is likely to point to ways of diminishing the harmful physical effects which occur on prolonged storage at higher temperatures. Other intriguing methods of providing large quantities of endocrine tissue may, however, forestall the low temperature bank, e.g., the large-scale *in vitro* cultivation of tissues being developed by Earle and his coworkers (Earle, 1953; Evans *et al.*, 1951).

The most striking application of biological studies on freezing has so far been in cattle breeding. The demonstration that glycerol-treated bull spermatozoa possessed normal fertilizing capacity both before and after freezing at −79°C. has been fully confirmed. The storage of semen treated in this way is now coming widely into practice and up to a period of one year, the longest so far recorded, there has been no loss of functional activity (Polge, 1952; Polge and Rowson, 1952a, b; Polge, 1953a, b; Polge and Rowson, 1953). The method, which is now being applied in Europe, Asia, Africa, Australia, New Zealand and in North and South America, as well as in Great Britain, promises to economize in the number of bulls required for breeding, to permit of progeny testing without wasting the most useful part of the bull's life, to facilitate the use of nominated sires, and to make possible global transport of semen.

## ACKNOWLEDGMENTS

I am much indebted to Dr. A. S. Parkes, F.R.S., who suggested the arrangement and revised the manuscript of this chapter. My best thanks are also due to Dr. J. E. Lovelock who has given me unstinted advice, to Mr. J. Smiles who collaborated in microscopic studies of freezing and has allowed me to use his photomicrographs in Fig. 8a and b, to Dr. O. G. Edholm who lent me a draft of his unpublished monograph, to Dr. C. Lutwak-Mann and Dr. E. H. Callow who drew my attention to some relevant literature, and to Miss S. Carswell who compiled the bibliography. The Librarian and various colleagues at the National Institute for Medical Research have assisted me in other ways.

## REFERENCES

It has been possible to make reference to only a few of the many relevant papers published in 1953.

Anderson, J. 1945. The Semen of Animals and Its Use for Artificial Insemination. *Tech. communs. Imp. Bur. Animal Breed. and Genet. (Edinburgh)* **viii,** 151; *Animal Breed. Abstr.* **13,** 118–119.

Andjus, R. 1951. Sur la possibilité de ranimer le rat adulte refroidi jusqu'à proximité du point de congélation. *Compt. rend.* **232,** 1591–1593.

Bate-Smith, E. C. 1944. The Quick Freezing of Meat. *Modern Refrig.* **47,** 267.

Becquerel, P. 1905. Action de l'air liquide sur la vie de la graine. *Compt. rend.* **140,** 1652.

Becquerel, P. 1932a. La vie latente des spores des mousses aux basses températures. *Compt. rend.* **194,** 1378–1380.

Becquerel, P. 1932b. La reviviscence des plantules desséchées soumises aux actions de vide et très basses températures. *Compt. rend.* **194,** 2158–2159.

Becquerel, P. 1936. La vie latente de quelques Algues et Animaux inferieurs aux basses températures et la conservation de la vie dans l'univers. *Compt. rend.* **202,** 978.

Becquerel, P. 1938. La congélation cellulaire et la synérèse. *Compt. rend.* **206,** 1587.

Becquerel, P. 1950. La suspension de la vie des spores des bacteries et des moisissisures desséchées dans le vide vers le zéro absolu. Ses conséquences pour la dissémination et la conservation de la vie dans l'univers. *Compt. rend.* **231,** 1392–1394.

Becquerel, P. 1951. La suspension de la vie au confins du zéro absolu entre 0,0075°K. et 0,047°K. Role de la synérèse reversible cytonucléoplasmique. *Proc. 8th Intern. Congr. Refrig.* P. 326.

Bělehrádek, J. 1935. *Temperature and Living Matter.* Protoplasma-Monographien No. 8. Borntraeger, Berlin.

Bell, L. G. E. 1952. The Application of Freezing and Drying Techniques in Histology, in *International Review of Cytology,* Vol. 1, pp. 35–63. Edited by G. H. Bourne, and J. F. Danielli, Academic Press, New York.

Billingham, R. E., and Medawar, P. B. 1952. The Freezing, Drying and Storage of Mammalian Skin. *J. Exptl. Biol.* **29,** 454–468.

Birdseye, C., and Fitzgerald, G. A. 1932. History and Present Importance of Quick Freezing. *Ind. Eng. Chem.* **24,** 676–678.

Blanchard, K. C. 1940. Water, Free and Bound. *Cold Spring Harbor Symposia Quant. Biol.* **8,** 1–8.

Blumenthal, H. T., and Walsh, L. B. 1950. Survival of Guinea-Pig Thyroid and Parathyroid Autotransplants Previously Subjected to Extremely Low Temperatures. *Proc. Soc. Exptl. Biol. Med.* **73,** 62–67.

Breedis, C. 1942. The Action of Extreme Cold on Leukemic Cells of Mice. *J. Exptl. Med.* **76,** 221–240.

Breedis, C., Barnes, W. A., and Furth, J. 1937. Effect of Rate of Freezing on the Transmitting Agent of Neoplasms of Mice. *Proc. Soc. Exptl. Biol. Med.* **36,** 220–224.

Briggs, R., and Jund, L. 1944. Successful Grafting of Frozen and Thawed Mouse Skin. *Anat. Record* **89,** 75–86.

Britton, S. W. 1923. Effects of Lowering the Temperature of Homoiothermic Animals. *Quart. J. Exptl. Physiol.* **13,** 55–70.

Brown, H. T., and Escombe, F. 1897. Note on the Influence of Very Low Temperatures on the Germinative Power of Seeds. *Proc. Roy. Soc. (London)* **62,** 160–165.

Bullough, W. S. 1950a. Mitotic Activity in the Tissues of Dead Mice and in Tissues Kept in Physiological Salt Solutions. *Exptl. Cell. Research* **1,** 410–420.

Bullough, W. S. 1950b. Completion of Mitosis after Death. *Nature* **165,** 493.

Callow, E. H. 1925. The Velocity of Ice Crystallization through Supercooled Gelatin Gels. *Proc. Roy. Soc. (London)* **108A,** 307–323.

Callow, E. H. 1951. Discussion in Commission III. *Proc. 8th Intern. Congr. Refrig.* P. 360.

Callow, E. H. 1952. Frozen Meat. *J. Sci. Food Agr.* **3,** 145.

Carr, C. J., and Krantz, J. C. 1945. Metabolism of the Sugar Alcohols and Their Derivatives. *Advances in Carbohydrate Chem.* **1,** 175–192.

Cattell, M. 1936. The Physiological Effects of Pressure. *Biol. Revs.* **11,** 441–476.

Chambers, R., and Hale, H. P. 1932. The Formation of Ice in Protoplasm. *Proc. Roy. Soc. (London)* **110B,** 336–352.

Chang, M-C., and Walton, A. 1940. The Effects of Low Temperature and Acclimatization on the Respiratory Activity and Survival of Ram Spermatozoa. *Proc. Roy. Soc. (London)* **129B,** 517–527.

Chaplin, H., and Mollison, P. L. 1953. Improved Storage of Red Cells at −20°C. *Lancet* **i,** 215.

Chaplin, H., and Veall, N. 1953. Removal of Glycerol from Previously Frozen Red Cells. *Lancet* **i,** 218.

Coggeshall, L. T. 1939. Preservation of Viable Malaria Parasites in the Frozen State. *Proc. Soc. Exptl. Biol. Med.* **42,** 499–501.

Cook, W. H., and Lusena, C. V. 1951. The Mechanism of Freezing in Food Products. *Proc. 8th Intern. Congr. Refrig.* P. 357.

Craigie, J. 1949. The Preservation of Suspensions of Tumour Cells in Dextrose at Low Temperatures. *Brit. J. Cancer* **3,** 268–274.

Craigie, J., Lind, P. E., Hayward, M. E., and Begg, A. M. 1951. Preliminary Observations on a Dormant State of Sarcoma Cells with Special Reference to Resistance to Freezing and Drying. *J. Pathol. Bacteriol.* **63,** 177–178.

Crismon, J. M. 1951a. Pathology and Physiology of Frost-Bite. *National Research Council Sub Committee on Vascular Surgery,* pp. 110–111.

Crismon, J. M. 1951b. Animal Studies. *Trans. 1st Conf. on Cold Injury* (*Josiah Macy, Jr., Foundation*). Edited by M. I. Ferrer. Hildreth Press, Bristol, Conn.

Cwilong, B. M. 1945. Sublimation in a Wilson Chamber. *Nature* **155,** 361–362.

Cwilong, B. M. 1947. Sublimation in a Wilson Chamber. *Proc. Roy. Soc. (London)* **190A,** 137–143.

Deanesly, R. 1953. Histological Evolution of Rat Gonadal Tissue Transplanted after Freezing and Thawing, in *The Preservation of Normal Tissues for Transplantation.* Ciba Foundation Symposium. In press.

Earle, W. R. 1953. Long-Term, Large-Scale Tissue Culture, in *The Preservation of Normal Tissues for Transplantation.* Ciba Foundation Symposium. In press.

Edholm, O. G. 1952. The Effects of Excessive Cold and Their Treatment. *Practitioner* **168,** 583–592.

Edholm, O. G. 1953. In press.

Emmens, C. W. 1948. The Effect of Variations in Osmotic Pressure and Electrolyte Concentration on the Motility of Rabbit Spermatozoa at Different Hydrogen-Ion Concentrations. *J. Physiol. (London)* **107,** 129–140.

Emmens, C. W., and Blackshaw, A. W. 1950. The Low Temperature Storage of Ram, Bull and Rabbit Spermatozoa. *Australian Vet. J.* **26,** 226–228.

Empey, W. A. 1933. Studies on the Refrigeration of Meat. Conditions Determining the Amount of "Drip" from Frozen and Thawed Muscle. *J. Soc. Chem. Ind. (London)* **52T,** 230–236.

Evans, V. J., Earle, W. R., Sanford, K. K., Shannon, J. E., and Waltz, H. K. 1951. The Preparation and Handling of Replicate Tissue Cultures for Quantitative Studies. *J. Natl. Cancer Inst.* **11,** 907–926.

Ferrer, M. I. 1951. Cold Injury. *Trans. 1st Conf. on Cold Injury* (*Josiah Macy, Jr., Foundation*). Edited by M. I. Ferrer. Hildreth Press, Bristol, Conn.

Fidler, J. C. 1952. Some Effects of Low Temperatures on Biological Systems. *Food Sci. Abstr.* **24,** 401.

Finn, D. B. 1932. Denaturation of Proteins in Muscle Juice by Freezing. *Proc. Roy. Soc. (London)* **111B,** 396–411.

Fisher, E. A. 1924. The Freezing of Water in Capillary Systems: a Critical Discussion. *J. Phys. Chem.* **28,** 360–367.

Flosdorf, E. W. 1950. Quick Freezing and the Freeze-Drying Process, in *Biophysical Research Methods*. Edited by F. M. Uber. Interscience Publishers, New York and London.

Fry, R. M., and Greaves, R. I. N. 1951. The Survival of Bacteria during and after Drying. *J. Hyg.* **49,** 220–246.

Fulton, J. D., and Smith, A. U. 1953. Preservation of *Entamoeba histolytica* at −79°C. in Presence of Glycerol. *Ann. Trop. Med.* **47,** 240–246.

Gagge, A. P., and Herrington, L. P. 1947. Physiological Effects of Heat and Cold. *Ann. Rev. Physiol.* **9,** 409–428.

Gaillard, P. J. 1948. Growth, Differentiation and Function of Explants of Some Endocrine Glands. *Symposia Soc. Exptl. Biol.* **2,** 139–144.

Gaillard, P. J. 1953. Transplantation of Cultivated Parathyroid Gland Tissue in Man, in *The Preservation of Normal Tissues for Transplantation*. Ciba Foundation Symposium. In press.

Gehenio, P. M., and Luyet, B. J. 1947. Improved Method of Obtaining the Survival of Vinegar Eels after Their Solidification at Low Temperatures. *Biodynamica* **6,**141.

Gehenio, P. M., and Luyet, B. J. 1951. Effect of a Preliminary Slight Dehydration on the Survival of Vinegar Eels Frozen at −77°C. *Biodynamica* **7,** 41–52.

George, W. 1953. Some Animal Reactions to Variations of Temperature. *Endeavour* **12,** 101–105.

Gersh, I. 1932. The Altmann Technique for Fixation by Drying while Freezing. *Anat. Record* **53,** 309–337.

Gersh, I. 1951. Some Recent Experiments in Fixation by Freezing and Drying, in *Freezing and Drying*. Edited by R. J. C. Harris. The Institute of Biology, London. Pp. 165–167.

Gibson, K. D. 1953. True and Apparent Activation Energies of Enzymic Reactions. *Biochim. et Biophys. Acta* **10,** 221–229.

Godfrey, T. M. 1953a. Natural Source and Occurrence, in *Glycerol*. A.C.S. Monograph No. 117. Edited by C. S. Miner and N. N. Dalton Reinhold Publishing Corp., New York.

Godfrey, T. M. 1953b. Methods of Production, in *Glycerol*. A.C.S. Monograph No. 117. Edited by C. S. Miner and N. N. Dalton. Reinhold, Publishing Corp., New York.

Godston, J. 1934. Keeping the "Core" out of Canned Egg Yolks. *Food Inds.* **6,** 201–203.

Gonzales, F., and Luyet, B. J. 1950. Resumption of Heart-Beat in Chick Embryo Frozen in Liquid Nitrogen. *Biodynamica* **7,** 1–5.

Gonzales, F., and Luyet, B. 1951. Resumption of Development in Chick Embryos after Solidification in Liquid Nitrogen. *Federation Proc.* **10,** 52.

Gorke, H. 1907. Über chemische Vorgänge beim Erfrieren der Pflanzen. *Landwirtsch. Vers.-Sta.* **65,** 149 (quoted by Kidd, 1929; Luyet and Gehenio, 1940).

Greaves, R. I. N. 1944. Centrifugal Vacuum Freezing. Its Application to the Drying of Biological Materials from the Frozen State. *Nature* **153,** 485–487.

Greely, A. W. 1901–2. On the Analogy between the Effects of Loss of Water and Lowering of Temperature. *Am. J. Physiol.* **6,** 122.

Greene, R. 1941. Frost-Bite and Kindred Ills. *Lancet* **ii,** 689–693.

Greene, R. 1942. Cold in the Treatment of Damage Due to Cold. *Lancet* **ii,** 695–697.

Greene, R. 1943. The Immediate Vascular Changes in True Frost-Bite. *J. Pathol. Bacteriol.* **55,** 259–267.

Gye, W. E., Begg, A. M., Mann, I., and Craigie, J. 1949. The Survival of Activity of Mouse Sarcoma Tissue after Freezing and Drying. *Brit. J. Cancer* **3,** 259–267.

Haines, R. B. 1934. The Minimum Temperatures of Growth of Some Bacteria. *J. Hyg.* **34,** 277–282.

Haines, R. B. 1937–8. The Effect of Freezing on Bacteria. *Proc. Roy. Soc. (London)* **124B,** 451–463.

Hampil, B. 1932. The Influence of Temperature on the Life Processes and Death of Bacteria. *Quart. Rev. Biol.* **7,** 172–196.

Hanke, M. E. 1953. The Physiological Action of Glycerol, in *Glycerol.* A.C.S. Monograph No. 117. Edited by C. S. Miner and N. N. Dalton. Reinhold Publishing Corp., New York.

Hardy, W. 1926. A Microscopic Study of the Freezing of Gel. *Proc. Roy. Soc. (London)* **112A,** 47.

Hawke, E. L. 1944. Thermal Characteristics of a Hertfordshire Frost Hollow. *Quart. J. Roy. Meteorol. Soc.* **70,** 23–48.

Hazel, J. F., and Schipper, E. 1950. Low Temperature Studies with Colloidal Silicic Acid. *J. Colloid Sci.* **5,** 532–540.

Hegarty, C. P., and Weeks, O. B. 1940. Sensitivity of *Escherichia coli* to Cold-Shock during the Logarithmic Growth Phase. *J. Bacteriol.* **39,** 475–484.

Heilbrunn, L. V. 1943. *An Outline of General Physiology,* Second edition. W. B. Saunders Co., Philadelphia.

Hepburn, J. S. 1915. The Influence of Low Temperatures upon Enzymes. A Review. *Biochem. Bull.* **4,** 136–150.

Hilliard, C. M., and Davis, M. A. 1918. The Germicidal Action of Freezing Temperatures upon Bacteria. *J. Bacteriol.* **3,** 423–431.

Hoagland, H., and Pincus, G. 1942. Revival of Mammalian Sperm after Immersion in Liquid Nitrogen. *J. Gen. Physiol.* **25,** 337–344.

Hoerr, N. L. 1936. Cytological Studies by the Altmann-Gersh Freezing-Drying Method. I. Recent Advances in the Technique. *Anat. Record* **65,** 293–313.

Iljin, W. S. 1934. Über den Kältetod der Pflanzen und seine Ursachen. *Protoplasma* **20,** 105 (quoted by Luyet and Gehenio, 1940).

Ingram, J. T. 1949. Chilblains. *Brit. Med. J.* **ii,** 1284–1286.

Irving, L. 1951. Physiological Adaptation to Cold in Arctic and Tropic Animals. *Federation Proc.* **10,** 543–545.

Jacobs, M. H., Glassman, H. N., and Parpart, A. K. 1950. Hemolysis and Zoological Relationship. Comparative Studies with Four Penetrating Non-Electrolytes. *J. Exptl. Zool.* **113,** 227–299.

Jensen, A. B. 1943. Über die Austrocknungsresistenz der Wirbeltierzellen einige kritische Betrachtungen. *Arch. exptl. Zellforsch.* **25,** 67–73.

Johnson, V., Carlson, A. J., and Johnson, A. 1933. Studies on the Physiological Action of Glycerol on the Animal Organism. *Am. J. Physiol.* **103,** 517–534.

Jones, P. F. 1953. The Use of Foetal and Neonatal Endocrine Homografts: an Experimental and Clinical Study, in *The Preservation of Normal Tissues for Transplantation.* Ciba Foundation Symposium. In press.

Joslyn, M. A. 1949. Enzyme Activity in Frozen Vegetable Tissue. *Advances in Enzymol.* **9,** 613–651.

Joslyn, M. A. 1951. The Action of Enzymes in the Dried State and in Concentrated Solution. *Proc. 8th Intern. Congr. Refrig.* Pp. 331–334.

Kauzmann, W. 1948. The Nature of the Glassy State and the Behaviour of Liquids at Low Temperatures. *Chem. Revs.* **43,** 219–256.

Keilin, D., and Hartree, E. F. 1949. Effect of Low Temperature on the Absorption

Spectra of Haemoproteins; with Observations on the Absorption Spectrum of Oxygen. *Nature* **164,** 254–259.

Kidd, F. 1929. Cantor Lectures: Biology and Refrigeration. I. Refrigeration in Nature. *J. Roy. Soc. Arts* **77,** 269–285.

Kidd, F., and West, C. 1924. Temperature and Metabolic Balance in Living Plant Tissues. *Proc. 4th Intern. Congr. Refrig.* P. 170.

de Klerk, D. 1952. Adiabatic Demagnetization and the Temperature Scale below 1°K. *Science* **116,** 335–339.

Koonz, C. H., and Ramsbottom, J. M. 1939. A Method for Studying the Histological Structure of Frozen Products. I. Poultry. *Food Research* **4,** 117–128.

Kreyberg, L. 1949. Development of Acute Tissue Damage Due to Cold. *Physiol. Revs.* **29,** 156–167.

Kyes, P., and Potter, T. S. 1939. The Resistance of Avian Tubercle Bacilli to Low Temperatures with Especial Reference to Multiple Changes in Temperature. *J. Infectious Diseases* **64,** 123–134.

Kylin, H. 1917. Über die Kälteresistenz der Meeresalgen. *Ber. deut. botan. Ges.* **35,** 370 (quoted by Luyet and Gehenio, 1940).

Lake, N. C. 1917. An Investigation into the Effects of Cold upon the Body. *Lancet* ii, 557–562.

Lavin, G. I., and Northrop, J. N. 1935. The Ultra-Violet Absorption Spectrum of Pepsin. *J. Am. Chem. Soc.* **57,** 874–875.

Lea, C. H., and Hawke, J. C. 1952. Lipovitellin. 2. The Influence of Water on the Stability of Lipovitellin and the Effects of Freezing and of Drying. *Biochem. J.* **52,** 105–114.

Lépine, P., Barski, G., and Reinié, L. 1951. Action de la congélation prolongée sur la vitalité des tumeurs spontanées de la souris. *Ann. Inst. Pasteur* **80,** 571–581.

Levaditi, J. C. 1952. Possibilité de conserver *Tr. Congolense* et *Pl. Berghei* à −70°C. *Compt. rend. soc. biol.* **146,** 179–181.

Lidforss, B. 1907. Die Wintergrüne Flora. *Lunds Univ. Arsskr.* (N.F.) **2,** 1.

Lipschütz, A. 1928. Histologie des ovaires isolés et transplantés. *Compt. rend. soc. biol.* **99,** 533–534.

Lipschütz, A. 1929. Transplantation d'ovaires après dessiccation. *Compt. rend. soc. biol.* **100,** 95–97.

Lovelock, J. E. 1952. Resuspension in Plasma of Human Red Blood-Cells Frozen in Glycerol. *Lancet* **i,** 1238–1239.

Lovelock, J. E. 1953a. The Haemolysis of Human Red Blood-Cells by Freezing and Thawing. *Biochim. et Biophys. Acta* **10,** 414–426.

Lovelock, J. E. 1953b. The Mechanism of the Protective Action of Glycerol against Haemolysis by Freezing and Thawing. *Biochim. et Biophys. Acta.* **11,** 28–36.

Lovelock, J. E. 1953c. Biophysical Aspects of the Freezing of Living Cells, in *The Preservation of Normal Tissues for Transplantation.* Ciba Foundation Symposium. In press.

Lovelock, J. E. 1953d. Personal communication.

Lusena, C. V., and Cook, W. H. 1953. Personal communication.

Luyet, B. J. 1937. Sur le mécanisme de la mort cellulaire par les hautes pressions; l'intensité et la durée des pressions léthales pour la lévure. *Compt. rend.* **204,** 1214–1215.

Luyet, B. J. 1939a. Vitrification of Water. *Physiol. Revs.* **56,** 1244.

Luyet, B. J. 1939b. The Devitrification Temperatures of Solutions of a Carbohydrate Series. *J. Phys. Chem.* **43,** 881–885.

Luyet, B. J. 1939c. Water and the Ultra-Structure of Protoplasm. *Arch. exptl. Zellforsch.* **22,** 487–491.

Luyet, B. J. 1941a. The Vitreous State of Matter and the Devitrification Temperatures, in *Temperature: Its Measurement and Control in Science and Industry.* American Institute of Physics. Reinhold Publishing Corp., New York. Pp. 420–424.

Luyet, B. J. 1941b. The Resistance of Living Matter to Very Low Temperatures, in *Temperature: Its Measurement and Control in Science and Industry.* American Institute of Physics. Reinhold Publishing Corp., New York. Pp. 425–427.

Luyet, B. J. 1944. The Physical States of Protoplasm Compatible with Life. *Colloid Chem.* **5,** 859–863.

Luyet, B. J. 1949. Ultra-Rapid Freezing as a Possible Method of Blood Preservation, in *Preservation of the Formed Elements and of the Proteins of the Blood.* American National Red Cross. Pp. 141–146.

Luyet, B. J. 1951. Survival of Cells, Tissues and Organisms after Ultra-Rapid Freezing, in *Freezing and Drying.* Edited by R. J. C. Harris. The Institute of Biology, London. Pp. 77–98.

Luyet, B. J., and Gehenio, P. M. 1940. *Life and Death at Low Temperatures.* Monograph published by Biodynamica, Normandy, Miss.

Luyet, B. J., and Gehenio, P. M. 1952. On the Mode of Action of Glycerol in Preventing Injury by Freezing in Embryonic Tissues of Chick. *Science* **116,** 526.

Luyet, B. J., and Gonzales, F. 1950. Réprise des contractions rhythmique du muscle amniotique après congélation dans l'azote liquide. *Compt. rend.* **230,** 2331–2333.

Luyet, B. J., and Gonzales, F. 1951a. Recording Ultra-Rapid Changes in Temperature. *Refrig. Eng.* **59,** 1191–1193.

Luyet, B. J., and Gonzales, F. 1951b. Survival of Cells in Embryonic Heart of Chick after Freezing. *Biodynamica* **7,** 61–66.

Luyet, B. J., and Hartung, M. C. 1941a. Survival of *Anguillula aceti* after Solidification in Liquid Air. *Biodynamica* **3,** 353–362.

Luyet, B. J., and Hartung, M. C. 1941b. Factors in Revival of *Anguillula aceti* after Its Solidification in Liquid Air. *Am. J. Physiol.* **133,** 368.

Luyet, B. J., and Hartung, M. C. 1941c. Death by Devitrification in the Nematode *Anguillula aceti. Biodynamica* **3,** 363–367.

Luyet, B. J., and Hodapp, E. L. 1938. Revival of Frog's Spermatozoa Vitrified in Liquid Air. *Proc. Soc. Exptl. Biol. Med.* **39,** 433–434.

Luyet, B. J., and Menz, L. 1951. Haemolysis by Freezing. *Federation Proc.* **10,** 87.

Luyet, B. J., and Schmidt, P. 1950. Determination of Amount of Ice Formed in Blood at Various Freezing Temperatures. *Federation Proc.* **9,** 81.

Macfadyen, A. 1900. On the Influence of the Temperature of Liquid Air on Bacteria. *Proc. Roy. Soc. (London)* **66,** 180–182.

Macfadyen, A., and Rowland, S. 1900a. Further Note on the Influence of the Temperature of Liquid Air on Bacteria. *Proc. Roy. Soc. (London)* **66,** 339–340.

Macfadyen, A., and Rowland, S. 1900b. Influence of the Temperature of Liquid Hydrogen on Bacteria. *Proc. Roy. Soc. (London)* **66,** 488–489.

Macfarlane, M. G., and Knight, B. C. J. G. 1941. The Biochemistry of Bacterial Toxins. *Biochem. J.* **35,** 884–902.

McFarlane, V. H., and Hall, H. H. 1943. Experimental Preparation and Preservation of Glycerine Egg Yolk. *U.S. Egg Poultry Mag.* **49,** 224–225, 230–231, 239.

Manley, G. 1952. *Climate and the British Scene.* Collins, London.

Mann, I. 1949. A Study of Cell Survival in Embryonic Tissue Grafts in Inbred Strains of Mice under Various Conditions. *Brit. J. Cancer.* **3,** 255–259.

Manwell, R. E., and Edgett, R. 1943. The Relative Importance of Certain Factors in the Low Temperature Preservation of Malaria Parasites. *Am. J. Trop. Med.* **23,** 551–557.

Marsland, D. 1950. The Mechanism of Cell Division; Temperature-Pressure Experiments on the Cleaving of Eggs of *Arbacia punctulata. J. Cell. Comp. Physiol.* **36,** 205–227.

Maximov, N. A. 1938. *Compt. rend. acad. sci. U.R.S.S.* **21,** 183 (quoted by Luyet and Gehenio, 1940).

Medawar, P. B., and Billingham, R. E. 1951. The Viability of Mammalian Skin after Freezing, Thawing and Freeze-Drying, in *Freezing and Drying.* Edited by R. J. C. Harris. The Institute of Biology, London. Pp. 55–62.

Mendelow, H., and Hamilton, J. B. 1950. A New Technique for Rapid Freezing and Dehydration of Tissues for Histology and Histochemistry. *Anat. Record* **107,** 443–451.

Mider, G. B., and Morton, J. J. 1939. The Effect of Freezing *in Vitro* on Some Transplantable Mammalian Tumors and on Normal Rat Skin. *Am. J. Cancer* **35,** 502–509.

Modlibowska, I. 1951. Low Temperature Injury and Frost Resistance of Plant Tissues with Special Reference to Fruit Trees. *Proc. 8th Intern. Congr. Refrig.* Pp. 331–336.

Modlibowska, I., and Field, C. P. 1942. Winter Injury to Fruit Trees by Frost in England, 1939–40. *J. Pomol. and Hort. Sci.* 197–207.

Mollison, P. L., and Sloviter, H. A. 1951. Successful Transfusion of Previously Frozen Human Red Cells. *Lancet* **ii,** 862–864.

Mollison, P. L., Sloviter, H. A., and Chaplin, H., Jr. 1952. Survival of Transfused Red Cells Previously Stored for Long Periods in the Frozen State. *Lancet* **ii,** 501–505.

Moran, T. 1925. The Effect of Low Temperatures on Hen's Eggs. *Proc. Roy. Soc. (London)* **98B,** 436–456.

Moran, T. 1926. The Freezing of Gelatin Gel. *Proc. Roy. Soc. (London)* **112A,** 30–46.

Moran, T. 1929–30. Critical Temperature of Freezing: Living Muscle. *Proc. Roy. Soc. (London)* **105B,** 177–197.

Moran, T. 1930. The Frozen State in Mammalian Muscle. *Proc. Roy. Soc. (London)* **107B,** 182–187.

Moran, T. 1935. *Post-Mortem* and Refrigeration Changes in Meat. *J. Soc. Chem. Ind. (London)* **54T,** 149–151.

Moran, T., and Hale, H. P. 1932. Rapid Freezing. Temperature of Storage. *J. Soc. Chem. Ind. (London)* **51T,** 20–23.

Moulton, C., and Lewis, W. L. 1940. *Meat through the Microscope.* Institute of Meat Packing. University of Chicago Press.

Nilsson-Leissner, G. 1929. Death from Low Temperature and Resistance of Plants to Cold. *Quart. Rev. Biol.* **4,** 113–117.

Nord, F. F., and Lange, F. E. M. 1935. Cryology, Diffusion and Size of Particles. *Nature* **135,** 1001.

Owston, P. G. 1951. The Structure of Ice. *Quart. Rev. Chem. Soc.* **5,** 344–363.

Parkes, A. S. 1945. Preservation of Human Spermatozoa at Low Temperatures. *Brit. Med. J.* **ii,** 212–213.

Parkes, A. S. 1951. Preservation of Spermatozoa, Red Blood-Cells and Endocrine Tissue, in *Freezing and Drying.* Edited by R. J. C. Harris. The Institute of Biology, London. Pp. 99–105.

Parkes, A. S. 1953. Preservation of Living Cells, in *Scientific Basis of Medicine.* British Postgraduate Medical Federation. In press.

Parkes, A. S., and Smith, A. U. 1953. Regeneration of Rat Ovarian Tissue Grafted after Exposure to Low Temperatures. *Proc. Roy. Soc.* (*London*) **140B,** 455–470.

Passey, R. D., and Dmochowski, L. 1950. Freezing and Desiccation of Mouse Tumours. *Brit. Med. J.* **ii,** 1129–1134.

Payne, N. M. 1926. Freezing and Survival of Insects at Low Temperatures. *J. Morphol.* **43,** 521–546.

Payne, M. A., and Meyer, R. K. 1942. Endocrine Function of Ovarian Tissue after Growth and Storage *in Vitro. Proc. Soc. Exptl. Biol. Med.* **51,** 188–189.

Pearce, J. A., and Lavers, C. G. 1949. Liquid and Frozen Egg. V. Viscosity, Baking Quality and Other Measurements on Frozen Egg Products. *Can. J. Research* **27F,** 231–240.

Phillips, P. H., and Lardy, H. A. 1940. A Yolk-Buffer Pabulum for the Preservation of Bull Semen. *J. Dairy Sci.* **23,** 399.

Pirie, N. W. 1937. The Meaninglessness of the Terms "Life" and "Living," in *Perspectives in Biochemistry.* Cambridge University Press.

Polge, C. 1951a. Functional Survival of Fowl Spermatozoa after Freezing at −79°C. *Nature* **167,** 949–950.

Polge, C. 1951b. Preservation of Fowl Spermatozoa at Low Temperatures. *Rept. 9th World's Poultry Congr.* **3,** 11–14.

Polge, C. 1953. Personal communication.

Polge, C., and Lovelock, J. E. 1952. Preservation of Bull Semen at −79°C. *Vet. Record* **64,** 396–397.

Polge, C., and Parkes, A. S. 1952. Possibilities of Long-Term Storage of Spermatozoa at Low Temperatures. *Animal Breed. Abstr.* **20,** 1–5.

Polge, C., and Rowson, L. E. A. 1952a. Fertilizing Capacity of Bull Spermatozoa after Freezing at −79°C. *Nature* **169,** 626–627.

Polge, C., and Rowson, L. E. A. 1952b. Results with Bull Semen Stored at −79°C. *Vet. Record* **64,** 851.

Polge, C., and Rowson, L. E. A. 1952c. Long-Term Storage of Bull Semen Frozen at Very Low Temperatures (−79°C.). *2nd Intern. Congr. Physiol. Pathol. Animal Reprod. and Artif. Insem.* **3,** 90.

Polge, C., and Rowson, L. E. A. 1953. Storage of Bull Semen at −79°C. and Fertility Results for up to Twelve Months. *Vet. Record* **65,** 677–679.

Polge, C., Smith, A. U., and Parkes, A. S. 1949. Revival of Spermatozoa after Vitrification and Dehydration at Low Temperatures. *Nature* **164,** 666.

Ponder, E. 1948. *Hemolysis and Related Phenomena.* J. & A. Churchill Ltd., London.

Pound, G. M., Madonna, L. A., and Peake, S. L. 1953. Critical Supercooling of Pure Water Droplets by a New Microscopic Technique. *J. Colloid Chem.* **8,** 187–193.

Proom, H., and Hemmons, L. M. 1949. The Drying and Preservation of Bacterial Cultures. *J. Gen. Microbiol.* **3,** 7–18.

Pryde, J. A., and Jones, G. O. 1952. The Properties of Vitreous Water. *Nature* **170,** 685–688.

Pütter, A. 1927 (quoted by J. Bělehrádek, 1935).

Rahn, O. 1945. Physical Methods of Sterilization of Microorganisms. *Bacteriol. Revs.* **9,** 1–47.

Réaumur, R. A. F. 1736. *Mémoires pour servir à l'histoire des insectes* (quoted by Luyet and Gehenio, 1940).

Reay, G. A. 1933. The Influence of Freezing Temperatures on Haddock's Muscle. *J. Soc. Chem. Ind.* (*London*) **52T,** 265–270.

Reay, G. A. 1935. The Preservation of Fresh and Thawed Fish in Ice. *J. Soc. Chem. Ind.* (*London*) **54T,** 96–98.

Reay, G. A. 1951. The Preservation of White Fish at Sea. *Proc. 8th Intern. Congr. Refrig.* P. 374.

Robinson, J. R. 1953. The Active Transport of Water in Living Systems. *Biol. Revs.* **28,** 158–194.

Rogers, W. S. 1952. Some Aspects of Spring Frost Damage to Fruit and Its Control. *Proc. 13th Intern. Horticultural Congr.*

Rogers, W. S. and Modlibowska, I. 1953. Communication to the Society for Experimental Biology.

Rostand, J. 1946. Glycérine et la resistance du sperme aux basses températures. *Compt. rend.* **222,** 1524–1525.

Rostand, J. 1952. Sur le refroidissement des cellules spermatiques en présence de glycérine. *Compt. rend.* **234,** 2310–2312.

Sair, L., and Cook, W. H. 1938. Relation of pH to Drip Formation in Meat. *Can. J. Research* **16D,** 255–267.

Salisbury, G. W., Fuller, H. K., and Willett, E. L. 1941. Preservation of Bovine Spermatozoa in Yolk-Citrate Diluent and Field Results from Its Use. *J. Dairy Sci.* **24,** 905–911.

Salt, R. W. 1936. *v.* Wigglesworth, 1947.

Salt, R. W. 1950. Time as a Factor in the Freezing of Undercooled Insects. *Can. J. Research* **28D,** 285–291.

Scholander, P. F., Hock, R., Walters, V., and Irving, L. 1950a. Adaptation to Cold in Arctic and Tropical Mammals and Birds in Relation to Body Temperature Insulation and Basal Metabolism. *Biol. Bull.* **99,** 259–271.

Scholander, P. F., Hock, R., Walters, V., Johnson, F., and Irving, L. 1950b. Heat Regulation in Some Arctic and Tropical Mammals and Birds. *Biol. Bull.* **99,** 237–258.

Scholander, P. F., Walters, V., Hock, R., and Irving, L. 1950c. Body Insulation of Some Arctic and Tropical Mammals and Birds. *Biol. Bull.* **99,** 225–236.

Schumacker, H. B., Jr. 1951. Animal Studies. *Trans. 1st Conf. on Cold Injury* (*Josiah Macy, Jr., Foundation*). Edited by M. I. Ferrer. Hildreth Press, Bristol, Conn.

Segur, J. B. 1953a. Chemical Properties and Derivatives of Glycerol, in *Glycerol.* A.C.S. Monograph No. 117. Edited by C. S. Miner and N. N. Dalton. Reinhold Publishing Corp., New York.

Segur, J. B. 1953b. Uses of Glycerine, in *Glycerol.* A.C.S. Monograph No. 117. Edited by C. S. Miner and N. N. Dalton. Reinhold Publishing Corp., New York.

Segur, J. B. 1953c. Physical Properties of Glycerol and Its Solutions, in *Glycerol.* A.C.S. Monograph No. 117. Edited by C. S. Miner and N. N. Dalton. Reinhold Publishing Corp., New York.

Shaffner, C. S. 1942. Longevity of Fowl Spermatozoa in Frozen Condition. *Science* **96,** 337.

Shaffner, C. S., Henderson, E. W., and Card, C. G. 1941. Viability of Spermatozoa of the Chicken under Various Environmental Conditions. *Poultry Sci.* **20,** 259–265.

Sherman, J. M., and Cameron, G. M. 1934. Lethal Environmental Factors within Natural Range of Growth. *J. Bacteriol.* **27,** 341–348.

Siminovitch, D., and Scarth, G. W. 1938. A Study of the Mechanism of Frost Injury to Plants. *Can. J. Research* **16C,** 467–481.

Sizer, I. W. 1943. The Effects of Temperature on Enzyme Kinetics. *Advances in Enzymol.* **3,** 35–62.

Sizer, I. W., and Josephson, E. S. 1942. Kinetics as a Function of Temperature of Lipase, Trypsin, and Invertase Activity from −70° to 50°C. (−94 to 122°F.). *Food Research* **7,** 201–209.

Sloviter, H. A. 1951a. Recovery of Human Red Blood-Cells after Freezing. *Lancet* **i,** 823–824.

Sloviter, H. A. 1951b. *In Vivo* Survival of Rabbits' Red Cells Recovered after Freezing. *Lancet* **i,** 1350–1351.

Sloviter, H. A. 1951c. Personal communication.

Sloviter, H. A. 1952. Recovery of Human Red Cells after Prolonged Storage at −79°C. *Nature* **169,** 1013–1014.

Smart, H. F. 1935. Growth and Survival of Microorganisms at Sub-Freezing Temperatures. *Science* **82,** 525.

Smith, A. U. 1949. Cultivation of Rabbit Eggs and Cumuli for Phase-Contrast Microscopy. *Nature* **164,** 1136–1137.

Smith, A. U. 1950. Prevention of Haemolysis during Freezing and Thawing of Red Blood-Cells. *Lancet* **ii,** 910–911.

Smith, A. U. 1952a. Cultivation of Ovarian Granulosa Cells after Cooling to Very Low Temperatures. *Exptl. Cell. Research* **3,** 574–583.

Smith, A. U. 1952b. Behaviour of Fertilized Rabbit Eggs Exposed to Glycerol and to Low Temperatures. *Nature* **170,** 374–375.

Smith, A. U. 1953a. *In Vitro* Experiments with Rabbit Eggs, in *Mammalian Germ Cells.* Ciba Foundation Symposium. J. & A. Churchill, London. Pp. 217–222.

Smith, A. U. 1953b. Unpublished results.

Smith, A. U., and Parkes, A. S. 1951. Preservation of Ovarian Tissue at Low Temperatures. *Lancet* **ii,** 570–572.

Smith, A. U., and Parkes, A. S. 1953. Storage and Homografting of Endocrine Tissues, in *The Preservation of Normal Tissues for Transplantation.* Ciba Foundation Symposium. In press.

Smith, A. U., and Polge, C. 1950a. Survival of Spermatozoa at Low Temperatures. *Nature* **166,** 668–669.

Smith, A. U., and Polge, C. 1950b. Storage of Bull Spermatozoa at Low Temperatures. *Vet. Record* **62,** 115–116.

Smith, A. U., Polge, C., and Smiles, J. 1951. Microscopic Observation of Living Cells during Freezing and Thawing. *J. Roy. Microscop. Soc.* **71,** 186–195.

Smith, A. U., and Smiles, J. 1953. Microscopic Studies of Mammalian Tissues during Cooling to −79°C. *J. Roy. Microscop. Soc.* **73,** 134–139.

Smith, L. S., and Krueger, A. P. 1952. Thermal Shock in a New Vibrio Phage. *Proc. Soc. Exptl. Biol. Med.* **81,** 254–259.

Smith, S. E. 1953. Personal communication.

Smyth, H. F., Jr., Carpenter, C. P., and Weil, C. S. 1950. Toxicology of Polyethylene Glycols. *J. Am. Pharm. Assoc.* **39A,** 349–354.

Spallanzani, L. 1787. *Opuscules de physique animale et vegetale.* Vol. 1. Traduit par J. Senebier. Chez Pierre Duplain, Pavie et Paris.

Stewart, D. L. 1951. Storage of Bull Spermatozoa at Low Temperatures. *Vet. Record* **63,** 65–66.

Stiles, W. 1922. The Preservation of Food by Freezing with Special Reference to Fish and Meat: A Study in General Physiology. *Food Invest. Board, Spec. Rept.* **7.** H. M. Stationery Office, London.

Stiles, W. 1930. On the Cause of Cold Death of Plants. *Protoplasma* **9,** 459–468.

Streicher, E., Hackel, D. B., and Fleischman, W. 1950. Effects of Extreme Cold on Fasting Pigeons with a Note on Survival of Fasting Ducks at −40°C. *Am. J. Physiol.* **161,** 300.

Strumia, M. M. 1949a. Freezing of Whole Blood. *Science* **110,** 398–400.

Strumia, M. M. 1949b. Freezing of Whole Blood, in *The Preservation of the Formed Elements and of the Proteins of the Blood.* American National Red Cross. P. 160.

Strumia, M. M., and Hodge, C. C. 1945. Frozen Human Skin Grafts. *Ann. Surg.* **121,** 860–865.

Sumner, J. B., and Somers, G. F. 1943. *Chemistry and Methods of Enzymes.* Academic Press, New York.

Szent-Györgyi, A. 1949. Free Energy Relations and Contraction of Actomyosin. *Biol. Bull.* **96,** 140–161.

Szent-Györgyi, A. 1951. *Chemistry of Muscular Contraction.* Academic Press, New York.

Tamman, G. 1898a. Über die Abhängigkeit der Zahl der Kerne, welche sich in verschiedenen unterkühlten Flüssigkeiten bilden, von der Temperatur. *Z. phys. Chem.* **25,** 441.

Tamman, G. 1898b. *Z. phys. Chem.* **25,** 472 (quoted by Luyet and Gehenio, 1940; Luyet, 1941, 1944; and Kauzmann, 1948).

Tanner, F. W., and Williamson, B. W. 1927–28. The Effects of Freezing on Yeasts. *Proc. Soc. Exptl. Biol. Med.* **25,** 377–381.

Taylor, A. C. 1949. Survival of Rat Skin and Changes in Hair Pigmentation Following Freezing. *J. Exptl. Zool.* **110,** 77–111.

Thiselton-Dyer, W. 1899. On the Influence of the Temperature of Liquid Hydrogen on the Germinative Power of Seeds. *Proc. Roy. Soc. (London)* **65,** 361–368.

Thoennes, G. 1940. Properties of Muscle Fibres Subjected to Vitrification by Extremely Rapid Cooling. *Biodynamica* **3,** 145–156.

Tosic, J., and Walton, A. 1947. Effect of Egg Yolk and Its Constituents on the Respiration and Fertilizing Capacity of Spermatozoa. *J. Agr. Sci.* **37,** 69–76.

Turner, T. B., and Brayton, N. L. 1939. Factors Influencing the Survival of Spirochaetes in the Frozen State. *J. Exptl. Med.* **70,** 639–650.

Uber, F. M. 1950. *Biophysical Research Methods.* Interscience Publishers, New York and London.

Ungley, C. C. 1949. The Immersion Foot Syndrome. *Advances in Surg.* **1,** 269–336.

Waldschmidt-Leitz, E. 1929. *Enzyme Actions and Properties.* Translated by R. P. Walton, 1929. Chapman and Hall, London.

Walsh, L. B., Blumenthal, H., and Grieg, D. 1949. The Effect of Environmental Temperatures on Cells; 1. Effect upon the Morphology and Viability of Neoplastic Cells. *Proc. Am. Soc. Zool., Anat. Record* **105,** 572.

Warner, P. T. J. C. P., Gostling, J. V. T., and Thackray, A. C. 1950. The Fate of Grafts of Sarcoma 37 Mince after Exposure to Low Temperature and Freeze-Drying. *Brit. J. Cancer* **4,** 396–404.

Webster, J. P. 1944. Refrigerated Skin Grafts. *Ann. Surg.* **120,** 431–439.

Weinman, D., and McAllister, J. 1947. Prolonged Storage of Human Pathogenic Protozoa with Conservation of Virulence: Observations on the Storage of Helminths and Leptospira. *Am. J. Hyg.* **45,** 102–121.

Weiser, R. S., and Osterud, C. M. 1945. Studies on the Death of Bacteria at Low Temperatures. I. The Influence of the Intensity of the Freezing Temperature, Repeated Fluctuations of Temperature, and the Period of Exposure to Freezing Temperatures on the Mortality of *E. coli. J. Bacteriol.* **50,** 413–439.

Werkman, C. H. 1953. Biochemical Use of Glycerol, in *Glycerol.* A.C.S. Monograph No. 117. Edited by C. S. Miner and N. N. Dalton. Reinhold Publishing Corp., New York.

Wheatley, D. 1950. Chilblains and Prothrombin Levels. *Lancet* i, 712–714.

White, J. C. 1943. Vascular and Neurologic Lesions in Survivors of Shipwreck. I. Immersion Foot Syndrome Following Exposure to Cold, in *Rehabilitation of the War Injured.* Edited by W. B. Doherty and D. C. Runes. Chapman and Hall, London.

Wigglesworth, V. B. 1947. *The Principles of Insect Physiology.* Third edition. Methuen, London.

Williams, H. 1933. *Mechanical Refrigeration.* Fourth edition. Pitman and Sons, London.

Wilson, G. S., and Miles, A. A. 1946. *Topley & Wilson's Principles of Bacteriology and Immunology,* Vol. I. Third edition. Arnold. London.

CHAPTER 2

# The Development of Freeze-Drying

E. W. FLOSDORF

*Director, Research and Development Division, F. J. Stokes Machine Co., Philadelphia, Pennsylvania*



## I. GENERAL CONSIDERATIONS

Terrestrial sublimation of ice no doubt first occurred when the Earth cooled sufficiently to produce an area of subfreezing temperature having frozen water exposed to an unsaturated atmosphere. It was not until the nineteenth century, however, that air was removed by pumps experimentally in the laboratory to accelerate the process, and not until the present century that the vacuum process was applied by Shackell (1909) to the drying of biological material.

Freeze-drying was first reduced to practice by Flosdorf and Mudd (1935) a few years prior to World War II for biological therapeutic agents such as human serum and plasma for injection. This was a result of the successful active application of heat for the first time to the drying materials from a temperature source as high as that of the room or higher. The material itself remained aseptic and at a temperature well below 0°C. during drying and until the ice phase disappeared. Then the material was taken to the ambient temperature with a final reduction of the moisture to the proper level, i.e., below 1.0%, which was found to be necessary for most of the therapeutic products then being studied (Flosdorf and Mudd, 1935).

Application to a wider range of products quickly followed. During World War II a tremendous expansion took place in the preparation of human blood plasma and serum as blood substitutes for military use in Canada, the United States, and England. Later in the war, the preparation of amorphous penicillin in a properly stable and clinically acceptable form was made possible by this "heated-vacuum" process. During and since that war, industrial and laboratory applications have been extended to other antibiotics and to many other preparations.

A detailed review of the literature has already appeared (Flosdorf, 1949). This chapter includes the earlier literature reports followed by a discussion of the rapid growth after 1935 with particular reference to World War II and postwar developments.

In reports in earlier literature it appears that the process was regarded as more or less of a laboratory curiosity. Shackell (1909), for example, had experimented with the preservation of complement, antisera, rabies virus, and other materials, Harris and Shackell with rabid brain (1911), and Hammer (1911) with the preservation of bacteria. Swift (1921) extended the technique to the preservation of bacterial strains for the purpose of maintaining unaltered biological characteristics, and Sawyer *et al.* (1929) to serum infected with yellow fever virus. Craigie (1931) also reported on the preservation of complement. Elser *et al.* (1935) dried various products, including many bacteria and some laboratory reagents. In none of the work reported in the above literature was heat actively applied; in fact, the materials were either vacuum-insulated from the atmosphere, or the whole apparatus was placed in a cold room.

The first use of a high-temperature source for drying as well as for production of low final moisture content was reported by Flosdorf and Mudd in 1935. Human convalescent and normal human serum and plasma were prepared and dried aseptically and then distributed for successful parenteral use by the Philadelphia Serum Exchange.

In order to achieve successful freeze-drying while heating the product from a high-temperature source, it was necessary to establish the proper surface relationships between the evaporating area and the area for absorption of the heat of sublimation. A simple, solid carbon dioxide type of condenser was used with a manifold to which were attached containers with suitable connectors for the maintenance of sterility. This, too, was original. Apparatus of this type is still used for experimental work, generally on a laboratory scale, but vast changes and improvements have subsequently been made in industrial applications (Flosdorf, 1949).

From 1935 to 1940 the literature contains many references to the application of this simple apparatus to the preservation of microorganisms, including viral cultures. Application has also been made to bacterial toxins and fractionated portions, and to vaccines, hormones, vitamins, and pharamceuticals.

In the same period the firm of Sharp & Dohme, Inc., in Philadelphia, recognized the commercial potentialities of this new process. They installed the first market-container machine in 1935, built under the author's direction at the University of Pennsylvania, and then took over the processing of human serum for clinical distribution by the Philadelphia Serum Exchange. The firm also made other products which appeared on the market in 1935 and the first commercial frozen-dried blood plasma in 1940.

It was at this time that the United States military medical departments recognized the value of frozen-dried blood plasma. About six months before the entrance of the United States into World War II, the decision was taken to begin the accumulation of military stores of this material. This decision to proceed with a vast plasma program was strengthened after Alexis Carrell had addressed the annual meeting of the American Human Serum Association in New York City in June, 1940. He had just returned from France, and he described graphically the utter collapse of the French blood bank system during the rapid advance of the German army which preceded the fall of France.

The contrast under such emergency conditions, when dried human plasma was available, was shown by I. S. Ravdin (*v.* Flosdorf, 1949) in a brochure published by the Southeastern Pennsylvania Chapter of the American Red Cross on February 9, 1942, entitled "A Philadelphia Doctor's Story of Pearl Harbor." Dr. Ravdin said of liquid plasma that it "saved the lives of more men than it will ever be possible for you or me to tell," and went on to state: "Now, a second type of plasma which was available, and which has been made available to the armed forces and civilian aid, almost entirely through the efforts of the Red Cross, is the dry plasma. That is the same material which you have just seen, but it is dried by a method which was originally developed at the University of Pennsylvania, in the Department of Bacteriology, by Doctors Flosdorf and Mudd. This has certain advantages, in that the material can be transported over long distances and at extremes of temperature and, merely by adding sterile water, can be regenerated and given intravenously." Ravdin further quoted Mr. Alfred Castle, who was Chairman of the American Red Cross in Honolulu at the time of the raid, as follows: "We have got a problem here. We are now collecting large amounts of plasma. We can't store all of this wet plasma. We must have some mechanism for drying it. Do you know where such apparatus is to be obtained?" Ravdin said, "I told him such apparatus was made in Philadelphia and he wanted to know how much it would cost. I told him perhaps a minimum of $12,000. He said, 'Well, you just ask the Red Cross when you get back in Washington, whether they would be willing to foot the bill. If the Red Cross won't pay the bill, send the apparatus, and have it charged to me. I'll foot the bill.'" Here we have the first graphic account of how frozen-dried plasma successfully met an unexpected emergency such as was experienced at Pearl Harbor and the appraisal made of the situation by those present at the scene.

Meanwhile, the production of frozen-dried human serum for transfusion had been under way in 1940 in Toronto, using blood collected by the Canadian Red Cross. This was done at the Connaught Laboratories under the direction of C. H. Best and D. Y. Solandt with the cooperation and consultation of the author. The firms of Sharp & Dohme, Inc. and F. J. Stokes Machine Company, and the University of Pennsylvania and the Philadelphia Serum Exchange of the Children's Hospital assisted in various ways. The production in Canada soon reached about 2000 units a week and ultimately was expanded severalfold (Flosdorf, 1949).

In the United States, Sharp & Dohme was producing commercial frozen-dried blood plasma in 1940 and so was ready in 1941 for the Red Cross program when the United States military forces had made their decision. Sharp & Dohme processed and dried the plasma prepared from blood collected by the American Red Cross for the Army and Navy. This program was later extended to centers throughout the country, processing and drying being carried out at the laboratories of Ben Venue, Cutter, Eli Lilly, Hyland, Lederle, Parke-Davis, and Reichel (later Wyeth). Peak production for the entire country ultimately reached about 100,000 units per week (Flosdorf, 1949).

Pilot-plant production in England began at Cambridge in 1940, with a full-scale production of 2500 units a week in 1943. This has been described by Greaves in 1946 and in subsequent publications.

The first large-scale production of amorphous penicillin was also about to get under way in 1943. The full experience of the blood plasma program was utilized with some necessary modifications for the processing of this antibiotic. By this time, the freeze-drying process had fully justified itself, and there was never any doubt concerning its use for penicillin. This, in some measure, was a mistake which could have been serious because there were certain factors in the processing of penicillin which required different techniques but fortunately it was possible to make the required changes quickly.

## II. EQUIPMENT DEVELOPMENTS

The first major attempt in the earlier years to obtain increased capacity was made by Elser *et al.* (1935). A manifold was provided for handling a number of ordinary, round-bottom flasks containing the frozen material.

The manifold itself was used as condenser simply by placing carbon dioxide snow over it and connecting a vacuum pump to the end. The apparatus operated inefficiently, however, and was finally set up in the subfreezing vaults of the firm of Sharp & Dohme at their laboratories in Glenolden, Pennsylvania. Even under these conditions, the apparatus did not perform properly; the copper manifold-condenser was subject to frequent freezing-up within, low final moisture content was unobtainable, and furthermore the products could not be handled aseptically.

Reichel, Masucci, and Boyer in 1931 and 1932 (unpublished) developed a procedure for rapid freezing and rapid dehydration of serum in large, round-bottom Pyrex flasks. These were connected to a large, metal-bulb condenser which was refrigerated in a bath of solid carbon dioxide and acetone. The plant was in operation at Glenolden and was used for a time for bulk preservation of excess quantities of commercial antitoxins. Antitoxins could not, however, be distributed in an aseptic and properly dried form. The serum was therefore restored, sterilized by filtration, and then dispensed in appropriate amounts for distribution as liquid. In other words, the purpose of drying was solely to preserve the material as part of a manufacturing operation for the production of a liquid serum for final distribution.

Flosdorf and Mudd had developed in 1935 the convenient and simple method of aseptic drying *in vacuo* from the frozen state in the individual containers in which the material was to be distributed. The initial freezing was accomplished rapidly by immersion of the containers in a bath at −78°C. The containers were then attached to a manifold constructed either of Pyrex glass or metal. The water vapor was removed by a set of metal or glass condensers maintained at −78°C. with solid carbon dioxide. The final moisture content was reduced to the necessary less than 1% at the end of this desiccation, and the containers were finally sealed off individually without breaking the original vacuum.

The essential problems that had to be solved in the development of the apparatus to be described were (a) to secure automatic regulation of the temperature of the product during the processing in the individual containers in which it was to be stored and distributed, (b) to complete the dehydration within reasonable time, (c) to provide practical means of sealing and severing the containers individually without loss of the original vacuum, and (d) naturally, to preserve sterility throughout the entire process.

Temperature control was made simple and automatic by regulating the rate of sublimation of water vapor from the product undergoing desiccation. This regulation of the rate of sublimation was accomplished by apparatus which satisfied certain critical relationships between the rate of heat intake from the atmosphere at the exterior glass surface of the containers, the rate of heat loss at the evaporating surfaces of the product, and the rate of escape of water vapor from the product to condensers, which were adequate in surface area. The essential features which established this automatic regulation of temperature on a satisfactory basis were as follows:

1. The product was frozen in containers of proper size and shape, in such a way as to give the correct relationship of the evaporating surface of the frozen product to the surface adjacent to the glass, through which atmospheric heat was transferred to the frozen solid.
2. The product was brought to a very low temperature before attachment to the desiccating apparatus.
3. The containers were rapidly attached to the manifold.
4. All connections between the containers and the condensers had an internal diameter large enough to offer a sufficiently free passage to the water vapor.
5. A high free-air vacuum was rapidly established and maintained throughout the apparatus.

Completion of the process within a reasonable time was effected by regulation of the relationship between the above-mentioned surfaces of the frozen product and its volume and depth.

This type of apparatus was constructed both for general research laboratory use in small sizes and in larger sizes suitable for what, at that time, was modest production. A 24-outlet glass manifold apparatus with a Dry Ice condenser of this type was demonstrated by the author in London in 1936 at the Second International Congress of Microbiology (Flosdorf and Mudd, 1937).

In 1938 an improved procedure was published by Flosdorf and Mudd, using a regenerable chemical desiccant to replace Dry Ice (Flosdorf and Mudd, 1938). Dry Ice for freezing was also dropped in favor of slow, vacuum "degassing" followed by final, rapid "self-freezing," now frequently called "snap-freezing," as suggested by Greaves. The regenerable desiccant removed the water vapor by formation of a fixed chemical hydrate, a most desirable development for equipment which could be operated in out-of-the-way places where low-cost solid carbon dioxide was unavailable. Such equipment has operated satisfactorily for many years in Kenya for the production of rinderpest vaccine; in fact the original unit has been in use there since 1938 (Flosdorf, 1949). This type is also still widely used for laboratory purposes, since operating costs are minimal. However, when large-capacity machines are required, the initial cost of the equipment is high.

The next development, historically, was the use of direct pumping to eliminate the need for either the cold trap or the desiccant (Flosdorf *et al.*, 1940). The initial form of this equipment employed a large, mechanical, oil-sealed rotary pump, the water vapor being condensed in the oil of the pump. This oil was continuously clarified centrifugally so that water-free oil was returned to the intake side of the pump. The large size of the equipment was again a limiting factor for high-capacity units, and this method is no longer widely used. Large multistage steam ejector pumps have been developed for the same purpose, and these are still used where low-cost, high-pressure steam and adequate condenser water are available.

Concurrently with these advances, drying chambers were developed to replace manifolds for large-scale production. With great numbers of single-size containers having the same product to be dried, the vacuum chambers soon proved to be more convenient. They eliminated expensive multiport manifolds, the source of many leaks. It was necessary, however, to develop different methods for introducing the necessary heat of sublimation into the drying product, since this was now contained in a vacuum-insulated chamber (Flosdorf, 1949; Flosdorf *et al.*, 1940).

At this time, too, low-temperature, mechanical refrigerators came into use for cooling the water-vapor traps at a relatively low cost and thus replacing cooling by Dry Ice. Compound ammonia and Freon systems were used in the United States and Canada, and other refrigerants were applied in England (*v. infra*). Two developments made possible the use of mechanical refrigeration in the United States; the first was the advance made in low-temperature refrigeration engineering generally, and the second was the development of a condenser with a greatly extended cold surface. Under such conditions it is possible to use a higher condenser temperature than the −78°C. of Dry Ice (Flosdorf *et al.*, 1945).

The important developments made by Greaves during this time are well known (Greaves, 1942, 1944). In his experimental drying plant, the desiccator was made from glass cylinders, and the refrigerator was operated by a small sulfur dioxide unit. The lowest temperatures obtained with the plant were around −20°C., but the results obtained by Greaves showed that the principle was sound and enabled preliminary experiments on automatic heat control to be carried out successfully.

In his original pilot plant, the sulfur dioxide compressor was replaced by a three-cylinder "Hallmark" methyl chloride machine giving a temperature below −40°C., with a heat exchange of 250 watts. This machine could dry 5 liters at a time from a 25-liter bottle. In the final pilot plant, the head accommodated 35 M.R.C. transfusion bottles, each of which held 400 ml. of serum or plasma. Greaves developed the method of "spin-freezing" to produce a frozen shell of the product on the inner periphery of the bottle. That is, the bottles were spun vertically in a cold room at a high enough speed to fling the product onto the periphery by centrifugal force and to hold it there until it had frozen. This method produced a very uniform layer and gave excellent results. It is in contrast to the method used in the United States where the bottles are rotated at slower speed on their horizontal axes in a refrigerated bath.

Finally, Greaves developed a method for "vacuum spin-freezing." The spinner is located directly in the vacuum drying chamber. When the bottles are rotating sufficiently rapidly, the chamber is evacuated and freezing occurs as a result of the rapid evaporation. Because of the rapid spinning, "degassing" is not required. This type of equipment designed by Greaves was ultimately developed into a large plant for producing all the dry human blood serum and plasma in England for military purposes in World War II.

Many other types of freeze-drying apparatus, generally differing in small details, have been reported during the past ten or twelve years, and some of these have already been briefly summarized (Flosdorf, 1949).

## III. APPLICATION DEVELOPMENTS

### 1. *Histology*

Freeze-drying has been employed for many years by histologists and cytologists. The technique and equipment are quite different from those used for drying laboratory and clinical prophylactic and therapeutic reagents. The temperatures are maintained at a much lower level, active application of heat is not made, and the whole procedure is much slower. Altmann (1890) over 60 years ago reported the usefulness of freeze-drying biological materials without shrinkage in connection with his cytological investigations of bioblasts. Forty years later Gersh (1932) described equipment for fixation involving the use of liquid ammonia as a refrigerant and a diffusion pump and phosphorus pentoxide for removal of the water. With this equipment Gersh was able to confirm the value of the procedure for the fixation of some organs and tissues (skin, cartilage, smooth muscle, liver, pancreas). Gersh applied the technique successfully to the investigation of the excretion of uric acid and ferricyanide, the chemical nature of some intracellular constituents, and the intracellular distribution of glycogen. The method has also been used for the preservation of vitally, or supravitally, stained preparations which fade in fixation or are incapable of satisfactory preservation by other means. Gersh found that fixation of organs other than those just mentioned was often less satisfactory and that central nervous system material was exceedingly difficult to fix. The developments in techniques and the very interesting results obtained have been summarized (Flosdorf, 1949) and are also the subject of a later chapter in this book.

### 2. *Microorganisms*

The early laboratory uses of freeze-drying, apart from histology, concerned the preservation of microorganisms. The efficiency of the freeze-drying was not an important factor in the days of simple equipment. Samples to be dried were small in size, and the rapid attainment of low final moisture content was not necessary. Neither a high activity nor a high survival rate was important. In other words, the absence of any active means for applying heat from a high-temperature source was not much of a handicap. This type of equipment could not possibly be used today for preserving such delicate materials as modified hog cholera virus where high yields of active vaccines are required on a large production basis.

Hammer (1911) applied desiccation from the frozen state to various bacteria. Rogers (1914) employed the method successfully for lactic acid-forming bacilli, and Swift used a similar desiccation in his work with streptococci and pneumococci (1921). Elser *et al.* (1935), Swift, and others have reported successful preservation of some organisms for long periods of time. *Neisseria meningitidis, N. gonorrhoeae, H. influenzae, H. pertussis, E. typhosa,* and other similar organisms have been kept viable for periods of many years. The percentage viability was undoubtedly very low, but after reconstitution the growth could be started again to produce subcultures having unaltered characteristics. An apparatus was developed by Sawyer and his associates (1929) with which serum infected with yellow fever virus was so preserved as to retain its infectivity over a period of years. Not all microorganisms behave in the same way.

Eagle (Mudd *et al.*, 1936) showed that *Spirochaeta pallida* does not survive the freeze-drying process. Rabbit chancres were emulsified, shown to be infectious for rabbits, and frozen-dried by Flosdorf; the residue was re-emulsified and injected intratesticularly into six new rabbits. These rabbits showed no signs of syphilis, and after a year four survivors were tested and found to be susceptible to this strain of fresh *Spirochaeta pallida.* More recently, Probey (1947) has reported similar findings.

Flosdorf and Kimball (1940) reported the freeze-drying of *H. pertussis.* Agglutinin absorption was used as the index to demonstrate that no dissociation occurred during storage of the dry organisms over a twelve-year period. The fundamental importance of the combination of agglutinins with surface antigens of bacteria in antibacterial immunity is well established. With non-flagellated organisms such surface reactions as agglutination or phagocytosis therefore provide distinguishing methods of assay for effective surface reactants in either serum or antigen. Complement fixation and precipitin testing with soluble antigens are of diagnostic value but do not distinguish surface antigen-antibody combination from phenomena involving other antigens.

Appleman and Sears (1946) reported that frozen-dried legume nodule bacteria (*Rhizobium leguminosarum*) retain completely both viability and their capacity to nodulate plant hosts and to fix nitrogen after four years of storage. The bacteria tested were isolated originally from alfalfa, lespedeza, cowpea, pea, soybean, vetch, crown vetch, and clover host plants. The cultures were grown on asparagus-mannitol medium and then emulsified in sterile water for drying. Frozen-dried viable cultures of molds and bacteria are now available commercially in the dairy industry as "starters" for innoculum propagation in production of cottage cheese, buttermilk, butter acidophilus, bulgarian, and yoghurt in the United States and in France.

Speck and Meyers (1946) reported that spray-dried cultures of *Lactobacillus bulgaricus*, when reconstituted with fluid at 37° to 50°C., give a higher percentage viability than at 21° to 25°C. Reconstituting at the lower temperature with subsequent warming does not produce the same result. They found that frozen-dried cultures gave the opposite temperature effect.

Lord Stamp (1947) has compared what he terms "slow drying of bacterial cultures in a desiccator over dehydrating agents *in vacuo*" with "more rapid freeze-drying." He states that the former is simple drying in the unfrozen state, although the vacuum was 100 to 300 microns of mercury and phosphorus pentoxide was the desiccant. In view of these conditions, Lord Stamp might well have been drying from the frozen state. It would depend entirely upon whether or not the small quantity (1 mm. thickness) in Petri dishes was completely dried during evacuation and before freezing had occurred. If not, there would be nothing to prevent the residue from freezing. Because of the absence of controlled means of heating, the rate of subsequent drying would be indeterminate and slow. When drying in a desiccator in this fashion, it is quite possible that in some cases there would be partial freezing, in others complete freezing, and in still others no freezing at all. In other words, because of the absence of control and of any means of knowing how well or how poorly the product had frozen, any conclusions must be indefinite. This may, in fact, account for the variable results which Lord Stamp reported; for example, *Chromobacterium prodigiosum* in one experiment gave an 86.1 to 90.2%

survival, and in another case 60.7%. Also, Lord Stamp has pointed out that his slow method proved unsatisfactory for preservation of more delicate organisms, such as *Neisseria meningitidis, Vibrio cholerae,* and *Fusiformis fusiformis,* whereas these and *N. gonorrhoeae* were successfully preserved by "rapid" freeze-drying.

Better results were obtained by Stamp with these methods when gelatin was used as a suspending medium. Beef extract and peptone were also incorporated. Except where a low pH is harmful (e.g., with *Haemophilus pertussis*) Stamp found that ascorbic acid further improved the results, which he attributed to its action as an antioxidant.

The difference in results obtained by Lord Stamp by the so-called "slow method" in a desiccator as compared with rapid freeze-drying is of interest as a demonstration of the great improvement obtained by the use of proper conditions of freezing, positive and controlled means of heating, and other factors. Lord Stamp states that a lower final content of moisture was obtained by use of the "rapid method" of freeze-drying, where the containers were exposed to the atmosphere while attached to a manifold connected with a Dry Ice condenser. Such uncertainty in the results and lack of dependability in its application to delicate organisms is characteristic of all similar desiccator methods, including those reported by Swift (1921), Elser *et al.* (1935), Hammer (1911), Rogers (1914), Shackell (1909), and others.

Weiser and Hennum (1947) reported a more rapid death rate in cultures of *Escherichia coli* which had been frozen-dried than in those which had been dried from the liquid state at 22°C. However, no determinations of residual moisture were made, and in view of this it seems doubtful whether definite conclusions can be drawn. Furthermore, this organism is scarcely representative of the more delicate ones which have been tested by freeze-drying.

When drying viruses, an initial loss of activity frequently occurs as a result of the processing, but the final, dry product is usually quite stable and no further loss occurs during storage (Scherp *et al.*, 1938). Viruses are, in general, more difficult to dry than other materials. A drying temperature must be maintained which is lower than that usually required for other products. Preferably it should be well below −20°C. (Flosdorf and Mudd, 1938), and in some cases as low as −35°C. Harris and Shackell (1911) presumably used freeze-drying in the preservation of rabid brains. Rivers and Ward (1935) relied widely on freeze-drying in their work on an intradermal vaccine for Jennerian prophylaxis. Siedentopf and Green (1942) reported great success in a similar preservation of modified canine distemper virus. It is known that some substances, after drying from the frozen state, do not retain activity in the presence of atmospheric oxygen, even though completely dry and hermetically sealed. Typical of such products are those high in lipoidal content. In these cases, sealing is necessary either under original vacuum or under an inert gas such as nitrogen or argon. Siedentopf and Green reported that this is particularly so with their distemper virus. It must be stressed that the release of the original vacuum with dry air and subsequent evacuation or replacement of this air with an inert gas does not work satisfactorily in all cases, since oxygen may be absorbed by the highly porous solid matter. Moreover, for ferret passage distemper virus, the nitrogen must be completely freed from oxygen by passing over hot copper.

Influenza virus may be successfully preserved (Scherp *et al.*, 1938), and freeze-drying is now used widely for carrying various strains of the virus in many research laboratories, (*v.* Harris, this volume). Hoffstadt and Tripi (1946), for example, report successful three-year preservation of Levaditi and Cutter strains of vaccinia, herpes simplex, laryngotracheitis of fowls, and Rous sarcoma viruses. On the other hand, they found inconstant maintenance of viability for the virus of infectious myxomatosis of rabbits over three-year periods; whether this was because of non-uniform residual content of moisture or other reasons was not determined. Their culture of OA strain of Shope's fibroma also did not survive this period. Other viruses which have been successfully dried are those causing hog cholera (Munce and Reichel, 1943), rinderpest, ovine ecthyma (sheep scabs), yellow fever, and various fowl diseases such as laryngotracheitis and fowl pox prepared from chick embryos. Wooley (1939) has reported that lymphocytic choriomeningitis and St. Louis encephalitis were preserved for at least 378 and 833 days, respectively, after freeze-drying.

Libby (1947) has experimented with freeze-drying in immunochemical studies using antigens "tagged" with radioactive phosphorus as a tracer for tobacco mosaic virus. Mice were injected with the "tagged" virus; 24 hours later the mice were killed in a Dry Ice–acetone bath, and 3- to 4-mm. sagittal sections were prepared with a band saw. These sections, after freeze-drying, were impregnated with paraffin, and 1-mm. sections were prepared with a microtome and placed in intimate contact with x-ray film for exposure for varying periods to obtain autoradiographs. In this way it was possible to locate regions and organs of greatest concentrations of radioactivity.

One of the earliest and most successful applications of freeze-drying has been in the control of rinderpest (cattle plague) in Africa. The mortality for this disease is high, sometimes reaching 50 to 75%. In the preparation of the virus the blood of infected animals is laked and centrifuged. This separates the leucocytes with which the live virus is associated. In liquid state the virus remains viable and effective as an immunizing agent for a matter of a few weeks only. It survives freeze-drying well, however, and its life is thus extended to months and years. Cattle are immunized by the simultaneous inoculation of living virus and protective immune serum.

Munce and Reichel (1943) showed that hog cholera virus of blood origin, when desiccated under high vacuum and stored *in vacuo* in flame-sealed ampoules, remained infective after exposure to a temperature of 60°C. for 96 hours. At 37°C. the infectivity was maintained for 328 days. Phenolized liquid virus from the same mixture was non-infective after exposure to the higher temperature for only 5 hours. At 37°C. the period of infectivity of the dried preparation was approximately twenty-three times as long as for the phenolized liquid virus. After storage at 20°C. the dried virus was still infective in these authors' last test, which was conducted after a storage period of 1125 days—twelve times as long as for the corresponding phenolized liquid virus.

One of the most recent developments is the widespread use in the United States of frozen-dried, live, modified hog cholera vaccine. The virus is modified by serial passage for many generations through hosts other than swine. Ultimately, a strain is obtained which is not infectious for swine but which still elicits the formation of protective antibodies (Baker, 1951).

Smadel *et al.* (1947) published a method for successfully freeze-drying Japanese encephalitis vaccine. This was ultimately supplied during World War II by the U.S. Army Medical Department, Research and Graduate School, for the Pacific Theater. The "Nakayama" strain was used as a 20% suspension of infected chick embryo tissue in buffered physiological saline containing sufficient formaldehyde to inactivate the virus. The formaldehyde was neutralized with sodium bisulfite, penicillin was added to the pools to a final concentration of five units per milliliter, and merthiolate at 1:10,000. The vaccine was finally frozen-dried in apparatus of a type similar to that used by Bauer and Pickels. By means of external deep-freeze type refrigeration around the equipment, the vials supported on a vertical manifold were kept in surrounding air of about −20°C. for several hours. The temperature was then allowed to rise slowly to reach 0°C. about 20 hours after starting. The temperature was then raised quickly to 30°C. and was maintained there for a 20- to 24-hour period. A pressure of 30 to 50 microns was sufficient initially, but at the end of the drying cycle the pressure was dropped to 2 or 3 microns.

When the purpose of preservation is the maintenance of a stock strain with unaltered characteristics, the percentage of the initial activity or viability which remains after drying does not have the same importance as it does with vaccines. For this reason, the pre-production stages for a new vaccine require extensive study to realize the optimum conditions for *maximum* survival.

The following vaccines are today in full-scale commercial production:

*Brucella abortus*
Canine distemper
*Erysipelothrix rhusiopathiae*
Fowl laryngotracheitis
Fowlpox
Modified hog cholera
Newcastle disease (live virus)
Newcastle disease (wing-web)
Pigeon Pox

### 3. *Therapeutic Agents*

#### a. Immune Sera

The first clinical application of freeze-drying was the production of convalescent human serum for injection (Flosdorf, 1949). In 1933 it was recognized that serum collected at the close of one epidemic, particularly in the case of children's diseases, might have much to offer for the prevention and control of further epidemics in subsequent years. The unknown and difficultly measurable degree of deterioration of the sera during intervening storage had been a deterrent to intensive investigation of their possible extended usefulness.

By 1935, sufficient favorable experience had been accumulated with the frozen-dried products prepared during this time to justify thoroughly the efforts spent in developing the freeze-drying procedure. The sera were collected in and distributed from the Philadelphia Serum Exchange which had been established for this purpose (Stokes *et al.*, 1934, 1935). Processing and drying of the sera was initially carried out by Flosdorf in the Bacteriological Department of the School of Medicine, University of Pennsylvania. The dried sera were used both for prevention and for treatment in clinical trials. All the sera distributed by the Philadelphia Serum Exchange since 1933 have been in this same form. Convalescent measles, scarlet fever, chicken pox, and mumps sera and pooled normal adult sera had been administered early in 1935 in "lyophile" form to a total of more than 600 persons. It was felt at that time that the distinctive advantage of "lyophile" sera was demonstrated for such work because it could be harvested at the optimum time and used when and where it was needed. It was pointed out that if the sera in question are especially perishable, as in the case of pooled normal adult sera, or are only occasionally needed, the method of preservation could make the difference between practicability and impracticability in the use of serum. It was also felt that the method of preservation could be a powerful aid in the utilization and further investigation of the value of sera and other products from human sources for many purposes.

Furthermore, convalescent sera were preserved from epidemics whose etiology and nosology were still under investigation. Convalescent sera from epidemics of influenza in Philadelphia and in Alaska (Flosdorf and Mudd, 1935) were collected and preserved for distribution to various investigators for parallel cross-protection tests.

Another interesting application has been the drying of human "hyperimmune" serum. This has been most widely employed for the prevention and treatment of whooping cough. The serum is obtained from the blood of individuals who are known to have had the disease in childhood and who, in addition, have received repeated injections of pertussis vaccine to produce a high agglutination titer. Such frozen-dried hyperimmune serum has had its usefulness well-proved in clinical experience (Flosdorf, 1949).

Also as a result of this early work, particularly of aseptic drying from the final containers, drying by sublimation spread rapidly as a major research tool. Among the projects to which it was applied was the utilization in 1941 of dry normal human serum and plasma in the treatment of hemorrhage, secondary shock, and burns (Flosdorf and Mudd, 1944). To this extent, development of drying by sublimation was one of three streams of investigation that joined to give rise to the blood plasma program for World War II. Another stream involved the laboratory study of the mechanism of secondary shock resulting from hemorrhage, trauma, toxemia, and burns. This investigation indicated that the major factor in shock was the reduction of the blood volume below the minimum capacity of the vascular system. The third stream was the accumulation of clinical experience with the administration of liquid human plasma and serum as a substitute for whole blood in the treatment of secondary shock and allied conditions. It was even found that in certain cases, for example where there is shock without hemorrhage, blood plasma is superior to whole blood since it is only the liquid part of the blood which has been lost from the circulation. It was the confluence of these three streams of investigation which resulted in the extensive program for taking dry and stable blood plasma to the battlefield and which enormously reduced the fatalities among war casualties.

The extended program to produce blood plasma and serum as blood substitutes thus came about as a direct outgrowth of the earlier work with dried human convalescent serum. Before 1941 it had been recognized that blood plasma or serum in a stable form had many advantages for emergency use (*v.*, e.g., the Medical Research Council's War Memorandum No. 1, published in London in 1941). In 1936 Hughes, Mudd, and Strecker first reported the use of *concentrated* solutions of human blood serum in the treatment of cases of increased intracranial pressure and shock (*v.* Hughes *et al.*, 1938). These were prepared by dissolving serum frozen-dried by Flosdorf. The great therapeutic value of dried human blood serum for reducing intracranial pressure lay in the fact that it could be given in concentrated form for its dehydrating effect, and also that even where such a concentration was not needed it could be more immediately available than either liquid serum or whole blood. Moreover, it could be given without regard to blood type. Following this clinical report, Bond and Wright (1938) investigated the effectiveness of concentrated serum in the treatment of experimental shock in animals. It is also worth commenting that the increasing use of serum regenerated from the dry state brought to the attention of clinicians the fact that fresh undried serum and plasma also had a wide usefulness. Although this was known in the scientific literature, it had been neglected by clinicians.

In 1934, Dr. Harry Eagle prepared various fractions of human serum, and these were frozen-dried by Flosdorf. In preparing fibrinogen and prothrombin it was noted that the dried material, on resolution, was often distinctly more alkaline than the original preparation, presumably because of loss of carbon dioxide during dehydration. In some cases this alkalinity was sufficient to inactivate the product unless due precaution was taken either to buffer the original solution strongly or to acidify it slightly just before processing. Eagle also observed a similar effect in guinea pig complement and in antisera from various sources. However, the alkaline shift was apparently insufficient to affect biological activity. Lens protein, serum albumin, and highly purified egg albumin were also dried and were found to maintain all their native characteristics for a period of years.

### b. Plasma Fractions

More recently, freeze-drying has been applied extensively to similar fractions prepared from some of the plasma collected in the military program. Cohn and his coworkers (1946) succeeded in preparing various components of blood in a high degree of purity so that they might be used in World War II for many specialized purposes. For example, serum albumin in high concentration may be used instead of whole blood plasma for its osmotic effects, etc. The main military advantage in serum albumin as a substitute for plasma was the smaller bulk. Moreover, the product is stable in solution, which contributes to ease in administration. However, the method of preparation involves the use of alcohol, and it was found that the most practical method of completely removing this without alteration of the protein was to dry the product from the frozen state. In this case, an extremely low final moisture content is unnecessary, since the product is redissolved for distribution. With respect to certain other fractions, such as thrombin and fibrin foam, the final product is dried from the frozen state for distribution but globulin is not distributed in frozen-dried form. Cohn made extensive use of freeze-drying in developing the new system of fractionation. Salting out, which is the classical procedure for separation of proteins, was avoided, and, as a result, subsequent dialysis was eliminated. The relative solubility of the various blood derivatives differ under differing conditions of salt content, pH, and temperature (especially at relatively low temperatures of 0° to −10°C.). By varying these conditions systematically, the proteins are precipitated and separated into different fractions (Cohn *et al.*, 1946). Many of these fractions are then dried from the frozen state to yield stable purified products which can be redissolved to any desired concentration in the appropriate diluent. An extended program is under way for large-scale production of gamma globulin to be used in the poliomyelitis program in the United States.

The same advantages that apply to frozen-dried human sera apply equally to frozen-dried animal sera. Sharp & Dohme in 1932 used this for bulk preservation of their excess stocks. It is a usual biological practice for stocks of horse sera and other similar products to be kept on hand in large amounts for immediate availability to meet any emergency. Bulk storage has several advantages. One is that the product may be given a final assay immediately prior to shipment. Another is that demands with respect to size and type of package are frequently not known in advance.

### c. Bone, Skin, Membrane, and Artery Grafts

The first frozen-dried tissue bank in the world has just recently been established at the U.S. Naval Hospital in Bethesda, Maryland. This came about as a result of the development by Flosdorf and Hyatt (1952) of a modified technique for freeze-drying of "live" bone collected from fresh cadavers. This method involves embedding the material in a block of ice by building up successive layers in and around the previously frozen bone. More recently the need for the ice block has been circumvented by drying in a chamber held initially below 0°C. This so controls the rate of drying that the resulting product can be successfully incorporated as a graft into the bone of the host. After trials in dogs, numerous casualties from Korea have received successful functional grafts and, more recently, the work has been extended to include artery and skin grafts (Hyatt *et al.*,

1952). Still more recently Flosdorf and Green (unpublished) have been successful with the use of amniotic membranes in a limited number of burn and ulcer cases as a substitute for skin homografts. If this is confirmed the value in stock-piling dry membranes to meet military and civil emergencies may be tremendous. Dr. Bradford Green has carried out the clinical work. It is reported (private communication) that frozen-dried bone and arterial grafts of bovine origin have been successfully received in humans in France (Lyon).

### d. Vitamins and Hormones

Commercially, one of the most important current applications of freeze-drying is in the field of pharmaceutical products. Parenteral vitamins have become an outstanding item and are produced in large volumes. The dry B complex preparations are of particular importance, for although these products can be dispensed in liquid form for distribution it is difficult to hold the type of formula in demand in good solution. The frozen-dried product has the excellent property of instantaneous solubility so that it can be restored for immediate use by the clinician at any time.

Clinical indications for parenteral use of vitamins include the treatment of various vitamin B complex deficiency states. Since normal vitamin absorption is through the gastrointestinal tract, any abnormality that impairs this function constitutes an indication for parenteral rather than oral administration (Ruffin, 1941; High, 1946; Jolliffe, 1943). Thiamine and riboflavin frequently produce almost immediate effects when given intramuscularly or intravenously after failure by oral administration, and many clinicians now prefer to initiate vitamin therapy parenterally for such conditions as clinical beriberi, ariboflavinosis, and pellagra (Sydenstricker, 1941).

Jolliffe and Smith (1943) have found an increased utilization of the water-soluble vitamins in the presence of infection, fever, and hyperthyroidism, and supplementary B vitamins have been used therapeutically for the treatment of typhoid (Stuart and Pullen, 1946).

A typical commercial B complex formula for a single dose is: thiamine hydrochloride (vitamin $B_1$), 25 mg.; riboflavin (vitamin $B_2$), 10 mg.; pyridoxine hydrochloride (vitamin $B_6$), 5 mg.; calcium pantothenate, 50 mg.; niacinamide, 250 mg.; and phenol (preservative), 0.5%. Ascorbic acid may also be included.

Three hormone preparations are produced in fairly large quantities. *Chorionic gonadotropin* is derived chiefly from human pregnancy urine, although some is of equine origin. *Pituitary gonadotropin* is extracted from equine pituitary for parenteral use in a variety of conditions such as ovarian failure, anomalous spermatogenesis, and testicular underdevelopment. *Adrenocorticotrophic hormone* (ACTH) is now available in ever-increasing amounts, subject only to the natural limitation imposed by the shortage of raw material from which to prepare it. The spectacular results achieved in the treatment of rheumatoid arthritis are well known, but the hormone is also being used in the treatment of acute rheumatic fever, non-Addisonian (familial) hypoglycemia, and myasthenia gravis.

e. Miscellaneous Pharmaceutical Products

Hyaluronidase (the "spreading factor"), an enzyme which acts on hyaluronic acid, has been obtained from many sources including bacteria, mammalian testes, leech extracts, and bee, snake, and spider venoms (Schwartzman, 1951). Frozen-dried preparations of the purified enzyme, usually derived from bull testes, are employed clinically to facilitate the subcutaneous administration of fluids.

Dried human blood cells are now available commercially for topical treatment of slowly healing wounds, burns, and ulcers. These are a by-product of plasma production. The product apparently has the property of stimulating the growth of healthy granulation tissue when applied liberally to the affected area, and it also serves as a medium for the growth and extension of epithelial cells over the granulating surface. In addition, the preparation contains a small amount of residual plasma, the stroma, and the contents of the cellular and acellular elements of the blood. The dried product is highly stable, is not absorbed by the dressing, and clings to the wound site.

Bile has similarly been prepared in a dry state so that a stable product may be available for the treatment of obstructive jaundice. The abnormal bleeding associated with this condition is believed to be due to the lack of absorption of vitamin K in the absence of bile in the intestines (Johnston, 1938).

Farr and Hiller (1946) have described the successful drying of hemoglobin. Application of freeze-drying to oxygenated hemoglobin solutions gave preparations in which the hemoglobin had lost 25 to 30% of its oxygen-binding capacity, by change to methemoglobin. However, when these hemoglobin solutions were first deoxygenated by repeated evacuation of all gases, so that over 99% of the oxyhemoglobin was changed to reduced hemoglobin, the reduced solutions could then be frozen and dried in ampoules and stored *in vacuo* for months without methemoglobin formation. In redissolving this reduced hemoglobin it was necessary to prevent even momentary access of atmospheric oxygen to the dried material before it was dissolved; otherwise, methemoglobin was formed. When the reduced hemoglobin was fully in solution, oxygenation did not inactivate it, and the solution was stable in air and could be kept at 4°C. for several weeks without significant change.

Drabkin (1946) reported that excellent results were obtained with hemoglobin which Flosdorf prepared for him in 1937 by freeze-drying. These original samples were dried on a manifold type of Dry Ice condenser apparatus (Flosdorf, 1949) and were sealed in individual containers. Drabkin stated that samples of dog cyanomethemoglobin were stored for nine years in a refrigerator without alteration. Preparations of hemoglobin tested over a five-year period were partially oxidized to methemoglobin but were undenatured in the sense that the total pigment was still completely convertible to hemoglobin by means of sodium hydrosulfite. This change toward ferrihemoglobin is not unusual; it occurs slowly and progressively in dilute solutions of oxyhemoglobin exposed to the air and also in the solid precipitate obtained in dialysis against saturated ammonium sulfate if this is not stored *in vacuo*. Drabkin found that cyanomethemoglobin proved to be the most stable, and in all his studies he has used frozen-dried preparations as his hemoglobin standard.

Chambers and Nelson (1950) have compared the properties of belladonna leaves dried in an oven at 50°C. or from the frozen state. From the data obtained in this investigation, the following conclusions were drawn:

1. The alkaloids were preserved as effectively by freeze-drying as by oven-drying, although there was no difference in extractability.

2. The water content after freeze-drying was the same as after oven-drying for 36 hours.

3. The leaf sugars were well-preserved by freeze-drying; there was less proteolysis by this method, and the chlorophyll was not destroyed.

In general it appeared that freeze-drying was a better preparative procedure than oven-drying and should be investigated for plants containing similar drugs.

Oven-drying is also being replaced by freeze-drying for the dehydration of materials such as feces, urine, and milk for analysis. The nitrogen contents of the frozen-dried products approximate to those of the fresh specimens, and such samples may be stored indefinitely (Teague *et al.*, 1942).

Flosdorf freeze-dried human milk for distribution from the Philadelphia Serum Exchange in 1934 (Flosdorf and Mudd, 1935). This is now being applied in Holland and to a limited extent in the United States.

### f. Commercial Production Cycles and Processing Information

The nature of the material to be dried determines very largely the operating conditions for a commercial plant. For example, serum will give a satisfactory product if the drying temperature is maintained at about −10°C. Plasma, however, must be kept below −15°C. and preferably at −18°C. Amorphous penicillin requires to be held initially at −25°C. and streptomycin, living virus vaccines, and bacteria at still lower temperatures.

During the desiccation, the temperature of the drying material is controlled by the temperature of the fluid circulating through the drying cabinet shelves. In general, the temperature of the shelves should be raised as quickly as possible in order to accelerate the drying, but the exact rate of rise must be evaluated for each plant and for each product. Towards the end of the cycle the temperature will tend to rise and should be held as high as possible to ensure complete desiccation. Subsequent handling of the dry product must, of course, be such as to ensure that rehydration is minimal, and vacuum-stoppering units are used to seal the containers as soon as possible *in vacuo* or in a suitable inert atmosphere.

It is convenient to employ a 20-hour drying cycle so that batches can be handled with only one 8-hour shift of personnel per day.

A typical drying cycle for 10- to 20-ml. quantities of serum, antitoxin, vitamin, or hormone might be:

1. Freeze initially to −30°C., or lower and transfer rapidly to drying chamber at or just below room temperature.
2. Evacuate.
3. Begin heating when (a) vacuum is less than 200 microns mercury (b) the product has cooled to −28°C. or lower, and (c) the condenser temperature (after the first rush of warm vapor) has fallen again to −30°C. or lower.
4. Heat the product at 37°C. for the next 5 hours, at 50°C. for 10 hours, and finally at 37°C. for 3 hours.

More labile materials such as *Brucella abortus* and modified hog cholera vaccines require a modified drying cycle. The plates of the drying chamber are cooled to −30°C. before the frozen vaccines are put in. The vacuum must be at least 150 microns mercury, and the condenser temperature −50°C. or lower. The heating cycle is also quite different. The temperature is maintained at −20°C. for the first 4 hours, is allowed to rise gradually to +20°C. over a period of 4 hours, then from +20° to +30°C. over a period of 8 hours, and is held at the high temperature for a final 4 hours.

## REFERENCES

Altmann, R. 1890. *Die Elementarorganismen und ihre Beziehungen zu den Zellen.* Veit and Co., Leipzig.

Appleman, M. D., and Sears, O. H. 1946. Studies on "Lyophiled" Cultures: "Lyophile" Storage of Cultures of *Rhizobium leguminosarum. J. Bacteriol.* **52,** 209–211.

Baker, J. A. 1951. The New Hog Cholera Vaccines. *Proc. 88th Ann. Meeting, Am. Vet. Med. Assoc.* Pp. 55–61.

Bond, D. D., and Wright, D. G. 1938. Treatment of Haemorrhage and Traumatic Shock by the Intravenous Use of "Lyophile" Serum. *Ann. Surg.* **107,** 500–510.

Chambers, M. A., and Nelson, J. W. 1950. An Investigation of High-Vacuum Freeze-Drying as a Means of Drug Preservation. I. *J. Am. Pharm. Assoc. Sci. Ed.* **39,** 323–326.

Cohn, E. J., Strong, L. E., Hughes, W. L., Mulford, D. J., Ashworth, J. N., Melin, M., and Taylor, H. L. 1946. Preparation and Properties of Serum and Plasma Proteins. IV. A System for the Separation into Fractions of the Protein and Lipoprotein Components of Biological Tissues and Fluids. *J. Am. Chem. Soc.* **68,** 459–475.

Craigie, J. 1931. Method of Drying Complement from the Frozen State. *Brit. J. Exptl. Pathol.* **12,** 75–77.

Drabkin, D. L. 1946. Spectrophotometric Studies. XIV. The Crystallographic and Optical Properties of the Hemoglobin of Man in Comparison with Those of Other Species. *J. Biol. Chem.* **164,** 703–723.

Elser, W. J., Thomas, R. A., and Steffen, G. I. 1935. The Desiccation of Sera and Other Biological Products (Including Microorganisms) in the Frozen State with the Preservation of the Original Qualities of Products so Treated. *J. Immunol.* **28,** 433–473.

Farr, L. E., and Hiller, A. 1946. Preparation of Dried Hemoglobin without Loss of Activity. *Federation Proc.* **5,** 133.

Flosdorf, E. W. 1949. *Freeze-Drying.* Reinhold Publishing Corp., New York.

Flosdorf, E. W., and Hyatt, G. W. 1952. The Preservation of Bone Grafts by Freeze-Drying. *Surgery* **31,** 716–719.

Flosdorf, E. W., and Kimball, A. C. 1940. Studies with *H. pertussis.* II. Maintenance of Cultures in Phase I. *J. Bacteriol.* **39,** 255–261.

Flosdorf, E. W., and Mudd, S. 1935. Procedure and Apparatus for Preservation in "Lyophile" Form of Serum and Other Biological Substances. *J. Immunol.* **29,** 389–425.

Flosdorf, E. W., and Mudd, S. 1937. Rapid Drying of Serum and Microorganisms from the Frozen State for Preservation. *Rept. Proc. 2nd Intern. Congr. Microbiol.* P. 45.

Flosdorf, E. W., and Mudd, S. 1938. An Improved Procedure and Apparatus for the Preservation of Sera, Microorganisms and Other Substances—the "Cryochem" Process. *J. Immunol.* **34,** 469–490.

Flosdorf, E. W., and Mudd, S. 1944. Blood Substitutes Used in Transfusion, in *Medical Physics.* Edited by O. Glasser. The Year Book Publishers, Chicago. Pp. 116–121.

Flosdorf, E. W., Hull, L. W., and Mudd, S. 1945. Drying by Sublimation. *J. Immunol.* **50,** 21–54.

Flosdorf, E. W., Stokes, F. J., and Mudd, S. 1940. The "Desivac" Process for Drying from the Frozen State. *J. Am. Med. Assoc.* **115,** 1095–1097.

Gersh, I. 1932. The Altmann Technique for Fixation by Drying While Freezing. *Anat. Record* **53,** 309–337.

Greaves, R. I. N. 1942. The Freezing of Human Serum and Plasma in Medical Research Council Transfusion Bottles before Drying by Sublimation from the Frozen State. *J. Hyg.* **41,** 489–495.

Greaves, R. I. N. 1944. Centrifugal Vacuum Freezing. *Nature* **153,** 485.

Greaves, R. I. N. 1946. The Preservation of Proteins by Drying with Special Reference to the Production of Dried Human Serum and Plasma for Transfusion. *Med. Research Council (Brit.) Spec. Rept. Ser.* No. **258.**

Hammer, B. W. 1911. A Note on the Vacuum Desiccation of Bacteria. *J. Med. Research* **24,** 527–530.

Harris, D. L., and Shackell, L. F. 1911. The Effect of Vacuum Desiccation upon the Virus of Rabies with Remarks upon a New Method. *J. Am. Public Health Assoc.* **7,** 52.

High, R. H. 1946. Treatment of Epidemic Diarrhea of Newborn. *Penn. Med. J.* **49,** 1334–1336.

Hoffstadt, R. E., and Tripi, H. B. 1946. A Study of the Survival of Certain Strains of Viruses after Lyophilization and Prolonged Storage. *J. Infectious Diseases* **78,** 183–189.

Hughes, J., Mudd, S., and Strecker, E. A. 1938. Reduction of Increased Intracranial Pressure by Concentrated Solutions of Human "Lyophile" Serum. *Arch. Neurol. Psychiat.* **39,** 1277–1287.

Hyatt, G. W., Turner, T. C., Bassett, C. A. L., Pate, J. W., and Sawyer, P. N. 1952. New Methods for Preserving Bone, Skin and Blood Vessels. *Postgrad. Med.* **12,** 239–254.

Johnston, C. G. 1938. Preoperative and Postoperative Treatment in Cases of Obstructive Jaundice. *Surgery* **3,** 875–883.

Jolliffe, N. 1943. Handbook of Nutrition; Conditioned Malnutrition. *J. Am. Med. Assoc.* **122,** 299–306.

Jolliffe, N., and Smith, J. J. 1943. Nutrition in Practice of Medicine. *Med. Clin. N. Amer.* **27,** 567–579.

Libby, R. L. 1947. The Use of Tagged Antigens in Immunochemical Studies. *Trans. N.Y. Acad. Sci.* **9,** 248–256.

Medical Research Council. 1941. *The Treatment of Wound Shock.* War Memorandum No. 1, London.

Mudd, S., Flosdorf, E. W., Eagle, H., Stokes, J., Jr., and McGuinness, A. C. 1936. The Preservation and Concentration of Human Serums for Clinical Use. *J. Am. Med. Assoc.* **107,** 956–959.

Munce, T. W., and Reichel, J. 1943. The Preservation of Hog-Cholera Virus by Desiccation under High Vacuum. *Am. J. Vet. Research* **4,** 270–275.

Probey, T. F. 1947. Loss of Virulence of *Treponema pallidum* during Processing of Dried Blood Serum. *Public Health Repts. (U.S.)* **62,** 1199–1202.

Rivers, T. M., and Ward, S. M. 1935. Jennerian Prophylaxis by Means of Intradermal Injections of Culture Vaccine Virus. *J. Exptl. Med.* **62,** 549–560.

Rogers, L. A. 1914. The Preparation of Dried Cultures. *J. Infectious Diseases* **14,** 100–123.

Ruffin, J. M. 1941. Diagnosis and Treatment of Mild Vitamin Deficiencies; Clinical Discussion. *J. Am. Med. Assoc.* **117,** 1493–1496.

Sawyer, W. A., Lloyd, W. D. M., and Kitchen, S. F. 1929. The Preservation of Yellow Fever Virus. *J. Exptl. Med.* **50,** 1–13.

Scherp, H. W., Flosdorf, E. W., and Shaw, D. R. 1938. Survival of the Influenzal Virus under Various Conditions. *J. Immunol.* **34,** 447–454.

Schwartzman, J. 1951. Hyaluronidase in Pediatrics. *N.Y. State J. Med.* **51,** 215–221.

Shackell, L. F. 1909. An Improved Method of Desiccation, with Some Applications to Biological Problems. *Am. J. Physiol.* **24,** 325–340.

Siedentopf, H. A., and Green, R. G. 1942. Factors in the Preservation of the Distemper Virus. *J. Infectious Diseases* **71,** 253–259.

Smadel, J. E., Randall, R., and Warren, J. 1947. Preparation of Japanese Encephalitis Vaccine. *Bull. U.S.Army Med. Dept.* **7,** 963–972.

Speck, M. L., and Meyers, R. P. 1946. The Viability of Dried Skim-Milk Cultures of *Lactobacillus bulgaricus* as Affected by the Temperature of Reconstitution. *J. Bacteriol.* **52,** 657–663.

Stamp, Lord. 1947. The Preservation of Bacteria by Drying. *J. Gen. Microbiol.* **1,** 251–265.

Stokes, J., Jr., McGuiness, A. C., and Mudd, S. 1935. Clinical Applications of the "Lyophile" Process. *Trans. Soc. Pediat. Research, Am. J. Diseases of Children* **50,** 535–536.

Stokes, J., Jr., Mudd, S., Roddy, R. L., Eagle, H., Flosdorf, E. W., and Lucchesi, P. 1934. The Use of Lyophile Human Serums for Prevention and Treatment in Infectious Diseases. *Trans. Soc. Pediat. Research, Am. J. Diseases of Children* **48,** 1428–1430.

Stuart, B. M., and Pullen, R. L. 1946. Typhoid; Clinical Analysis of 360 Cases. *Arch. Internal Med.* **78,** 629–661.

Swift, H. F. 1921. The Preservation of Stock Cultures of Bacteria by Freezing and Drying. *J. Exptl. Med.* **33,** 69–75.

Sydenstricker, V. P. 1941. Syndrome of Multiple Vitamin Deficiency. *Ann. Internal Med.* **15,** 45–51.

Teague, D. M., Galbraith, H., Hummel, F. C., Williams, H. H., and Macy, I. G. 1942. Effects of Desiccation Procedures on the Chemical Composition of Feces, Urine and Milk. *J. Lab. Clin. Med.* **28,** 343–348.

Weiser, R. S., and Hennum, L. A. 1947. Studies on the Death of Bacteria by Drying. I. The Influence of *in vacuo* Drying from the Frozen State and from the Liquid State on the Initial Mortality and Storage Behaviour of *Escherichia coli*. *J. Bacteriol.* **54,** 17.

Wooley, J. G. 1939. The Preservation of Lymphocytic Choriomeningitis and St. Louis Encephalitis Viruses by Freezing and Drying *in Vacuo*. *Public Health Repts.* (*U.S.*) **54,** 1077–1079.

CHAPTER 3

# Theoretical Aspects of Drying by Vacuum Sublimation

R. I. N. GREAVES

*Reader in Bacteriology,*
*University of Cambridge, Cambridge, England*



## I. INTRODUCTION

Water boils at 100°C. when the atmospheric pressure is 760 mm. Hg, or, expressed in another way, the vapor pressure of water at 100°C. is 760 mm. Hg. If the pressure above the water is progressively lowered, the boiling point of the water will also be lowered so that it may be boiled at temperatures well below 100°C. This method of low-temperature vacuum evaporation has been used for many years for concentrating and drying solutions which would be unstable at higher temperatures. Martin (1896), for example, made use of it for drying fairly stable solutions of antibodies. The procedure is not ideal, for, as the protein concentrates, the molecules tend to aggregate into glue-like scales which, being very impermeable to water vapor, result in a considerable prolongation of the drying time. Moreover, as the solution concentrates, the protein molecules are subjected to very high salt concentrations so that an irreversible aggregation, which is called denaturation, takes place. This denaturation becomes very obvious when re-solution of the dried scales is attempted, for the solution time is very protracted and probably solution is never complete. Although very stable proteins may survive this ill-treatment, those that are more delicate are completely destroyed and rendered totally insoluble.

If the pressure over the solution is reduced below 4 mm. Hg, which is below the vapor pressure of ice at 0°C., drying will occur from the frozen state. In freeze-drying the water is removed from the ice as vapor without passing through a liquid phase. Thus the ice scaffolding of the frozen protein solution disappears, leaving the protein and the salt molecules separate in a dry molecular skeleton resembling a spongy mass with a volume equal to that of the original frozen block. Thus a protein solution can be dried without the molecules aggregating or coming into contact with high salt concentrations. Such a process gives a product which is extremely rapidly and completely soluble, and even very delicate proteins, such as crystalline egg albumin, do not show any evidence of denaturation when dried in this way.

Denaturation is known to vary directly with time and temperature, and it is generally considered that the success of freeze-drying results from the low temperatures at which drying is carried out. Although this may be true, I have come more and more to the conclusion that the success of freeze-drying is due mainly to the fact that drying takes place from the solid state so that aggregation of molecules and concentration of salts cannot take place. Most proteins remain in solution only in the presence of salts, so if the above contention is correct, drying from the solid phase will occur only if the temperature of drying is lower than the eutectic temperature of the solvent salt solution.

Although the method had been known since the beginning of the century, the virtues of freeze-drying were not fully appreciated until just before the beginning of World War II, when apparatus for laboratory and small-scale commercial use was first becoming available. The war years produced a mushroom growth in apparatus for the freeze-drying of blood plasma and penicillin on a large scale, and the freeze-drying procedure emerged from the war as a major technique for the preservation of many biological preparations. Although the pendulum swings in favor of freeze-drying, a certain mysticism has sprung up round the technique and, as anyone who possesses the necessary apparatus knows, the technique is often used quite unnecessarily. There is a tendency to forget that other methods have been used and are being used for drying, at any rate for the tougher proteins, which attack the problem of denaturation as a "time-temperature" phenomenon by drying at high temperatures for very short times. The first of these methods was roller- or film-drying, originally introduced both in Britain and in Germany during the war years 1914–1918 for the drying of potato flour. These machines were used later for the production of dried milk powders. Roller driers have been superseded, for the drying of all materials that will pass through a small orifice, by spray driers. For spray-drying the liquid is atomized into very fine droplets, allowing a very large area to be exposed from which evaporation can take place. The fine droplets are injected into a current of hot air; drying is extremely rapid and, although the particles rise to the temperature of the hot air when they are dry, by this time they are relatively insusceptible to high temperatures. This method is widely and successfully used for the production of dried milk and coffee powders and, during the war, Wilkinson *et al.* (1942) showed that the method could also be used fairly successfully for the drying of blood plasma.

The use of the word "successfully" in the preceding paragraph needs explanation. What is meant by "successful drying"? Chemicals are often dried as a means of concentration, and as long as the drying process does not lead to changes in chemical constitution they may be said to have been dried successfully. Coffee extract has been successfully dried if it is readily soluble and has retained its aroma. Protein solutions and other biological materials are usually dried in order to preserve them at normal temperatures for long periods of time. It is necessary that the drying process shall not cause denaturation, but, however successful it may be in producing a product which is rapidly soluble immediately after drying, it will be useless if denaturation occurs on storage. For prolonged preservation it is important to be sure that the residual moisture content of the dried material is very low and also that it is packed in such a way that absorption of water cannot occur. Water seems to be the catalyst which is necessary for denaturation to occur, and, although it is probably impossible to remove every trace of water from a dried product, evidence indicates that, when the water content is very low, dried products show remarkable resistance to very high temperatures.

The word "denaturation" as applied to proteins also needs some explanation. It means the aggregation of protein molecules into an insoluble mass, and a good example is the coagulation that occurs on boiling the white of an egg. In this extreme degree denaturation is easy to recognize, but in its early stages recognition can be very difficult. Molecular aggregation may be observed by a change in osmotic pressure, by a change in electrophoretic mobility, by an increase in —SH groups, or by a change in sedimentation rate on ultracentrifugation. None of these methods is sensitive enough to show that any change has occurred on freeze-drying by different methods which may, however, be distinguished by such indirect tests as solubility times and the titration of some labile component such as the complement activity of guinea pig serum.

The technique of freeze-drying can be divided conveniently into the following stages.

1. Freezing.
2. Primary drying.
3. Secondary drying and packing.

It is proposed to consider the process under these headings in the following pages.

## II. FREEZING

### 1. *Eutectic Determinations and Their Significance*

Freeze-drying cannot be discussed without frequent reference to the eutectic point of the material being dried. It is necessary, therefore, to have a clear idea of what is meant by the word "eutectic" and of how eutectics may be determined.

If a solution of common salt is slowly frozen and a continuous record is made of its temperature, a curve similar to that shown in Fig. 1 will be obtained. The temperature will fall progressively with time until 0°C. is reached, when a plateau will occur on the curve, during which period pure water will be liberating its latent heat of fusion and freezing out as pure ice. Meanwhile the salt will be concentrating in the remaining unfrozen water until a certain concentration is reached, known as the eutectic concentration. If the original salt concentration is low, the proportion of eutectic mixture will also be small and the mixture will appear to be a solid block of ice, even at as high a temperature as −5°C. That this is not the state of affairs can be shown by measuring the electrical resistance of the ice block which will still be quite finite. If the temperature is now lowered further, between −21° and −22°C. a second plateau will appear on the curve as the eutectic mixture gives up its latent heat of fusion; this temperature is known as the eutectic temperature or the eutectic point. Beyond this second plateau further measurement will show that the resistance is now infinite, implying that all the water molecules have now been immobilized.

In practice it is usually more convenient, in order to avoid any difficulty from supercooling or uneven cooling, to measure the eutectic temperature by progressive warming of material which has been rapidly frozen below its eutectic point. The salt solution is placed in a conductivity cell made from hard glass and containing two platinum electrodes between which is placed a heat-measuring device such as a thermocouple. The platinum electrodes should be coated with platinum black. The fluid whose eutectic is to be measured is placed in the cell which is then plunged into a Thermos flask containing alcohol refrigerated with solid carbon dioxide to between −70° and −80°C. Rapid freezing occurs. The resistance of the ice is measured by connecting the electrodes in one arm of a Wheatstone bridge which is supplied with an alternating current,

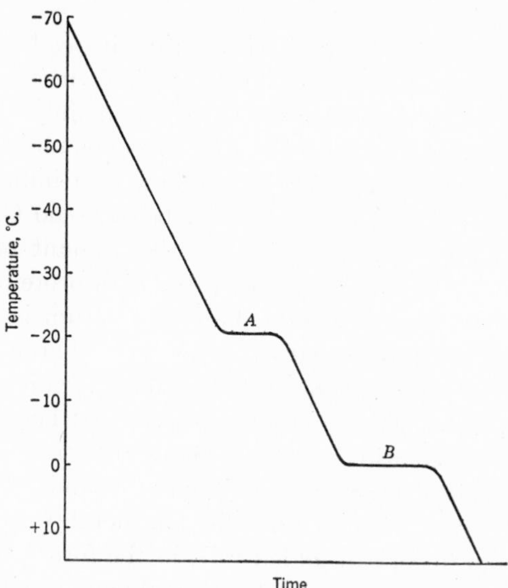


FIG. 1. Eutectic of sodium chloride. The curve was obtained by plotting temperature against time while warming a solution of sodium chloride. Plateau *A* was caused by the thawing of the eutectic mixture at the eutectic temperature. Plateau *B* was caused by the thawing of pure ice.

preferably from an oscillator giving a pure sine wave. The use of alternating current is necessary because a direct current would cause electrolysis of the solution which is being measured. The balance point is found at which the sine wave cannot be detected either by the use of telephones or, preferably, by the use of a "magic-eye" null-point indicator or an oscilloscope. The contents of the Thermos flask are now heated at a constant slow rate; this can conveniently be done with bubbles of air which are arranged to rise up regularly through the alcohol–solid carbon dioxide mixture. As the air bubbles rise through the freezing mixture, they stir it well so that the temperature throughout the flask is very even. Temperature and resistance measurements are made at regular intervals and, if required, both may be recorded continuously. At −70°C. the resistance of the cell is infinite, but as the temperature of the flask is raised the temperature within the cell also rises steadily and uniformly until the eutectic temperature is reached at which point the resistance of the cell suddenly falls and the temperature curve develops a plateau. This is the eutectic temperature of the solution.

The eutectic mixture now thaws, and the temperature rises once more until a temperature just below 0°C. is reached. A second plateau then occurs at the thawing point of ice which is slightly depressed below 0°C. by the presence of the salt.

If this experiment is repeated with serum instead of salt solution, one would expect to find plateaux on the thawing curve corresponding to eutectic mixtures of all the salts in the serum (mainly salts of calcium, potassium, and sodium). In practice the only detectable plateau is just below 0°C., but resistance measurements show that infinite resistance is not reached until the temperature is well below −60°C. The probable reason for this unexpected result is that the amount of each eutectic mixture is very small in comparison with the high protein content of the serum. Since the conductivity tests show that serum is not completely frozen at temperatures above −60°C., on theoretical grounds alone serum should be dried at temperatures below −60°C., which is not a very practicable proposition. The situation is saved, first because the amount of concentrated salt solution unfrozen below 0°C. is so small that the amount of protein in contact with it is minute, and second because at these low temperatures denaturation is considerably delayed. Plasma, however, has had a lot of salt added to it in the form of sodium citrate, and if the plasma has come from a whole blood bank it will also have been considerably diluted with glucose solution so that the protein content may well be below 5%. It is not surprising, therefore, that on empirical grounds it has been found better to dry plasma at a lower temperature than is necessary for serum.

It is often required to dry solutions in which the protein content is lower and the salt content higher than in serum or plasma. Broth and the early samples of penicillin are examples of such solutions. When such solutions are frozen to about −10°C. they appear to be solid, but the presence of the unfrozen portion of the solution becomes obvious as soon as the block is submitted to a vacuum, when the strange phenomenon occurs of the ice block emitting bubbles; Flosdorf (1949) expressively calls this condition "puffing." The presence of a liquid phase in early crude penicillin frozen at −20°C. could be demonstrated by inverting the bottle; an oily liquid then slowly separated from the frozen solid and ran down into the neck.

From a practical point of view these two tests, the frothing of the ice block under vacuum and the separation of liquid from the ice block, are good rough guides to the highest safe temperature at which drying can be carried out. On theoretical grounds drying should always take place below the lowest eutectic temperature of the solution, when the resistance of the block is infinitely large; in practice this is seldom possible, and, provided that the quantity of eutectic mixture present is small compared with the quantity of protein, which it usually is, the amount of denaturation of the product that occurs on drying will be undetectable by any of the present methods of testing.

As long, therefore, as no frothing occurs during drying and as long as there has been no reduction in volume from the size of the original ice block, the final dried product will be readily soluble and will exhibit no sign of denaturation.

### 2. *Necessity for Freezing*

Before drying can take place from the frozen state, it is necessary to freeze the solution. The properties of the final dried material can be very appreciably altered by the method used for freezing. Since drying can take place only from a surface, the rate of drying must vary with the surface area from which evaporation can take place, and this surface can often be regulated during the freezing process.

The size of the crystal that is formed during freezing greatly affects the time for solubility of the dried material and, as a general rule, it may be assumed that, the smaller the crystal size, the more rapidly soluble the dried material will be. This is hardly surprising for, since large crystals result from slow freezing, the presence of large crystals means that the protein has been subjected to the eutectic mixture of its solvent's salts for long periods, that the molecules have been given a maximum chance of aggregation, and that a consequent slight denaturation is probable. Conversely, small crystals formed during freezing generally result in rapid solubility of the dried product.

If a sample of serum is divided into two portions, one of which is rapidly frozen and the other slowly frozen, after drying the two dried materials will look quite different. The quickly frozen material will be a uniform light cream color; the slowly frozen will appear patchy and of a much darker hue, the darkest patches always coinciding with the largest crystal imprints. If the solubility times of the dried materials are compared, the quickly frozen will be found to redissolve appreciably faster than the slowly frozen.

The prefreezing also determines the surface area available for evaporation. Drying from an open dish or from a tray requires that a shallow layer on the bottom of the dish shall be frozen in order to expose a large evaporating surface. Often this method cannot be used, for it necessitates handling the dried material in order to pack it. Therefore bottles or ampoules have to be used, and, because their height is much greater than their diameter, very little material can be placed on the bottom of each container if only a thin layer is to be dried. An improvement will result if the bottle is frozen on its side or at a slight angle to the horizontal so that a wedge of frozen material is formed, but the best solution would be to freeze around the inside periphery of the ampoule or bottle.

If these simple objectives are kept in mind, the reasoning behind the various methods of freezing will be appreciated.

Freezing may be carried out by evaporation as the first stage of the drying process, or it may be conducted at atmospheric pressure as a preliminary procedure.

### 3. *Methods of Freezing*

Methods of freezing may be classified as follows:

a. Evaporative freezing.
   (1) "Degas" snap-freezing.
   (2) Vacuum spin-freezing.
b. Prefreezing.
   (1) Static freezing.
   (2) Shell-freezing.
   (3) Spin-freezing.

#### a. Evaporative Freezing

If a small amount of a protein solution is placed in a large basin in a desiccator containing a desiccant and the pressure in the vessel is rapidly reduced, a point is reached at which violent frothing occurs. Shortly after this the material suddenly freezes into a mass looking like a meringue and then dries from the frozen state in this meringue-like form. It was formerly thought that the frothing was due to rapid boiling at reduced pressure, but this is not strictly true. Nevertheless, at these reduced pressures, evaporation becomes more and more rapid, and unless the liquid can absorb its latent heat of evaporation from its surroundings it will get cooler and cooler until it eventually freezes. The temperature then continues to fall, but evaporation becomes less and less rapid until eventually a temperature is reached at which the rate of loss of heat by evaporation just balances the rate of uptake of heat from the surroundings, and freeze-drying continues at this temperature.

This method of freezing is very rapid. At one moment there is a soap-like mass of bubbles, at the next the whole mass is immobilized by freezing. Provided that the material is not subject to surface denaturation—e.g., crystalline egg albumin—a very rapidly soluble material results after drying.

This method of freezing, though excellent, is not often practicable, for it involves the handling of the dried product in order to pack it. More usually freezing has to be carried out in ampoules or bottles, and in these circumstances the liquid would froth out of the containers.

Hartley (1936), however, discovered that this frothing was not due to true boiling at reduced pressure; that is, it was due not to rapid evolution of water vapor but to the evolution of permanent gases dissolved in the liquid. Thus he found that if the chamber was evacuated to the point at which bubbles were just beginning to appear and then kept at this pressure, the gases could be removed quietly without excessive frothing. Eventually a fluid was left which was quiescent at still lower pressures.

Greaves and Adair (1936) and later Flosdorf and Mudd (1938) made use of this method of degassing to obtain quiescent fluids. The pressure was then lowered rapidly, resulting in very rapid evaporation and a sudden freeze.

If the bottles or ampoules are placed at a slight angle to the horizontal, freezing occurs as a wedge on one side of the vessel, thus giving a better surface-to-depth ratio than is possible if freezing is carried out with the bottles standing vertically.

This process has certain great advantages, for it allows freeze-drying to be carried out on a small scale with a minimum of apparatus—i.e., a vacuum pump, a laboratory desiccator, and a bottle of desiccant, either phosphorus pentoxide or Drierite. It is not quite a perfect method, however, for, although the contents of nearly all the ampoules will freeze perfectly, in a few the material will explode on freezing so that it is ejected from the ampoule. Moreover, it is impossible to freeze the material around the whole inside periphery of the bottle to give an optimal surface-to-depth ratio.

These difficulties can be overcome by the method of vacuum spin-freezing introduced by Greaves (1944). The most critical time in the formation of a bubble is at its birth. At this stage the surface tension tending to prevent expansion is very high, and a small increase in force will prevent frothing. It was found that, if the fluid is submitted to quite a small *g* by slow centrifugation, bubble formation will be completely inhibited, and if this centrifugation is carried out in the vacuum chamber, protein solutions can be subjected to high vacua while being spun, without any frothing occurring. Thus protein solutions can be frozen by evaporation without the necessity for any previous degassing. Anothre great advantage of this method is that the centrifugal force can be used also for distributing the liquid so that it freezes in a shape offering a good surface-to-depth ratio. If the bottle or ampoule is spun on its vertical axis, the liquid will be thrown up around the inside periphery of the bottle and will freeze in this shape. Alternatively, large numbers of small ampoules and tubes can be placed in an angle centrifuge head so that they incline inwards at an angle of about 10° to the vertical to give a wedge-shaped ice block on one side of the tube.

A fairly small increase in *g* is sufficient to prevent all frothing, for instance, spinning a 1-in. diameter ampoule on its vertical axis at 700 r.p.m. It is wise to use the lowest effective speed to minimize the danger of breakage of ampoules and also to reduce the need for balancing the centrifuge heads.

The evaporative freeze obtained by this centrifugal method is very rapid. Unlike freezing by immersion in an external refrigerant where ice forms first nearest the glass and then penetrates to the depths of the fluid, ice forms first on the surface of the fluid and then penetrates to the glass. Under certain conditions this may cause fracture of the glass. When freezing by spinning on a vertical axis, a cylinder of ice forms first in the cone in the center of the fluid, and the expansion of ice between the cylinder and the glass wall may fracture the glass outward. When wedge-freezing, either the surface of the wedge must move or else the glass will again fracture outward. This breakage very seldom occurs when protein solutions like serum or plasma are being frozen, but it is particularly liable to occur with solutions of albumin in distilled water and with distilled water itself. That the breakage is caused mechanically and is not due to heat changes in the glass is demonstrated by the fact that hard glasses such as Pyrex are just as liable to fracture as are the soft glasses such as soda glass. Solutions which might cause fracture of the glass on freezing should be frozen in glassware that is mechanically strong.

The method of vacuum spin-freezing has become very popular, particularly for small laboratory apparatus. Such an apparatus is always available for the drying of small quantities if phosphorus pentoxide is used as the desiccant. The method is excellent for drying cultures, for it can be used satisfactorily for very small quantities. The method is also suitable for large laboratories and for small industrial scale production, but it will probably be found to be more economical to substitute a refrigerated condenser for phosphorus pentoxide as the desiccant. An apparatus with a load capacity of about 1 liter and a mechanically refrigerated condenser is available. The method of vacuum spin-freezing is less suitable for large-scale drying installations in which prefreezing and low-temperature storage act as useful buffers against irregular intake.

b. Prefreezing

If frozen material is placed in a desiccator containing a desiccant and if the desiccator is then evacuated, no frothing will occur from the ice, provided that no thawing has occurred during the period of evacuation of the chamber. If the ice mass is large, partial thawing is not likely to occur, but thawing may be a considerable difficulty if large numbers of small ice blocks have to be handled. This difficulty can be avoided if the time taken to evacuate the chamber to a safe pressure (less than 1 mm. Hg) is made very short by using large clearance capacity vacuum pumps. Another way of avoiding this difficulty is to prefreeze actually in the vacuum chamber, by standing the batches of ampoules on refrigerated trays.

(1) *Static Prefreezing.* The aim, as in evaporative freezing, should be to keep the crystal size as small as possible by obtaining a rapid freeze and, having obtained a rapid freeze, to drop the temperature as quickly as possible below the eutectic of the solution. Much greater ambient temperatures are required in order to obtain a rapid static freeze than for methods, such as spin-freezing, in which there is active mixing. Even if Dry Ice is used as the refrigerant, it will be possible to get a rapid freeze only if the layer of liquid is very thin. The method is therefore of very limited application.

(2) *Shell-Freezing.* The desirability of freezing on the inside periphery of bottles or ampoules led to the introduction of shell-freezing in the United States by Flosdorf and Mudd (1935). Large bottles are supported at a slight angle to the horizontal in a tray of Dry Ice in alcohol and are rotated on their axes either mechanically or by hand. At this temperature, and with the assistance of the agitation that results from rotation, rapid freezing with a small crystal structure results. Hand rotation is excellent for small numbers of bottles, but it is not practicable on a larger scale. Therefore mechanical methods of rotation have been introduced. In turn these methods required the abandonment of Dry Ice baths and their substitution by mechanically refrigerated baths, but, to obtain temperatures comparable with those of Dry Ice, it was necessary to use compounded compressors of complex design.

Naturally enough, attempts were made to get satisfactory freezing at higher temperatures. Strumia and McGraw (1943) introduced a method of shell-freezing in a bath at −20°C. In this process the bottle was slowly rotated on its horizontal axis while immersed to a depth of only 0.5 cm. in the cold bath. Under these conditions the liquid supercooled and froze into a solid block. To overcome this, rotation was stopped when supercooling started so that a pencil of ice formed on the portion of the bottle that lay below the level of the liquid of the cold bath. When this had occurred, rotation was restarted and shell-freezing took place on the inside periphery of the bottle. Judging by the published photographs, large ice crystals were formed which, as we have already seen is indicative of salt concentration and delayed solubility of the dried product.

(3) *Vertical Spin-Freezing.* There is much to be said for avoiding liquid refrigerant baths because the solvent, Methyl Cellosolve or alcohol, is left on the bottle walls and must be removed before the bottles are

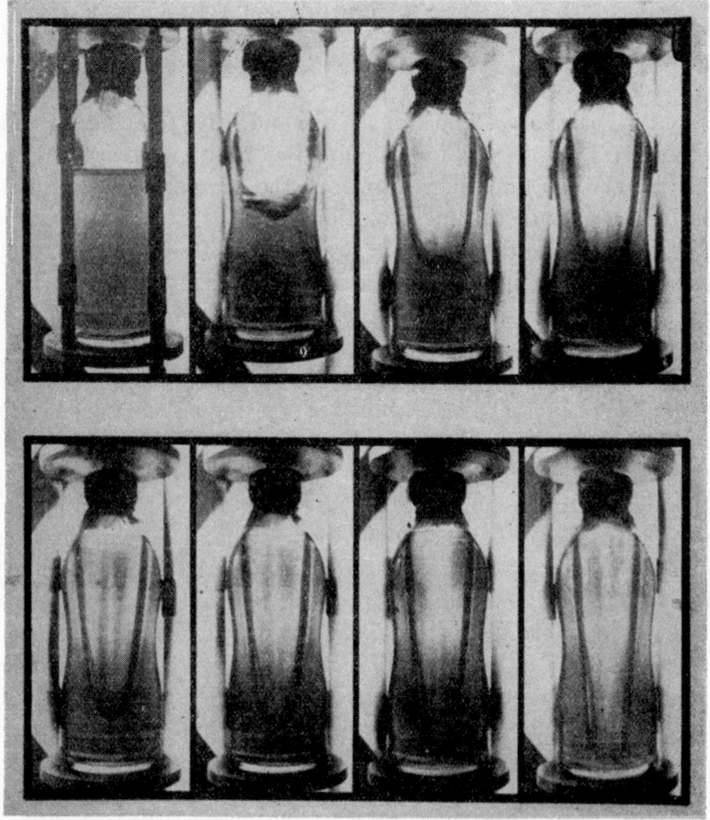

FIG. 2. Stages in the formation of a cone in a bottle of plasma which is being spun on its vertical axis. The photographs were taken at 4-second intervals.

placed in the desiccator. Lanyon (1941) described a method of shell-freezing by rotating the bottle on or near its horizontal axis in a blast of cold air at −18°C. With serum or plasma this caused a very satisfactory freeze, provided that the neck of the bottle was left open, but the moment this was closed supercooling occurred and the liquid froze into a solid block. Since, for reasons of sterility, the contents of the bottle can seldom be exposed to an air blast, this method can rarely be used.

The freezing that occurs after supercooling is usually very satisfactory in that a network of ice is rapidly formed throughout the liquid, preventing salt concentration and giving rise to small ice crystals. It occurred to Greaves (1942) that if the liquid could be held against the inside periphery of the bottle while the bottle was exposed to a cold air stream the freeze that follows supercooling might be used to advantage. Consequently the bottles were spun on a vertical axis so that a cone was formed down the center of the fluid which was consequently forced against the inside periphery of the bottle (see Fig. 2). If this spinning is carried out in a cold

FIG. 3. View of refrigerated room constructed for the vertical spin-freezing of 108 bottles of plasma at each operation. The fan, which causes a rapid circulation of air over refrigerated coils placed behind a baffle, can be seen at the far end of the room.

room in a blast of cold air at −18°C. a very satisfactory freezing occurs which is often called vertical spin-freezing. In order to obtain the small crystal size certain points of technique must be observed: the liquid must be freshly filtered so that it is very clean and free from small particles that might act as centers for crystal formation, the air blast should not be lower in temperature than −18°C., and the liquid should be precooled to +1°C. Mechanical spinners can be constructed to spin a number of bottles; Fig. 3 shows a cold room fitted for spinning over one hundred transfusion bottles at a time. The refrigerant coil is placed behind a baffle at the far end of the room, and a powerful draft is maintained by a fan which blows air through the baffle. The bottles of frozen plasma were stored in a room at −25°C. until required for drying.

Where large amounts of material must be dried and where the material is such that it can be forced through a fine orifice, it is often convenient to spray the material against the refrigerated side of a desiccator chamber. In this way very rapid freezing of small particles occurs, and by suitably directing the jet the whole inside periphery of the chamber can be covered to a considerable depth with rapidly frozen material.

## III. PRIMARY DRYING

### 1. *Removal of Water Vapor*

Before drying by vacuum sublimation can take place, it is necessary to reduce the total pressure in the drying chamber to less than 4 mm. Hg, which is the vapor pressure of ice at 0°C., and, in practice, the pressure should be very much lower still. The pressure in the drying system will be the sum of the pressure of the residual permanent gases and the pressure of the water vapor evolved from the drying material. At a pressure of 0.1 mm. Hg, 1 gram of water occupies 9500 liters as vapor, the removal of which is a far greater problem than the removal of the permanent gases in the system.

The water vapor can be removed by (a) mechanical pumping, (b) chemical desiccants, or (c) refrigerated condenser surfaces.

#### a. Mechanical Pumping

If mechanical pumps are to be used for removing both the permanent gases and the water vapor, then they must have very great clearance at low pressures and must also be provided with some method for removing the water from their oil. Such a pump was used by Flosdorf *et al.* (1940) in their Desivac process in which the water was continuously removed from the oil by centrifugation. When using these pumps, it is essential that the speed of drying be such that the pressure in the system can be kept sufficiently low by the pump. In practice, this means that very large pumps are necessary. Nevertheless, this method was used in the early days of World War II by the Canadian Red Cross for drying plasma on a large scale for transfusion purposes (Best *et al.*, 1942).

A more efficient method of direct pumping is the use of steam ejector pumps. Steam ejector pumps are built on the principle of the common laboratory water pump, and according to Levinson and Oppenheimer (1944) a four-stage pump can evacuate a chamber to 500 microns Hg, and a five-stage system can achieve 100 microns Hg. According to these authors, "An apparatus of this type, with a capacity for removing two liters of water per hour from the drying chamber, consumes 20 (sic) liters of water in the form of high pressure steam (10 atm.). The amount of water necessary to condense the steam is very large (approximately 220 liters per minute). This equipment is now in common use and is highly successful. It is practical if high-pressure steam and sufficient cold water is readily available. In general, it is not as efficient as a mechanically refrigerated condenser, and it involves very large apparatus and large installations."

It is more usual to treat the permanent and the condensable gases separately. If the water vapor can be removed in other ways, then small vacuum pumps will suffice to remove the small amounts of permanent gases which may gain access to the vacuum chamber, either through leaks in the system or by slow liberation during the drying of material which has not been "degassed" before freezing. The water vapor may be removed separately by chemical desiccants or by cold condensing surfaces.

b. Chemical Desiccants

Chemical desiccants are of two types, those that enter into chemical union with the water, and those that absorb the water physically. In the first category must be included phosphorus pentoxide, calcium chloride, and calcium sulfate. Phosphorus pentoxide is the classic desiccant. The dry powder unites with water to form metaphosphoric acid; this reaction is irreversible, and, as the metaphosphoric acid has a very low vapor pressure, phosphorus pentoxide may be used if very low residual moisture contents are desired. On this score it could be classed as a very efficient desiccant, but in other ways it is not so efficient. The chief difficulty is to ensure that sufficient surface is exposed. Fresh phosphorus pentoxide is very avid for water, but when small quantities have combined with it the surface forms into a "pan" which prevents the lower layers of the desiccant from uniting with the water vapor. This difficulty of adequate exposure and the further difficulty of removing the heat which is generated by the reaction make it an unsuitable desiccant unless only very small amounts of water vapor have to be removed over a fairly long period. Under these conditions it is unexcelled.

Calcium chloride is now very seldom used. For the removal of an equal amount of water very much larger amounts of calcium chloride are required than are needed with phosphorus pentoxide, which is, in consequence, used in preference. Calcium chloride is still occasionally used for removing moisture from refrigerator systems, but even in this field it has now largely been superseded.

The only advantage of calcium chloride over phosphorus pentoxide is cheapness, but if bulk can be tolerated then it will be found that calcium sulfate is an even cheaper desiccant. Anhydrous calcium sulfate takes up water to form the hemihydrate, and on heating to 180°C. it is converted back to the anhydrous state. Calcium sulfate is cheap to buy and, as it can be dehydrated by moderate heat at atmospheric pressure, it can be used over and over again. The only drawback is the very large amount that must be used. The Cryochem process of Flosdorf and Mudd (1938) makes use of this material.

In the adsorption group of desiccants Anhydrone and silica gel should be considered. Anhydrone adsorbs water and holds it at a very low vapor pressure; this adsorption can be reversed by heating in a vacuum. Anhydrone is an excellent desiccant, but its primary cost is very high and the fact that it has to be dehydrated in a vacuum is inconvenient. Silica gel is much cheaper, but unfortunately adsorption of water is accompanied by a fairly high temperature rise, and as this is also associated with a marked rise in vapor pressure the amount of desiccant that must be used in order to adsorb a given amount of water is very large. Hill and Pfeiffer (1940) overcame this difficulty in an ingenious way when they discovered that if silica gel is refrigerated it becomes far more efficient. The vapor pressure of wet silica gel at −20°C. was found to be approximately the same as the vapor pressure of an ice condenser at −40°C. Since refrigeration at −20°C. is a much cheaper, easier, and more efficient procedure than refrigeration at −40°C., the use of refrigerated silica gel became a practical proposition and was used by them in their Adtevac process.

c. Refrigerated Condenser Surfaces

Chemicals will act as desiccants if the compound which they form with water has a vapor pressure which is lower than the vapor pressure of ice at the temperature at which the material is to be frozen-dried. Similarly, if a cold surface is introduced into a vacuum system at a temperature lower than the drying temperature, the water vapor evolved by the drying material will be condensed as ice.

The nearer the temperature of the condenser is to the drying temperature, the more slowly will drying proceed. However, thinking in terms of temperature is apt to produce rather an erroneous impression, for what really matters is the vapor pressure difference between the two surfaces, and although vapor pressure is related to temperature this relationship is more nearly logarithmic than linear. Thus in the lower temperature ranges very large temperature differences would be equivalent in vapor pressure difference to quite small temperature differences in the higher temperature ranges.

The lower the condenser temperature, the more efficient the drying system will be, and for this reason liquid air is greatly favored by the author for small-scale laboratory work. Its chief disadvantage is its small latent heat, which means that the condenser has to be replenished very frequently. This limits the use of liquid air to drying cycles that can be completed during normal laboratory working hours.

Dry Ice with a temperature of −78°C. comes much higher in the temperature scale than liquid air. It has, however, a much higher latent heat than liquid air, and consequently when it is used to refrigerate liquids such as alcohol or Methyl Cellosolve which have freezing points below −80°C. the refrigerant mixture will cool a condenser for long periods.

Elser *et al.* (1935) and Flosdorf and Mudd (1935) used cold condensers refrigerated with Dry Ice. Flosdorf and Mudd in their "lyophile" process used condensers cooled with Dry Ice in Methyl Cellosolve, and their apparatus ranged in size from small laboratory plants to semicommercial plants in which they were the first to dry human serum and plasma for transfusion purposes. The small-scale "lyophile" apparatus has proved enormously successful for laboratory use, and apparatus of this nature will be found in many laboratories in all parts of the world.

For large-scale commercial work Dry Ice condensers are not to be recommended because of their high running costs, unless very advantageous conditions of supply exist. Even then the handling of large amounts of Dry Ice becomes a problem. It is at this stage that the use of mechanically refrigerated condensers becomes preferable, although, in the writer's opinion, mechanical refrigeration is justified even for large-scale laboratory apparatus. Figure 4 shows an apparatus which is mechanically refrigerated and which has a capacity of 400 ml.

The two most important considerations in the use of mechanically refrigerated condensers are the temperature to be maintained and the shape of the condenser.

The author prefers a condenser temperature of −40°C. This is because it is a temperature which can be achieved easily by standard small refrigerator units and which can be maintained against reasonable duty.

The lower the evaporator temperature, the smaller becomes the duty of the compressor. At −40°C., small single-stage compressors charged with methyl chloride or Freon 12 will deliver a useful duty. The substitution of Freon 22 for Freon 12 will usually produce temperatures from 5 to 10 degrees lower, but, owing to increased pressures, special gland seals may have to be fitted. A ¼-horsepower compressor charged with methyl chloride could be reasonably expected to maintain a condenser temperature of −40°C. with a drying rate of 50 ml. per hour. A condenser temperature of −40°C. should enable useful drying speeds to be obtained at temperatures of the order of −30°C.

If the condenser temperature is lowered from −40° to −80°C. while the same drying conditions are maintained so that the vapor pressure difference between the condenser and the drying material is not changed, the drying temperature only drops from $-30°$ to $-33°C$. This 3 degree fall in drying temperature would be dearly bought, for a condenser temperature of $-80°C$. can be obtained only by two-stage refrigeration.

Two-stage refrigeration involves either compounding or cascading. Compounded refrigerators consist of a high-pressure and a low-pressure

FIG. 4. Edwards Model 3 Centrifugal Freeze Drier with covers removed to show pumping and refrigeration systems. Courtesy of W. Edwards & Co. (London) Ltd.

compressor working on a common intercooler. In this way the swept volume of the low-pressure compressor can be made very much greater than the swept volume of the high-pressure compressor, resulting in a great increase in efficiency. Compounding either increases the efficiency of the compressor when it is working at comparatively high temperatures such as $-40°C$. or else enables a lower temperature to be reached than would be possible with the same compressor connected in a more normal manner. Compounding is particularly satisfactory when ammonia is used as the refrigerant.

Cascaded refrigerators use one compressor to cool the condenser of a second machine so that the liquid is cooled before expansion in the final evaporator. Different gases may be used for each of the machines, a common practice being to use methyl chloride to cool the condenser of a machine charged with propane. Such cascaded machines will produce a reasonable duty at temperatures as low as −80°C. or, alternatively, a very good duty at −40°C.

If the cost of drying is unimportant, it would be an advantage to run the condenser at the lowest possible temperature so that the lowest possible drying temperature is achieved. However, against this it must be remembered that mechanical refrigeration becomes less and less reliable as the temperature gets progressively lower, so that in practice it is usually wiser to use the highest condenser temperature which will yet give a sufficiently low drying temperature with a small margin of safety.

Much controversy surrounds the mechanical form that the condenser should take. It is frequently stated that, because ice is a poor conductor of heat, there will be a significant drop of temperature across the layer of ice on the condenser so that the effective temperature of the condenser will be much higher than the temperature of the expanding refrigerant gas. Those who hold this view maintain that either the surface of the condenser should be made very large or else some method should be developed for continuously removing the ice from the condenser. The author is unaware of any figures having been published for the conductivity of ice formed by condensation in vacuum, nor does he think that measurements would give constant values of conductivity, for direct observations of ice condensing in vacuum show that the physical form varies with the temperature of condensation and with the degree of vacuum in the chamber. At temperatures around −20°C. a transparent ice is formed, whereas at lower temperatures an opaque white ice appears. If the partial pressure of the permanent gases is high, then the ice tends to form on that part of the condenser which the water vapor first meets. If, however, the partial pressure of non-condensable gases is low, then the ice will form more or less evenly over the whole condenser surface. Thus the effective size of the condenser varies inversely with the partial pressure of the non-condensable gases.

With regard to condenser size, there are two schools of thought. One considers it is best to use small condenser surfaces working at low temperatures; the other prefers to use the largest possible condenser surface working at a correspondingly higher temperature.

If one holds this latter view, then the condenser should take the form of a coil of pipe, the size being determined by the optimal refrigeration duty required at the desired condenser temperature. This will result in a condenser of large surface area, and in order to obtain the maximum efficiency of this large surface it is important that the non-condensable gases should be maintained at a very low level.

Levinson and Oppenheimer (1944) prefer a condenser with a small surface maintained at a very low temperature, and they recommend a flat plate condenser placed fairly closely over the orifices of the bottles from which plasma is being dried. In America there is a preference for a condenser in the form of a tube down which the water vapor passes and around the outside of which the refrigerant is circulated. Ice is prevented from building up inside this tube by scraper blades which resemble the blades of a mowing machine and which are kept constantly rotating. The ice is thus separated as snow and falls into a cold collecting chamber. If two such chambers are provided with a changeover valve, then a continuously operating plant becomes possible.

The Chain Belt Company (1948) has introduced a liquid condenser for the continuous operation of a moving-belt freeze-drier. A salt solution with a low eutectic, and at its eutectic concentration, is refrigerated and sprayed into the vacuum chamber. Water vapor will condense in this cold brine solution, diluting it slightly. The diluted brine is removed from the drying chamber and concentrated back to the eutectic mixture by heating at atmospheric pressure. It is then refrigerated again and sprayed once more into the vacuum chamber. A suitable salt would be lithium chloride, although undoubtedly calcium chloride would be satisfactory for many purposes.

## 2. *Vacuum Requirements*

### a. Vacuum Chambers and "Plumbing"

Because freeze-drying can take place only in a comparatively high vacuum, specialized chambers and apparatus have to be used for the process. There are again two distinct schools of thought; one advocates carrying out the process in special vacuum chambers, and the other prefers manifolds to which each bottle or ampoule is individually attached. With either method, vacuum engineering techniques will have to be employed. These techniques are highly specialized, and it is not proposed to discuss them in detail here, but it may be helpful, particularly to those who contemplate building their own small-scale drying plants, if a few of the most widely used techniques are briefly described.

The simplest method of freeze-drying is to use a standard laboratory glass desiccator, to "degas" the material to be dried and to use phosphorus pentoxide as the desiccant. Such a desiccator can be connected to a single- or two-stage rotary vacuum pump by a length of rubber pressure tubing. This arrangement is not ideal, for the average vacuum desiccator is provided with a glass tap which has far too small a bore, and rapid evacuation is made even more difficult by the glass capillary tube which is often fitted in order to prevent the vacuum in the desiccator from being let down too rapidly. A simple improvement can often be effected by breaking off this glass capillary. The desiccator method also has the disadvantage that it is difficult to insert electric wires or attachments for vacuum measurements. A greatly improved and equally simple apparatus can be made by taking a glass cylinder and providing it with a bottom metal plate, a top metal ring, and finally a top metal lid. The glass cylinder is connected to the plate and ring by luting with a special vacuum "plasticine" such as Apiezon Q; the top plate may also be sealed to the top ring with the same compound, for such a seal can easily be broken with a knife when necessary. For connecting to the vacuum pump a large-bore glass tap can be sealed into the bottom plate with Apiezon W wax or good-quality sealing wax. Vacuum gauges and electric wires can also be sealed into the bottom plate in a similar manner. Such a simple apparatus can be used for experimental work and for small-scale laboratory production. These simple techniques can also be used for large machines, and a large-scale production plant based on these techniques has been described (Greaves, 1946).

The choice of material for a vacuum apparatus must depend on the ultimate vacuum to be achieved and on whether or not the apparatus will be continuously pumped. Fortunately with freeze-drying the ultimate vacuum required is not very high, and the vacuum pumps are usually running continuously. Thus rubber tubing may be used, although it is slightly permeable to certain gases, and metals and glass may also be used without preliminary outgassing. Cast metals should be avoided if possible, for slight faults in casting may cause vacuum leaks. Metals may be joined by soldering, brazing, or welding. Soldered joints require that the two surfaces to be joined should be perfectly tinned, after which the joint is preferably made with an iron. Brazed and welded joints should be tested with a hydrogen leak detector, and, if faulty, the bulk of the joint should be removed, preferably by turning in a lathe, and then the joint should be rewelded and the process repeated until a perfect weld is made.

When completed, the vacuum apparatus should be tested to determine that there are no leaks. Special leak detectors have been developed, most of which depend on the rapid diffusion of hydrogen. Tracing a leak is usually a fairly simple process with this apparatus but it is not likely to be available except in a vacuum engineering works. Often a leak which is passing gas can be blocked with a liquid, so that if the joints are painted with water it is often possible to block the leak temporarily and finally to locate it exactly. Alternatively the apparatus may be put under pressure (about 25 lb./sq. in. is adequate) and leaks looked for by painting all joints with soapy water.

Vacuum valves are of three types. First there is the ground-glass barrel-type valve lubricated with a vacuum grease such as Apiezon M or L. Such valves are entirely satisfactory in the small sizes, but with an increase in size the large ground surfaces become very difficult to move. Second there is the metal valve consisting of ground metal plates separated by a vacuum oil such as Apiezon J. The bottom plate has an entrance and an exit hole drilled in it, and the top plate has a channel which either connects or isolates the entrance and exit holes in the bottom plate. The Audco valve manufactured under a Metropolitan Vickers patent is of such a design. The third type of valve incorporates a rubber diaphragm and is eminently suitable for the order of vacuum required for freeze-drying. These valves are manufactured with both small and large bores and are used practically exclusively in modern freeze-drying apparatus.

If very large-bore valves are required for isolating large vacuum lines, the valve may have to be very complicated; for example, the closure may be a metal plate seating onto a rubber ring and operated by a threaded rod passing through a vacuum stuffing box.

The diameter of connecting pipes must be calculated from a knowledge of the volume of vapor which must pass and the maximum allowable pressure rise along the line; formulas for calculating the resistance of pipe lines are given by Barrett and Beckett (1951). If the line connects the condenser and the pump, it will have to pass only the non-condensable gases, and it can therefore be of quite small diameter compared with the size that would be required if it had to pass the water vapor before condensation. If manifolds are used instead of vacuum chambers, then the water vapor has to be piped to the condenser and, unless these pipes are of large diameter, there will be a large pressure rise along the line which will be reflected in a high drying temperature. This fact and the difficulty of getting reliable vacuum connections between the bottles and the manifold weigh the scales very heavily in favor of vacuum chambers, particularly for large-scale operation.

The strongest structure under a vacuum is the sphere, closely followed by the cylinder with hemispherical ends. If these shapes are adopted, quite light-gauge material may be used for constructing the vacuum chamber. A vacuum chamber designed with these favorable factors in mind is shown in Fig. 5. This shape is often not very convenient for accommodating material in the drying chamber, and for tray driers in particular a rectangular shape is to be preferred. A rectangular chamber would have to be made from very thick steel plates if it were to have adequate strength, but the steel plates can be reinforced by ribbing which is a common practice with pressure vessels. In order to withstand the atmospheric pressure, the ribbing should be within the chamber; it is always amusing to observe that the pressure technique is so ingrained in engineers, minds that they continue to place the ribbing on the outside of vacuum chambers. It can, however, be argued that if the ribbing is inside the chamber it is wasting valuable vacuum space.

FIG. 5. Edwards Model 1000 PS freeze-drying plant set up for testing before delivery. Courtesy W. Edwards & Co. (London) Ltd.

b. Vacuum Pumps

The choice of a suitable vacuum pump for a particular drying plant is of great importance. In the section on desiccants it was stated that certain types of vacuum pump were fitted with centrifuges which could separate the water from the oil, thus enabling the pumps to be used for freeze-drying without the need for a desiccant. The only disadvantage of this method is the necessity of using a pump with a very great clearance for drying quite small amounts of material. Unless the pump is fitted with some method of removing water from the oil, it is absolutely essential that water should not get into the oil.

If an avid desiccant like phosphorus pentoxide is being used in sufficient quantity, no water vapor will pass over to the pump and it will be an advantage to use a vacuum pump with a high clearance capacity at very low pressures so that the pressure of non-condensable gases is kept at the lowest possible level. A suitable pumping system consists of an oil diffusion pump backed by a rotary oil pump. Mercury should not be used in the diffusion pump in this system as mercury vapor might distill back into the vacuum system and contaminate the material being dried. A mercury diffusion pump may well be employed, however, if a liquid air condenser is being used to remove the water vapor, for the mercury vapor will also be condensed on the liquid air condenser and there will be no danger of contamination of material in the chamber.

When a refrigerated condenser at $-40°C.$ is employed, it would be futile to use a pumping system like that described in the previous paragraph. Such a system would have a very high clearance capacity at 0.1 mm. Hg (the vapor pressure of water at $-40°C.$), and consequently large amounts of water vapor would be sucked over by the diffusion pump and deposited in the oil of the rotary pump so that the whole pumping system would fail. Such an apparatus requires a pump with a high clearance capacity at high pressures so that the system can be evacuated rapidly from atmospheric pressure to a pressure well below the vapor pressure of ice at 0°C., e.g., 0.5 mm. Hg. The pumping speed should then fall so that it is very small at 0.1 mm. Hg. These pumping characteristics can be obtained with a single-stage rotary oil pump. The amount of water vapor that would get over into such a pump would be very small and would distill off rapidly from the hot oil so that the pump would maintain its pumping efficiency indefinitely. If a two-stage rotary oil pump were used in such a system, it would probably be necessary to provide some method for stripping the water from the oil to prevent the system from losing its efficiency. A simple stripper in which the oil is continuously circulated over a heated plate has been described by Greaves (1946).

A Dry Ice condenser, however, has a water vapor pressure of less than 0.001 mm. Hg, and to do it full justice an efficient two-stage rotary oil pump should be used.

A pump should be chosen that will evacuate the whole apparatus to a pressure of at least 0.5 mm. Hg in about 5 to 10 minutes. If it takes longer to reach this pressure, prefrozen material may thaw or, if evaporative freezing is being employed, a rather sluggish and unsatisfactory freeze may occur. If the system is leaky, then pumps of much greater capacity will be necessary and they, of course, will suck over more water vapor and will eventually fail. The necessity for a vacuum-tight system is obvious.

### 3. *Vacuum Measurement*

Pressure measurements are always referred to the height of a mercury column. In vacuum freeze-drying the range of vacuum encountered is usually between 1 and 0.001 mm. Hg. Rough vacua in the pressure range of several centimeters Hg may conveniently be read from the height of a mercury column, but this simple method is not applicable to measurement of pressures of a fraction of a millimeter Hg. Magnification of movement by lenses or levers is of no use in this range, for, as Flosdorf (1949) points out, "Inertia of movement under slight pressure differences, together with frictional resistance, nullifies the use of lever and float arrangements for increasing sensitivity."

Measurements in this pressure range are always referred directly or indirectly to measurements with a McLeod gauge. The necessary magnification is obtained with this gauge by trapping a known volume of the rarefied atmosphere and compressing it into a capillary of known volume per unit length. In its original form the McLeod gauge was large and clumsy, but the modern, small, portable form of the gauge is favored by some for pressure measurements in freeze-drying. In the author's opinion the McLeod gauge has two serious disadvantages for freeze-drying measurements: first, the gauge can be used only for sample measurements, so no continuous record of pressure can be made; and second, without considerable knowledge and experience it is difficult to know whether one is reading the absolute pressure or the partial pressure of non-condensable gases. This difficulty arises because the rarefied atmosphere has to be compressed into the capillary tube before it can be measured, and if this pressure is greater than the vapor pressure of water at the ambient temperature the water vapor will be condensed to a minute volume and the reading recorded by the gauge will be much lower than the total pressure in the system. Flosdorf (1949, pp. 54–61) discusses this point in detail, and describes how the difficulty may be avoided.

The Knudsen gauge is another absolute gauge which may be used for measuring total pressure and in which no difficulty from condensation is encountered. The McLeod gauge will give an unequivocal correct reading of the pressure of a dry rarefied atmosphere and may thus be used for calibrating other types of gauge.

Of other types of gauge that most useful for the pressure ranges encountered in freeze-drying is the thermal electric gauge. A current passed through a wire will heat it to a temperature depending on the rate of cooling, and the rate of cooling will depend on the nature and amount of the surrounding atmosphere. Thus the degree of vacuum will be found to bear a direct relationship to the temperature of the wire, which may be measured either directly with a thermocouple or indirectly as the resistance of the wire.

In the Pirani gauge the measuring filament is placed in one arm of a bridge circuit balanced at atmospheric pressure; any "out-of-balance" can be converted to a reading of vacuum on the scale of a meter and may even be recorded. Such a gauge will record the total pressure of a rarefied atmosphere, but because the thermal conductivity of different gases is different there will be an inevitable inaccuracy unless it is used for measuring a pure gas, which it will not be doing if used for measurements while freeze-drying. This is not the serious disadvantage that might be imagined, for it is seldom necessary to know the pressure with extreme accuracy, and if the Pirani gauge is calibrated against a McLeod gauge on dry air it becomes a very useful instrument for freeze-drying.

The Pirani gauge is sensitive only over the range from 1 to 0.001 mm. Hg, which is exactly the range of working for freeze-drying. At the higher pressure ranges it is advisable to balance the gauge filament with a similar filament at atmospheric pressure in the opposite arm of the bridge. At the lower pressure range it is advisable that the balancing filament should be sealed in a bulb evacuated to 0.001 mm. Hg.

The Pirani gauge can be made into an extremely sensitive type of leak detector. It is thus of great value during the initial testing of a drying plant; then, when the plant has been made leak-free and is being used for routine drying, as long as the gauge records a pressure which matches very closely the vapor pressure of ice at the condenser temperature one knows that satisfactory operation is occurring.

The Pirani gauge has the reputation of not maintaining its calibration and consequently requiring frequent recalibration against a McLeod gauge. This is because dirt collects on the filament, and it can be avoided if the filament is coated with glass. Unfortunately a glass-coated filament responds much more slowly to changes in pressure. This is not a disadvantage while freeze-drying, but it does decrease the usefulness of the gauge for leak detection. It has been found, however, that if the filament is heated to red heat in a vacuum the gauge regains its original calibration; provision for heat treatment of the filament is provided on some modern gauges.

### 4. *Heat Control*

The latent heat of evaporation of ice at different temperatures can be calculated from Clapeyron's equation:

$$\frac{dP}{dT} = \frac{\lambda}{T}(v_2 - v_1)$$

which gives a value of 672 cal. per gram between −25° and −30°C. Thus the speed of drying must depend solely on the rate of application of heat.

Freeze-drying on the small scale which is usual in the laboratory is accomplished either in a desiccator with phosphorus pentoxide as a desiccant or by using a manifold and a Dry Ice condenser. Using the chemical, one relies on a sufficiency of heat reaching the frozen product by radiation and conduction from the reaction between the water and the phosphorus pentoxide; with the manifold the ampoules are exposed to the air of the room and are heated by it. As the amount of heat absorbed in either method is usually insufficient to produce thawing, and as the time taken for drying is seldom important, complications due to the introduction of controlled heat can be avoided. Drying can, however, be speeded up with the manifold method if it takes place in an incubator, or conversely it can be slowed down if it is transferred to a refrigerator, as was done by Elser *et al.* (1935). The situation is very different, however, in drying plants which must handle large volumes of material or when it is desired to dry some particular product at a particular temperature.

If the material to be dried is suspended so that it is completely heat insulated from its surroundings and if a refrigerated condenser is used to absorb the water vapor that evolves, the temperature of the material at first falls rapidly and then progressively more slowly until it exactly equals the temperature of the condenser. At this temperature drying ceases, for the water vapor molecules are just as likely to return to the frozen mass as they are to go to the condenser, and similarly molecules emitted from the condenser might return to the frozen mass.

To disturb this equilibrium, heat would have to be applied to the frozen mass. This would cause a rise in its temperature, and a vapor pressure gradient between it and the condenser would be established, with a consequent flow of water molecules from the material being dried to the condenser. From Clapeyron's equation, if 672 cal. were applied, 1 gram of water would be transferred to the condenser and *pro rata.* In practice an efficiency of 672 cal. per gram is not likely to be achieved; in one plant in which the author tried to work out this value experimentally a figure of 901.5 cal. per gram was obtained. From this figure an approximate overall average value which has proved most useful for preliminary calculations is that "1 watt of heat input will dry 1 ml. in 1 hour"; thus to dry 1 liter in 1 hour, 1 kilowatt of heat will have to be applied. If, however, the liter is in the form of a cube of ice, each side 10 cm., and if the kilowatt is applied as heat to five of its six sides, local melting at the point of contact of the hot surface will undoubtedly occur. Clearly many other considerations are involved, and since they are all dependent variables a clear understanding of their interrelationship is essential before it is possible to design a plant to dry a given volume at a given temperature in a given time.

The rate of drying is directly related to the amount of heat applied to the frozen product. Claims of fast drying rates should be considered with caution. In a plant designed so that there is as little restriction of vapor flow as possible, the limiting factor to the speed of drying is the difficulty of applying the heat to the actual drying surface. Often for practical reasons restrictions to vapor flow have to be present in a drying system, e.g., necks of bottles or ampoules, drying caps, and plugs, which may be necessary for sterility. The price that has to be paid for the inclusion of these restrictions is a slowing of the drying rate because less heat can be applied if the same drying temperature is to be used.

It is common practice to apply the heat needed for evaporation by conduction. Either the material to be dried is placed in a glass dish supported on a metal plate heated electrically and controlled thermostatically, or else the material is shell-frozen on the inside periphery of a bottle

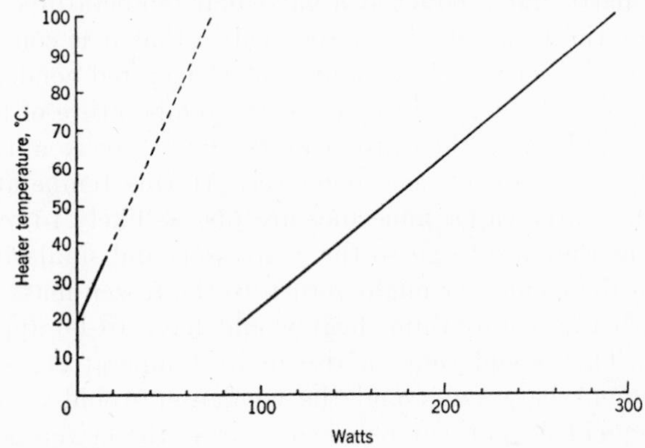


FIG. 6. Solid line represents the heat absorbed by 5 liters of serum, distributed so that it had a surface area of 2500 sq. cm., at different heater temperatures. The serum was in a glass bottle which was approximately 0.5 cm. thick, and the neck of the bottle was closed with a cotton-wool filter. Dotted line represents the heat loss of the system at different temperatures of the heater. The continuous line represents values actually plotted, and the dotted line represents assumed values.

which is placed in a metal container thermostatically controlled at a predetermined temperature.

The heat absorption at different heater temperatures can be determined and plotted if the surface area from which evaporation is occurring is known and the heat input to the heater plate is measured at different temperatures. Such an experiment is illustrated in Fig. 6. As the heater temperature is raised, more and more heat is absorbed and consequently the drying rate is increased. This experiment was conducted with rather a thick layer of serum in a very large bottle, the evaporation surface was 2500 sq. cm., and the bottle neck was plugged with cotton wool for the purpose of maintaining sterility. Even under these very adverse conditions there was no tendency for the ice to melt at its surface of contact with the glass, even when the outside of the bottle was heated to 100°C.

The maximum limit of the heater temperature is governed by two factors. First, the temperature of the ice–glass interface must not rise above the eutectic of the material being dried, and second some arrangement must be made to ensure that the dried material is not raised to a dangerously high temperature. To avoid this complication it is common practice to set the heater temperature well below what would otherwise be a safe maximum. In the example under discussion, if the heater temperature had been set at 40°C., 150 − 20, or 130 watts, would have been absorbed per hour. Thus on a 20-hour schedule 130 watts would dry 2.6 liters of serum spread out to give an evaporation surface of 2500 sq. cm; in other words, under these particular conditions the depth of material which could be safely dried in 24 hours is just over 1 cm. The conditions of this experiment were particularly disadvantageous; Flosdorf (1949) considers that it should not be difficult to arrange conditions so that 1 mm. depth can be dried per hour, i.e., twice the rate achieved here. Conditions can be envisaged in which even faster rates could be safely achieved. Often, however, unsuitable ampoules or bottles must be used, and conditions may be made even worse by insistence on the use of bacterial filters, so that the designer of freeze-drying apparatus has to make adjustments accordingly. Any claims that a particular apparatus will dry faster than another should be examined very carefully.

The rate of heat absorption in relation to heater temperature shown in Fig. 6 applies only to this particular experiment, for it is very much influenced by the thickness of the wall of the glass bottle, which was of the order of 0.5 cm. The heat conductivity of glass is very low, and across a width of 0.5 cm. it would be quite possible to have a gradient of temperature of 150°C. or more. If the frozen mass is in direct contact with the heater, an equivalent heat absorption would occur at a very much lower heater temperature; in fact, it would be impossible to raise the heater temperature even to +40°C., for before that temperature was reached the heat absorption would cause local thawing of the frozen mass. Thus with the frozen mass in contact with the metal heater one apparently gets a much higher rate of drying than occurs if glass intervenes.

If drying is to proceed, there must be a flow of vapor from the evaporating to the condensing surface, and a vapor pressure difference must exist between these two places. This condition can be expressed by the formula:

$$\frac{\text{Vapor pressure difference}}{\text{Resistance to flow}} = \text{Rate of flow} \qquad \text{or} \qquad \frac{VPD}{R} = C$$

It has already been explained that the rate of flow of the water vapor is directly proportional to the heat input in watts, so that the expression may be rewritten as:

$$\frac{\text{Vapor pressure difference}}{\text{Resistance to flow}} = K \text{ watts}$$

In the discussion of temperature gradients it was assumed for each example that the evaporating surface was $-25°C.$, and it was also stated that if the ice layer was infinitely thin then the heater temperature could be infinitely high without causing melting at the interface. From the formula given above it is clear that this could occur only if the obstruction to the vapor flow is infinitely small. Then and only then could the heat input ($K$ watts) be increased indefinitely without raising the vapor pressure difference and hence the temperature of the material being dried. Under these conditions, which obviously could never be achieved in practice, drying would be instantaneous.

It can also be deduced from the equation that if the heat input ($K$ watts) remains constant the vapor pressure difference between the evaporating and the condensing surfaces is directly proportional to the flow of vapor. If the condenser temperature is fixed then it follows that for a given rate of drying the temperature of the evaporating surface will vary with the degree of obstruction.

The obstruction to the vapor flow in a freeze-drying system is made up from a number of factors. In an ideal system if the evaporating molecules were being fired from the surface at right angles and if the condensing surface were very close to the evaporating surface, the only possible obstruction to vapor flow would be collision of the water vapor molecules with the molecules of permanent gas left in the necessarily imperfect vacuum. In practice the water vapor molecules must come off at all angles and must collide with each other. To quote Carman (1948): "The gap between the evaporating and condensing surface does not appear to be critical." Carman is, of course, referring to a system in which there is no mechanical constriction between the two surfaces such as would occur along a pipe. Certainly, within limits the distance to the condenser is of no significance compared with the obstructions introduced by the necks of ampoules and bottles and the plugs and caps that may be necessary to ensure sterility. Formulas that have been devised for calculating the effect of obstructions are quoted by Flosdorf (1949). Such formulas may be useful for preliminary calculations, but they tend to be extremely inaccurate in practice, for they are based on idealized conditions. It is impossible, for example, to predict how much of the obstruction produced by the neck of a bottle may be due to laminar flow and how much to turbulence in the neck. In so complex a system it may be concluded that as yet calculation is no substitute for direct measurement.

If the heat input that is necessary to give the desired drying time produces too high a drying temperature, it may be possible to lower this temperature by removing the sterility plug or by using a bottle with a wider neck. If this is impossible, then the heat input must be reduced and the drying time proportionately prolonged. If large thicknesses are to be dried, it may be found that the temperature at the evaporating surface is sufficiently low but that the temperature at the glass–ice interface is too high; again this will demand a decrease in the heat input and a lengthening in the drying time.

Bradish *et al.* (1947) claim drying rates much faster than those of Greaves (1946), which they attribute to placing the condenser immediately above the trays containing the material to be dried. The implication is that it is important that the condenser surface should be near the drying surface. From what has already been said, it should be clear that it is impossible to compare drying rates from open metal trays with drying rates from plugged glass bottles; arguments of this nature which neglect many relevant data are misleading. If an M.R.C. plasma drying plant is altered so that the condenser coils, instead of being at the bottom of the vacuum chamber, are placed round the necks of the bottles, and if all other conditions of drying are kept the same as in the original plant, the drying temperature is found to be raised. This unexpected result would seem to suggest that it is incorrect to imagine that all the water vapor molecules that hit the condenser stick there; if we assume that a proportion fail to stick, they would bounce back toward the neck of the bottle and collide with molecules leaving the bottle, so that there is an increased turbulence and an increase in the resistance to the flow of vapor. A similar rise in drying temperature has been observed when the necks of some ampoules were placed directly facing and about 1 inch away from a flat plate. Inclining the ampoules so that the vapor molecules hit the plate at an angle caused a progressive lowering of the drying temperature. In this instance the increase in temperature was obviously due to molecules that were reflected back from the plate, thus increasing the obstruction to the flow of water vapor molecules from the ampoules.

For rapid drying with conducted heat it is necessary for the depth of the material being dried to be kept small and for it to be in contact with a metal heating plate. These conditions can seldom be met in practice. Consequently Levinson and Oppenheimer (1944) investigated the possibility of heating by radiation. They reasoned that, if it were possible to find a wavelength which was not absorbed by glass but which was absorbed by frozen serum, it should be possible to avoid the heat gradient of the glass, thus making drying from a glass container as rapid as it would be from a metal container. These authors took ten bottles of plasma and surrounded each with one of ten heaters made from Nichrome resistance wire of varying lengths and gauges, so that with the same wattage the wires when placed in a vacuum would heat up to different temperatures from 100° to 1000°C. at 100°C. intervals. To quote from their paper: "After a complete drying cycle i.e., a total power consumption of 360 Watts for each heater over a ten hour period, all the plasma specimens were carefully examined. The plasma in the heaters burning at 400°, 500°, 600° and 700° were uniformly dry. In heaters operating at 100°, 200° and 300°C., melting had occurred in that part of the plasma adjacent to the wall of the glass bottle and all specimens contained a great deal of residual moisture. With heaters burning at 800°, 900° and 1000°C., the outer part of the plasma was definitely burned and discolored while the inner surface was still frozen. From these tests and results we came to the conclusion that infra-red radiation of a hot body of a temperature between 400° and 700°C. is most suitable and effective for drying frozen plasma in a bottle. It seems that this radiation penetrates Pyrex and Neutraglass bottles without appreciable absorption and further penetrates and is gradually absorbed by frozen and dried plasma." These authors then go on to describe a drying plant designed for infra-red heating of plasma in 300-ml. amounts, frozen on the inside periphery of a bottle, and they record a drying cycle of 10 hours. To quote: "For the first two hours each heater burns at a 100 Watt-hour rate. Then the heat is progressively reduced according to the schedule shown: one hour at 60 Watts; one hour at 40 Watts; one hour at 20 Watts; one hour at 12 Watts, and finally three hours at 9 Watts"; and "We have made the current regulation completely automatic by using a 'step-down' transformer." Surely this procedure must mean that the temperature of their heater wires is gradually reduced and consequently the wavelength of the radiant heat must alter. It is difficult to decide on the value of radiant heat for drying from this account.

If differential heating is really important, one has to consider whether dielectric heating or short-wave diathermy might not be a suitable method of heating. Experiment shows the dielectric constant to be very favorably different between frozen serum, dried serum, and glass. Thus, by suitable choice of frequency of operation, it theoretically should be possible to apply heat to the frozen serum only, without heating in any way the glass or dried serum. There are, however, certain technical difficulties which up till now have rendered this form of heating impracticable. First, the application of heat in this way in a partial vacuum leads to flashover and ionization discharge; second, any considerable uniform heating of the ice block would lead to an explosion and total disintegration of the block.

Thus for practical purposes we are nearly always forced back to direct conduction heating; the following paragraphs will discuss the methods which have been used for its control.

### 5. *Temperature Control*

For the greatest simplicity it will first be assumed that the material to be dried can be distributed in such a way and that the drying cycle can be so timed that it is unnecessary to raise the heater plates above the safe upper limit of temperature that the dried material can withstand; with serum or plasma this temperature might be +40°C. The heater plate may be heated by the circulation of a hot fluid or by contact with electrically heated resistance wires. If fluid is to be used to heat the plate, it is circulated from a tank which is thermostatically controlled at the desired temperature. If drying is to be a fixed routine, it may be possible to abolish thermostatic control and to substitute a continuously variable transformer, motor driven to follow a definite time-power schedule. Alternatively, the heating fluid may be heated by gas which is thermostatically controlled, or the hot gases from the compression side of the refrigerator may be led through the heating tank, the temperature of which is kept constant by adjusting the proportion of the hot gases which are allowed to circulate by this route.

The use of fluid as a heating medium involves the need for somewhat complex manufacture if the fluid is to be introduced into the vacuum chamber in a vacuum-tight manner and if the flow is to be so contrived that it is uniform throughout the whole mass of drying material. It is thus common practice to heat by passing an electric current through a resistance wire wound around a metal container inside which is placed the bottle containing the material to be dried. In its simplest form the heat is controlled by a bimetallic strip thermostat or contact thermometer fixed to the container and set so that the heat is cut off at a safe low temperature.

If the material being dried can be distributed in a very thin layer, then drying by this simple method can be very fast. If, however, the material is in thick layers, as is often unavoidable, then drying becomes slower than it need be. It would be possible to double or treble the amount of heat applied in the early stages if the heater temperature were allowed to rise well above +40°C., but it would then be necessary to provide some safety device to prevent the temperature of the material when dry from rising to too high a level. For routine drying a prearranged time schedule could be set up which progressively reduced the heat. Alternatively a thermocouple placed in the material being dried and recording the temperature on a recording galvanometer could be arranged to trip a contact at a certain temperature and consequently alter the heat control to a more conservatively set thermostat (Greaves and Adair, 1939).

The ideal control would be a continuous control from the temperature of the material being dried, so that in the early stages as much heat as possible would be utilized without raising the drying material above its eutectic temperature.

With all forms of heating so far described, the serum temperature starts to rise before drying is complete, so that it passes the eutectic and even 0°C. before it is absolutely dry. It is possible that this may be deleterious to certain materials. Theoretically the material should remain below the eutectic temperature until it is absolutely dry and should then be rapidly brought to a positive temperature and then removed.

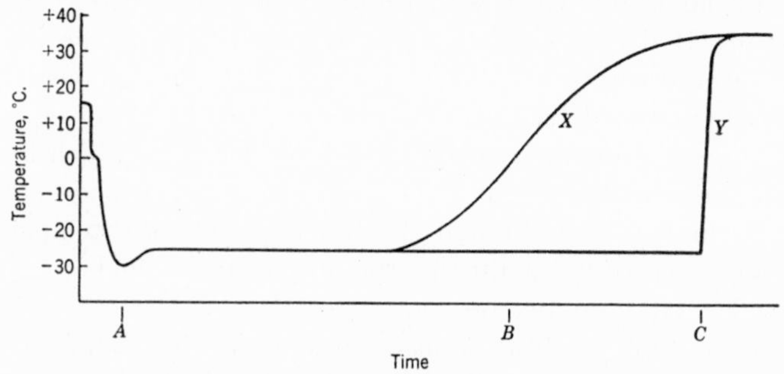


FIG. 7. Curve $X$ is obtained by controlling the heater temperature. Note that at point $B$ the serum temperature reaches 0°C. before drying is complete. Curve $Y$ is the ideal curve obtained by controlling the heat input from the serum temperature. At point $C$, when drying was complete, the temperature was raised rapidly to 37°C. Both drying curves were obtained after an evaporative freeze. Heating was started at point $A$.

Figure 7 shows the two types of drying curve. The theoretically optimal curve could be obtained if the heat were controlled directly from the serum temperature.

Although not impossible, it would be difficult to control from a thermocouple with its minute direct-current output requiring the use of a direct-current or magnetic amplifier. Alternatively the thermocouple output could be "chopped" mechanically and then treated as alternating current. Resistance thermometers can, however, be fed with alternating current, and the "out-of-balance" amplified on a normal alternating-current amplifier. Considerably less amplification need be used if a thermistor is substituted for the resistance thermometer. Figure 8 shows the circuit diagram of an arrangement which can be used to control the heating from a thermistor or resistance thermometer recording the actual drying temperature, see Roberts (1951). $V_2$ is made phase conscious so that control is in the correct direction. The saturable reactor in the plate circuit of $V_3$ can be made of almost any size, and control of 5 kw. or more can be effected by this simple device.

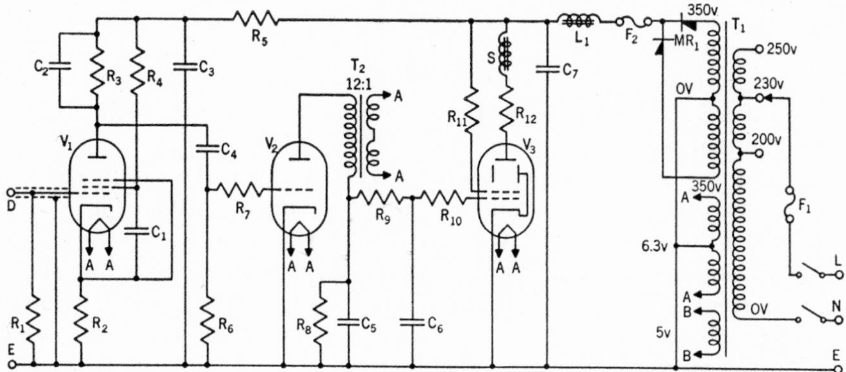


FIG. 8. Circuit diagram of apparatus for the continuous control of the drying temperature from a thermistor or resistance thermometer placed in the material being dried (Roberts, 1951).

$R_1$ = 1 megohm, $R_2$ = 1 kohm, $R_3$ = 220 kohms, $R_4$ = 1.5 megohms, $R_5$ = 100 kohms, $R_6$ = 1 megohm, $R_7$ = 220 kohms, $R_8$ = 47 kohms, $R_9$ = 47 kohms, $R_{10}$ = 10 kohms, $R_{11}$ = 6.8 kohms, 2 w., $R_{12}$ = 47 kohms, 2 w.
$C_1$ = 0.1 $\mu$F., $C_2$ = 0.005 $\mu$F., $C_3$ = 4 $\mu$F., $C_4$ = 0.01 $\mu$F., $C_5$ = 0.5 $\mu$F., $C_6$ = 0.5 $\mu$F., $C_7$ = 4 $\mu$F.
$V_1$ = SP61 (Mazda), $V_2$ = ECC32 (Mullard), $V_3$ = KT66 (Osram).
$T_1$ = 350-0-350 v., 150 ma., 6.3 v., 3 amp., 5 v., 2 amp.
$T_2$ = Wharfdale G.P.8.
S = Saturable inductor, Electro Methods, Type MAF 20/1150 w.
$F_1$ = 2 amp., $F_2$ = 250 ma., $L_1$ = 20 H., 150 ma., $MR_1$ = S.T.C. V 25, 40 IL.

## 6. *Temperature Measurement*

In simple forms of apparatus commonly used in laboratories and in which no additional heat need be used, temperature measurement is seldom required. The apparatus is so designed that dried materials cannot get too hot and the time required for drying various quantities has been worked out to allow a good margin of safety. In an all-glass apparatus the inclusion of a mercury-in-glass thermometer in a large ampoule may give some useful information as to drying temperatures and may also be used as a rough guide to the dryness of the material. When the temperature recorded by this thermometer placed in the material being dried equals that of another thermometer placed on the heating plate, dryness is achieved.

In large drying plants temperature measurement becomes very important, not only as a check that all is functioning correctly but also as a means of determining when drying is complete. As these large plants are nearly always made of metal, mercury-in-glass thermometers are of no use and temperatures must be measured electrically. When temperatures are being measured electrically, it is comparatively simple to record them continuously and even to use the electrical output from the thermometer to control the amount of heat applied. Once recorded, the picture obtained is a valuable guide to the correctness or otherwise of the drying schedule that has been used.

The three common types of electric thermometer, the thermocouple, the resistance thermometer, and the thermistor, are all suitable for recording and, if necessary, for controlling freeze-drying temperatures.

Thermocouples are the most common form of electric thermometer used in freeze-drying. The thermocouple is easily made by spot-welding or even soft-soldering a constantan wire to a copper wire. If the other end of the constantan wire is also made into a junction with copper and if the second junction is placed in a Thermos flask which is kept at 0°C. with an ice-water mixture, the voltage output from the copper wires will be related to the temperature of the measuring junction. Once calibrated, thermocouples keep their calibration indefinitely and may be readily matched by using further portions of constantan of the same length. The shorter the length of the constantan wire and the larger its gauge, the greater is the output from the couple for a given temperature difference; thus, a few preliminary experiments will enable a couple to be constructed which will match the sensitivity of the measuring instrument that is to be used over the range of temperature that is to be recorded. Unfortunately the output from the couple is small, so that very sensitive, and thus costly, measuring instruments have to be used. However, even galvanometers can be made to record, and a thread-recording galvanometer becomes a very useful addition to any drying plant. Such a galvanometer could conveniently have a scale from −50° to +50°C., with a central zero if 0°C. is being used as the temperature for the reference couple, or a side zero if a thermostatically controlled hot junction is being used. The thermocouple can be made to control the temperature if contacts are fitted to the chopper-bar of the thread-recording galvanometer as described by Greaves and Adair (1939).

The two main drawbacks to the use of thermocouples are the small output and the necessity for maintaining a constant temperature for the reference junction. The constant temperature junction can be avoided if resistance thermometers are substituted for the thermocouples. The output is still very small, but because the resistance thermometer may be fed with alternating current ordinary alternating-current amplifiers may be used to increase the output, which is much more simple than trying to increase the output of thermocouples with direct-current amplifiers. The author has successfully used very small resistance thermometer elements made from the coiled tungsten filaments of 20-watt electric light bulbs.

Both drawbacks to the use of thermocouples are removed by the use of thermistors. Thermistors show a very marked resistance change with temperature so that, once calibrated, temperatures can be measured with a simple ohm-meter. Very small thermistors can also be obtained which are thus suitable for temperature measurements in the smallest of ampoules.

When recording drying temperatures it is convenient to use two temperature elements, one being placed near the surface of the material being dried, the other placed next to the glass of the bottle or ampoule at the point where the thickness of the material being dried is greatest. The first element will then record the actual drying temperature, while the second will record the highest temperature reached by the material during drying and also the time at which drying is completed. If a third element is available, it should be placed on the heater plate.

## IV. SECONDARY DRYING AND PACKAGING

How dry should one attempt to make a frozen-dried product? There is no simple answer to this problem. There is some evidence that it is an advantage not to make bacterial cultures too dry (Fry and Greaves, 1951), but what little evidence there is suggests that with proteins the drier they are, the better they will be preserved. It is often said that the final moisture content should be reduced below 1% of the dry weight for satisfactory preservation, but there is little justification for this figure. Greaves (1949) reported some experiments in which it was shown that the ability of dried blood-grouping serum to withstand boiling varied directly with the length of time taken over secondary desiccation over phosphorus pentoxide; after 12 hours of secondary desiccation the titer of the serum showed a fourfold drop after 3 hours of boiling; after 36 hours of secondary desiccation the same fall in titer occurred after 4 hours of boiling; and after 108 hours of secondary desiccation no fall could be observed after 5 hours of boiling.

The accurate determination of the residual moisture content of frozen-dried samples is discussed in another section of this book. If the residual moisture content is plotted against time, the curve so formed is found to be exponential. Although the residual moisture content can be reduced quite quickly below 1%, it would take an infinite time to reach absolute dryness. Thus the degree of dryness to which a product is eventually taken becomes a matter of economics and will depend very largely on the value of the product and the length of time and the conditions under which it is to be stored.

What has been said applies only to drying over a desiccant such as phosphorus pentoxide when an irreversible reaction with water takes place. It does not apply when a refrigerated condenser is used to remove the water, for, depending on the temperature of the condenser, the dried material would eventually reach an equilibrium with a certain water vapor pressure. This equilibrium will be determined by the vapor pressure of water at the temperature of the condenser, the temperature of the dried protein, and the hydration value of the protein. Thus, for a certain condenser temperature the residual moisture content of the dried protein will depend on the temperature to which it is raised at the end of the drying cycle; the higher this temperature, the lower will be the residual moisture content. With a condenser temperature of −40°C. and a final serum temperature of +40°C. it should be possible to reach an equilibrium with a residual moisture content of about 1%, but in practice this figure is usually nearer 4%. For valuable materials it is usually well worth while to reduce the residual moisture content much further, and this is done by secondary drying over a chemical desiccant such as phosphorus pentoxide.

Nothing short of the most perfect drying is good enough for laboratory materials, so that secondary drying should be as prolonged as possible. A good rule for laboratory sera is that secondary drying should be for a minimum of 3 weeks, and if space allows this period should be further prolonged. This secondary drying is carried out on a manifold which is connected *via* a phosphorus pentoxide trap to a small, two-stage rotary oil pump. The manifold consists of a number of sockets into which fit headers complete with rubber teats which make a vacuum seal when the necks of ampoules are pushed over them. The ampoules of dried material, when they are removed from the primary drier, have their necks constricted in a flame down to a capillary before they are placed on the secondary drying headers so that at the end of secondary drying they may be sealed in vacuum by means of a small crossfire burner. Thus the dried material is packed in an all-glass container which has been sealed in high vacuum.

This counsel of perfection cannot always be attained. Dried plasma transfusions have to be dispensed in standard transfusion bottles, and in England these are fitted with aluminium caps and rubber washers. Since rubber is permeable to water vapor, if these bottles were evacuated the vacuum would slowly be replaced by water vapor which would wet the dried material. It is best to evacuate the bottles and then fill them with a dry inert gas such as nitrogen; even dry air would be preferable to vacuum packing. In the United States the standard transfusion bottle is capped with an all-rubber closure. The procedure adopted with these bottles is to evacuate them and then place them in tins which are also evacuated. Such a method of closure is ideal but expensive. It is useless to give prolonged secondary desiccation to material that is to be stored in rubber-capped bottles, but since gas packing can so easily be combined with secondary desiccation a short period of 2 to 3 days will help to prolong the useful period of storage.

Although the sealed-glass evacuated ampoule is the ideal package for dried material, it is not liked by the clinician. To overcome this objection the rubber stopper covered with a spun-aluminium cap has been used successfully, but unless an all-glass container is employed it is wise to stipulate that the material should be stored at as low a temperature as possible and preferably in a very constant temperature.

## V. SOME DIFFICULTIES

Smith (1951) reported difficulty when he attempted to dry influenza virus antigen which had been purified by adsorption onto red blood cells followed by elution in saline. On drying, the material was found to be ejected from the tubes. Smith found that the addition of 0.5% Difco proteose peptone prevented this phenomenon.

Cowan (1951) reported a similar difficulty leading to cross infection when drying cultures of different organisms at the same time in the same apparatus.

When it is realized that 1 gram of water at a pressure of 0.1 mm. Hg produces 9500 liters of water vapor, it is not surprising that light particles may be carried away in the vapor stream. The difficulty can obviously be overcome by reducing the speed of drying so that the velocity of the vapor stream is slowed sufficiently. If possible a more satisfactory solution would be to add some neutral binding agent, such as a protein, which would give solidity to the cake of dried material.

It has been pointed out that in order to prevent "puffing" it is necessary to dry below the eutectic of the solution. If sugars are present, even this precaution may not be successful. Materials containing more than a small percentage of sugars are very apt to "puff," and they are also very difficult to get really dry. This property that sugars exhibit of holding onto water is possibly of value in the drying of bacteria, as the sugars prevent the cultures from becoming too dry. The sugars may make the drying of certain fruit juices very difficult. Gane (1951) states: "One phenomenon that was noted but not explained was the change in physical state that occurred in the powders from sugar-containing liquids. These caked or even partially liquefied on storage and it is suggested that this is due to the rapid rate of freezing whereby the sugars are thrown out of solution in an amorphous form to crystallise later with liberation of water." The author has noted this effect with frozen-dried apple juice.

The freeze-drying of tissues for microscopical investigation has posed many problems. The water is largely contained within the cell membranes, which offer considerable obstruction to the flow of vapor. The speed of evaporation is insufficient to keep the tissue frozen, external cooling is required, and drying times are greatly prolonged. Gersh and Stephenson deal with solutions to such difficulties as these in Chapter 14.

## REFERENCES

Barrett, A. S. D., and Beckett, L. G. 1951. Aspects of the Design of Freeze-Drying Apparatus, in *Freezing and Drying*. Edited by R. J. C. Harris. The Institute of Biology, London. Pp. 41–49.

Best, C. H., Solandt, D. Y., and Ridout, J. H. 1942. The Canadian Project for the Preparation of Dried Human Serum for Military Use, in *Blood Substitutes and Blood Transfusion*. Edited by S. Mudd. Charles C Thomas Co., Springfield, Ill. Pp. 235–241.

Bradish, C. J., Brain, C. M., and McFarlane, A. S. 1947. Vacuum Sublimation of Ice in Bulk. *Nature* **159,** 28–29.

Carman, P. C. 1948. Molecular Distillation and Sublimation. *Trans. Faraday Soc.* **44,** 529–536.

Chain Belt Company. 1948. Continuous Low-Temperature Dehydration. British Patent No. 604, 955.

Cowan, S. T. 1951. Infection and Drying Techniques, in *Freezing and Drying*. Edited by R. J. C. Harris. The Institute of Biology, London. Pp. 127–132.

Elser, W. J., Thomas, R. A., and Steffen, G. I. 1935. Desiccation of Sera and Other Biological Products (including Microorganisms) in the Frozen State with Preservation of the Original Qualities of Products So Treated. *J. Immunol.* **28,** 433–473.

Flosdorf, E. W. 1949. *Freeze-Drying*. Reinhold Publishing Corp., New York.

Flosdorf, E. W., and Mudd, S. 1935. Procedure and Apparatus for Preservation in "Lyophile" Form of Serum and Other Biological Substances. *J. Immunol.* **29,** 389–425.

Flosdorf, E. W., and Mudd, S. 1938. An Improved Procedure and Apparatus for Preservation of Sera, Microorganisms and Other Substances—the "Cryochem" Process. *J. Immunol.* **34,** 469–490.

Flosdorf, E. W., Stokes, F. J., and Mudd, S. 1940. The "Desivac" Process for Drying from the Frozen State. *J. Am. Med. Assoc.* **115,** 1095–1097.

Fry, R. M., and Greaves, R. I. N. 1951. The Survival of Bacteria during and after Drying. *J. Hyg.* **49,** 220–246.

Gane, R. 1951. Freeze-Drying of Foodstuffs, in *Freezing and Drying*. Edited by R. J. C. Harris. The Institute of Biology, London. Pp. 31–39.

Greaves, R. I. N. 1942. The Freezing of Human Serum and Plasma in Medical Research Council Transfusion Bottles, before Drying by Sublimation from the Frozen State. *J. Hyg.* **41,** 489–495.

Greaves, R. I. N. 1944. Centrifugal Vacuum Freezing. Its Application to the Drying of Biological Materials from the Frozen State. *Nature* **153,** 485–487.

Greaves, R. I. N. 1946. The Preservation of Proteins by Drying. *Med. Research Council* (*Brit.*) *Spec. Rept. Ser.* No. **258.**

Greaves, R. I. N. 1949. Some Recent Advances in Technique for Drying from the Frozen State. *Brit. Sci. News* **2,** 173–176.

Greaves, R. I. N., and Adair, M. E. 1936. A Simple Method for Preservation of Sera by Desiccation in the Frozen State without the Use of Refrigerants. *J. Hyg.* **36,** 507–513.

Greaves, R. I. N., and Adair, M. E. 1939. High Vacuum Condensation Drying of Proteins from the Frozen State. *J. Hyg.* **39,** 413–445.

Hartley, P. 1936. A Simple Laboratory Method for the Desiccation of Serum and other Protein Solutions. *Quart. Bull. Health Organization League Nations* **5,** 735–745.

Hill, J. M., and Pfeiffer, D. C. 1940. A New and Economical Desiccating Process Particularly Suitable for the Preparation of Concentrated Plasma or Serum for Intravenous Uses, the "Adtevac" Process. *Ann. Internal Med.* **14,** 201–214.

Lanyon, E. C. G. 1941. An Apparatus for Spin-Freezing Serum or Plasma in Circular Bottles. *J. Hyg.* **41,** 111–116.

Levinson, S. O., and Oppenheimer, F. 1944. *Drying by Ice Sublimation. The Principle of Infra-red Radiation for Rapid Desiccation of Plasma and Other Biologics.* Samuel Deutsch Serum Center, Chicago.

Martin, C. 1896. A Simple and Rapid Method of Desiccating Serum and Keeping It Sterile during the Process. *J. Pathol. Bacteriol.* **3,** 507–509.

Roberts, M. H. 1951. Electric Controllers for Laboratory Furnaces. *Electronic Eng.* **23,** 51–54.

Smith, W. 1951. A Difficulty in the Quantitative Freeze-Drying of Certain Materials, in *Freezing and Drying.* Edited by R. J. C. Harris. The Institute of Biology, London. Pp. 139–142.

Strumia, M. M., and McGraw, J. J. 1943. A Method and Apparatus for Shell-Freezing and Rapid Drying of Plasma and Other Products from the Frozen State by Low Temperature Water Vapor Condensation *in Vacuo. J. Lab. Clin. Med.* **28,** 1140–1155.

Wilkinson, J. F., Bullock, K., and Cowen, W. 1942. A Continuous Method of Drying Plasma and Serum. *Lancet* **i,** 281–284.

CHAPTER 4

# The Preservation of Blood Plasma and Blood Products by Freezing and Drying

MAX M. STRUMIA

*Associate Professor, Graduate School of Medicine, University of Pennsylvania; Director, Laboratory of Clinical Pathology, Bryn Mawr Hospital*

*Page*



## I. GENERAL CONSIDERATIONS

Specific presentation of data on the preservation of plasma and blood products by freezing and drying must be preceded by consideration of some questions of a more general nature. One of the most urgent is the transmission of infectious diseases in general and of homologous serum hepatitis in particular. This danger, unless practically controlled, affects the clinical value of plasma and, consequently, also the justification for at least a part of this contribution. It prospects the necessity of further study on the effect which various sterilizing agents, now under experimental trial, may have on the properties of plasma. In such a group of agents one must include heat, ultraviolet irradiation, cathode rays, nitrogen mustard, sulfur mustard, $\beta$-propiolactone, etc.

The great contributions made in the field of the cold ethanol-water fractionation (Cohn, 1941, 1947; Janeway, 1947) and the expectancy of similar results by the use of metal interactions with the various proteins (Cohn *et al.*, 1950) promise the availability, in the not-too-distant future, of a supply of at least some of the most important plasma fractions in a readily available form. But it is difficult to anticipate that purified plasma fractions could ever replace entirely the use of whole plasma for many reasons. Among these reasons we may list the simplicity, convenience, economy, and availability of plasma and its multiplicity of action. These attributes add up to great economy in the cost of production, which can be carried out by many centers not equipped for the preparation of plasma fractions.

Another reason is that, as yet, fractionation of plasma proteins has failed to preserve some of the important fractions of plasma, namely the prothrombin, the thromboplastin, and complement complexes. On the other hand plasma when properly dried retains unaltered all its specific components with the possible exception of the lipoproteins.

Granted that, with the development of better methods of plasma fractionation, the use of plasma fractions will become more widespread, the need for whole plasma will remain, and with this need the necessity for improved methods of sterilization and preservation. It appears desirable, until dependable and practical methods of plasma sterilization are developed, to reduce the number of individual plasma units in a pool to a minimum compatible with a reasonable reduction in isoagglutinins titer. At present, in our laboratory, only two to three units are pooled to obtain approximately 500 ml. of plasma containing 32 to 34 grams of plasma proteins.

In this paper the terms of "frozen" and "dried" plasma will generally be used with a rather narrow meaning. No attempt to formulate a rigid definition of these terms will be made, as the full meaning will become evident from the context.

It is more important to discuss briefly what is meant by the term "normal human plasma." This is very important, because the value of any means of preservation must be based on differences, or rather on the lack of differences, between the "fresh" normal plasma and the product resulting from the procedure used, such as freeze-drying. Here again it would be futile to attempt a definition of so complex a fluid, but it may be taken for granted that for normal human plasma is meant a fluid obtained from whole blood, in which coagulation has been impeded, generally with the use of citrate, and which has all the specific properties of blood, except those related to the presence of erythrocytes and leucocytes, which elements are removed in the preparation of plasma, usually by centrifugation.

Concerning the third formed element, the platelets, although in most instances only relatively few are found in the plasma, some of their essential activities (particularly the thromboplastic) are transferred to the plasma during the process of preparation.

The labile plasma components, and therefore their physiological and pharmacological properties, deteriorate at various rates, but generally fairly rapidly, if plasma is preserved in the liquid state. This is especially true of the complement, the prothrombin, the thromboplastin complexes, and the antihemophilic globulin. The deterioration of these labile elements becomes extremely slow when blood is preserved in the frozen state or in the dry state. In using, therefore, the term "liquid plasma" to indicate plasma stored in the liquid state for periods of time longer than a few days, or possibly less, we must accept the implicit limitation that many properties of the fresh plasma are no longer present. The term "liquid plasma" used in the sense of "normal human plasma" is greatly misleading.*

A second and equally important consideration concerns the relative ease with which plasma in the liquid state may be rendered unsafe by bacterial contamination. Bacterial growth, from a minimal chance contamination not always readily detected by bacterial control, may develop sufficient pyrogens to cause very severe and even fatal reactions. Although preparation of liquid plasma in a competent laboratory is a relatively safe procedure, in smaller institutions it is inadvisable, as it may lead to very serious reactions.

One possible advantage of preservation of plasma in the liquid state has been that of reducing or eliminating the danger of transmission of viral hepatitis (Allen *et al.*, 1950). While final proof of this effect is awaited, even if convincing evidence be presented, it would hardly justify the procedure, for the reasons discussed above. It appears entirely unjustifiable to destroy all the specific properties of plasma and to use it simply for its osmotic colloidal properties and nutritional value. Some of the plasma substitutes and expanders would accomplish as much.

This paper is not intended to present fundamental data on the process of freeze-drying, for Greaves has already dealt with these, but simply to present practical data as they apply to the drying of plasma.

## II. PREPARATION OF PLASMA

It is quite evident that no method of preservation can possibly put back into plasma something which through improper processing has been lost or destroyed. Therefore, the first consideration must be given to the preparation of plasma.

### 1. *Anticoagulant*

At least two anticoagulants have been thoroughly studied and found to be equally satisfactory. These are plain citrate solution and acid citrate

* United States Pharmacopeia.

dextrose (ACD) solutions. The plain citrate is generally used as a 4% solution, 50 ml. being employed for 500 ml. of blood. This solution has been found to be entirely satisfactory for the preparation of plasma to be stored in the frozen or in the dried state. Although it is not the purpose of this chapter to discuss the preservation of erythrocytes, this problem cannot be ignored in approaching a practical solution of the problem of plasma procurement. The human body can replace plasma-protein losses much more readily than losses of red cells. The large-scale destruction of large quantities of red cells left over from plasma preparation is absolutely inexcusable. A good proportion of patients requiring whole blood transfusions could be adequately treated with red cells only. This poses the question of choice of an anticoagulant. Red cells collected in plain citrate solution, centrifuged at room temperature for the purpose of separating plasma, and indifferently treated as far as temperature of storage is concerned are generally of no practical value for transfusion.

It becomes necessary, therefore, for the salvage of red cells (1) to choose a proper ACD solution and (2) to control strictly the temperature before and during the process of red cell separation. A number of ACD solutions have been proposed. For the purpose of blood storage for 21 days or less at temperatures between 4° and 8°C., little difference has been found between any of them. The volume of water and the dextrose concentration, however, become important when plasma is to be dried.

Let us consider some of the types of ACD solutions in general use and then discuss the effect of their composition on the process of plasma drying. Some formulas use a rather large volume of water and maximal quantities of dextrose, such as the widely used formula B, proposed by the National Institutes of Health of the United States and extensively used by the American Red Cross. This formula closely resembles the one originally suggested by Loutit and Mollison.*

Experience has shown that ACD solutions of this type are consider-

* Loutit and Mollison formula for ACD solution:

| | |
|---|---|
| Disodium citrate | 2 grams |
| Dextrose | 3 grams |
| Distilled water to | 120 ml. |

The pH of this solution is ca. 5, and the 120-ml. quantity is recommended for approximately 430 ml. of blood.

Formula B is as follows:

| | |
|---|---|
| Trisodium citrate dihydrate | 1.71 grams |
| Citric acid | 0.62 gram |
| Dextrose | 2.0 grams |
| Water | 130 ml. (this amount recommended for 500 ml. of blood) |

ably hypotonic and contain an excess of dextrose. Trisodium dihydrate is isotonic in a concentration of 3%. Dextrose, being freely diffusible, does not exert any useful osmotic effect on the erythrocytes. The acidity of the medium, especially at the start of the collection of blood, increases the ionization of hemoglobin. This phenomenon and the presence of excessive amounts of diffusible dextrose concur in producing excessive swelling of the erythrocytes. At the end of 21 days of storage at 4° to 6°C., an excess of dextrose is still present in blood collected in this type of ACD solution.

The use of large volumes of water and of maximal amounts of dextrose cannot, therefore, be justified on the ground that they aid the preservation of erythrocytes. Both factors are equally undesirable in so far as the preparation of plasma is concerned. To start with, it appears economically unsound to add an excess of water which later has to be removed by a lengthy and fairly expensive process of sublimation. Second, final concentrations of dextrose in the whole citrated blood substantially above 200 mg. % yield a plasma which appears to be difficult to dry with the commercial apparatus generally available for this purpose in most biological houses, at least in the United States.*

For the purpose of obtaining a red cell residue which can be used for whole blood transfusion and of securing a plasma optimal for drying from the frozen state, it is therefore desirable to use an ACD solution of small volume and low dextrose content.

Experimental work by a number of investigators has shown that ACD solutions with a volume of water of 75 ml. for 500 ml. of blood are entirely satisfactory for the purpose of blood preservation and drying of plasma. We have had considerable experience in drying plasma from blood collected in the ACD formula B.M. No. 3 (Strumia *et al.*, 1947). Formula A of the National Institutes of Health is very similar.† More recent experimental studies have shown that the amount of water of the ACD B.M. No. 3 can be readily reduced to 66 ml., thus obtaining an isoösmotic medium.

* Although it is possible to dry plasma with practically any concentration of dextrose, the fact remains that commercial houses in the United States have complained of their inability to do so with the present equipment and cycle of operations.

† B.M. No. 3 formula:

| | |
|---|---|
| Trisodium citrate | 1.6 grams |
| Citric acid | 0.56 gram |
| Dextrose | 1.5 grams |
| Water | 75 ml. |

Formula A:

| | |
|---|---|
| Trisodium citrate | 1.65 grams |
| Citric acid | 0.60 gram |
| Dextrose | 1.84 grams |
| Water | 75 ml. |

Plasma from blood collected in 75 ml. of an ACD solution has a higher concentration of plasma protein than plasma from blood collected in 50 ml. of 3% sodium citrate. The higher concentration of plasma proteins in the plasma from ACD blood, notwithstanding the higher volume of diluent, is due to the passage of water from the suspending medium into the erythrocytes because of the conditions of hypotonicity and excess dextrose already mentioned. For a mass of erythrocytes of 220-ml. volume, the amount of water thus removed from the suspension medium amounts to 30 to 35 ml. Another reason for the difference is that the 4% solution of trisodium citrate dihydrate is hypertonic, so that water is added to the plasma. In our experience the mean concentration of proteins in oxalated plasma from normal individuals is 6.8 grams %; in plain citrated blood it is 5.75, and in ACD plasma 6.22 grams %.

Addition of citrate as anticoagulant to whole blood is surely not the only method of obtaining plasma. The use of ion exchange resins (Buckley *et al.*, 1950) and of chelating compounds, such as Sequestrene* (Proesher, 1951) yield plasma which can be readily dried; however, little or no experience is available concerning such plasmas, particularly their behavior after reconstitution with water.

### 2. *Collection of Blood*

Regardless of the type of container used, good mixing of the anticoagulant and the blood must be secured. This is particularly important when ACD solutions are used as anticoagulants.

Poor mixing of blood and ACD solutions results in a very unstable fibrinogen, which precipitates readily on storage in the liquid state and after reconstitution of dried plasma with diluent.

The use of plastic bags yields plasma indistinguishable from that obtained with the use of the conventional glass bottles as far as freeze-drying is concerned.

### 3. *Separation of Formed Elements*

Centrifugation with the conventional bucket-type centrifuge is the method of choice, because of simplicity, safeguard against contamination, and preservation of intact erythrocytes for transfusion.

## III. FREEZING OF PLASMA

It is essential for the drying of plasma that prefreezing be properly carried out. Prefreezing can be simply accomplished by cooling the material by the use of high vacuum and the consequent rapid heat loss due to evaporation. When plasma is frozen in this manner, however,

* Sequestrene is a brand of crystalline sodium ethylenediamine tetraacetic acid obtained from the Alrose Chemical Company, Providence, Rhode Island.

partial denaturation occurs, owing to increased solute concentration as the water separates as ice. This results in a partial loss of labile components, decreased solubility, and increased turbidity of the regenerated material.

The optimal procedure for prefreezing is the same for plasma to be stored in the frozen state and for plasma to be dried from the frozen state, except that in the latter instance consideration must be given to the thickness of the frozen material, as this will greatly influence the duration of the process of sublimation.

It is most desirable to freeze-dry plasma in the final container because thus sterility of the material is more readily maintained. Consideration must be given therefore to the choice of a container suitable for the purpose.

Because of the desirability of "shell-freezing of plasma" to obtain a thin uniform layer, the most desirable form for the container is that of a uniform cylinder, with a capacity approximately 25% greater than the volume of plasma to be processed. Finally, the size of the neck should be determined in consideration of the very large volume of water vapor to be transferred from the interior of the bottle to the condenser—especially during the first few hours of the processing. At a temperature of 0°C. and a pressure of 100 microns the volume of 1 gram of water vapor is 9500 liters.

Extensive experience has shown that for the conventional unit of 250 to 300 ml. of citrated plasma in the standard 400-ml. bottle (Strumia *et al.*, 1941), shell-frozen as a hollow cylinder approximately 6.5 cm. outer diameter and 3.2 cm. inner diameter, and from 10 to 12 cm. in length, the neck opening must be no less than 12 mm. in diameter to achieve near-optimal escape of water vapor during sublimation.

Very rapid freezing of plasma is not essential to obtain an optimal result from freeze-drying. Freezing can be carried out at temperatures much higher, and thus more economically, than the temperature of Dry Ice, which is so commonly in use for this purpose. In our experience plasma can be properly prefrozen at temperatures as far apart as −12° and −72°C. without essential difference in the final product. However, at the higher temperatures (−12° to −35°C.), when the bottles are rotated, there is a tendency for slushing and the formation of soft, crumbly ice and of irregular lumps, as well as a greater tendency for separation of lipids, with resulting longer periods of drying and greater turbidity in the reconstituted plasma. At even higher temperatures of freezing (−6° to −12°C.), heat dissipation is often sufficiently slow to produce prolonged supercooling, with resulting instability of some of the plasma proteins. Temperatures in the neighborhood of −30°C., readily achieved with standard, one-stage commercial compressors utilizing Freon 12, are considered both economical and suitable. However, shell-freezing of plasma at such temperatures must be done with certain precautions.

"Shelling" is generally carried out by rotation of the cylindrical glass bottle containing the plasma partially immersed in a coolant liquid bath. When the temperature of the coolant is −50°C. or lower, snap-freezing of a thin layer of plasma and fixing of the frozen mass to the glass are readily achieved without difficulty. At −30°C., however, there is little or no tendency for the ice to adhere to the glass while the bottle is in motion. Consequently, a lumpy, irregular shell of frozen plasma is formed, with considerable lengthening of the time of drying. When employing temperatures for prefreezing considerably higher than −50°C., it is desirable to cool the plasma to substantially near 0°C. by slow rotation and then to arrest the rotation until local initial snap-freezing occurs, with fixation of the ice to the glass container. Once this has occurred, rotation is resumed and continued until the entire mass of plasma is shell-frozen. To obtain good results the bottle must be immersed in the coolant to a depth of about 12 mm. It has been pointed out that the time for the complete freezing of plasma from the initiation of cooling should not exceed 6 hours; otherwise flocculation may occur (Strumia, 1942; Strumia and McGraw, 1943; 1949). Spin-freezing of plasma at temperatures of −18° to −20°C., in a strong jet of cold air and at a velocity of 900 r.p.m., achieves similar results but requires somewhat more expensive and bulky apparatus. Under these conditions greater separation of lipids occurs.

It is possible to freeze and thaw plasma once before freeze-drying, without loss of any of the essential properties. However, repeated freezing and thawing results in instability of plasma proteins.

Freezing in shell form is not necessary when the volume of fluid to be frozen is small, provided that the mass of ice thus formed is not too thick. Bottles containing the material to be frozen are simply placed in a freezing cabinet at about −20° to −25°C. or immersed in a liquid coolant and allowed to freeze. Properly frozen plasma is stable over periods of several years if maintained at temperatures of −20°C. or lower.

Special precautions must be taken when drying very small volumes of material, such as some plasma fractions. In these cases the small thermal capacity of the frozen material would not be sufficient to maintain the material frozen while a suitably high vacuum is being produced. Therefore the drying chamber must be provided with a means of maintaining the material frozen until such a vacuum has been obtained. This can be achieved by circulating in the supporting shelves or in hollow cylinders surrounding the bottles a coolant sufficient to maintain the frozen material at the proper temperature. For plasma and most plasma fractions the temperature of the coolant should be at −12°C. or lower.

If the drying chamber is not provided with means for cooling, small amounts of material can be satisfactorily dried by placing the containers in a shallow pan and filling the pan with water to a depth slightly above the level of the material to be dried. The entire mass is then frozen. The mass of cold ice outside the containers will maintain the small amounts of material frozen, while a satisfactory vacuum for sublimation is achieved. This ice will subsequently be removed by sublimation along with the water from the samples.

## IV. DRYING OF PLASMA FROM THE FROZEN STATE

The advantages of preserving plasma in the dry state have been discussed in many previous publications. It can be briefly stated that the advantages do not rest in a *better* preservation but rather in a much more practical way of preserving plasma as compared with the optimal, i.e., preservation in the frozen state at temperatures of −20°C. or lower. Under ordinary conditions prevailing in hospitals and similar institutions, preservation of plasma in the frozen state appears to be the method of choice, but when transportation and preservation under unknown temperature conditions are important then drying of plasma becomes the method of choice.

Although there is practically no end to the possibilities in the design of apparatus satisfactory for drying plasma and plasma fractions, the general basic principles of design and construction apply equally to all types of apparatus. Such principles have been extensively dealt with by Greaves and Adair (1939), Flosdorf (1949), Barrett and Beckett (1951), Bradish *et al.* (1947), Carman (1948), and in earlier chapters of this volume. We will limit our comments to the practical application of these principles to the freeze-drying of plasma. First the conditions and details of design related to removal of water will be discussed, and later the construction and operation of a typical medium-sized apparatus for shell-freezing and drying of plasma will be described.

## V. CONDITIONS AND DETAILS OF DESIGN RELATED TO REMOVAL OF WATER

### 1. *Temperature of Plasma and Pressure of Water Vapor*

Water vapor from frozen plasma can be removed in a variety of ways, some of which will be briefly discussed later. But the speed with which water vapor is removed must be at least sufficient to maintain plasma frozen at a temperature compatible with optimal preservation of the most labile fractions; simply to avoid thawing is not sufficient. The safe maximal temperature, although theoretically related to the eutectic point of plasma (Barrett and Beckett, 1951) can best be determined empirically by drying plasma at various temperatures under controlled conditions. As a measure of the effect of the temperature of the plasma during drying, we have studied the solubility of the dried product, the turbidity and stability of the regenerated material, and the prothrombin and complement contents. In this way the maximum safe temperature for human plasma has been established at −12°C. It should be noted that for long periods of preservation in the frozen state −16°C. is the maximum safe temperature. However, for the period of time and experimental conditions prevailing during the freeze-drying period, temperatures of −12°C. are well tolerated. At −5° to −6°C., frozen plasma becomes soft, especially at the lipid-rich surface, and foaming occurs under the high vacuum.

Plasma subjected to temperatures in excess of −12°C. for any length of time, especially during the early phases of drying when the water content is high, shows deterioration of one or more of the labile fractions. This deterioration comes as a consequence of the separation out of ice which makes the remaining solution more concentrated.

Lowering the temperature of frozen plasma substantially below −15°C., on the other hand, does not improve the final product but serves simply to lengthen the period of drying because of the rapidly diminishing ice vapor pressure that results. For plasma, water-vapor pressures between 200 and 300 microns are sufficiently safe and effective during the early phase of drying. Five hundred microns can be considered to be the upper limit.

### 2. *Heat Supply to the Frozen Plasma and Heat Loss*

The critical relationship between heat supply by means to be mentioned later and the heat lost through evaporation is mediated by a variety of factors, of which the most important are the surface of evaporation in relation to the mass of ice and the efficiency with which water vapor is removed. Shell-freezing of plasma, already mentioned, ensures a relatively large surface in a conveniently small vessel.* Pan-drying, where the surface-to-mass relationship can be almost optimal, is not readily applicable to plasma, because of the difficulty in maintaining sterility. Rapid removal of the water vapor is most essential, the two limiting factors here being the water vapor pressure near the evaporating surface and the resistance to the flow of the water vapor.

* For the conventional 250 ml. of plasma frozen in the standard bottle, the evaporation surface is initially about 100 sq. cm. Increase of the surface of evaporation as drying progresses and improved heat transfer through the thinner mass of ice are responsible for the acceleration of the rate of drying as the process goes on.

Greaves (1946) has discussed the above factors extensively and has proposed several formulas to determine the heat requirements and the rate of flow, as expressed in units of obstructive resistance. His analysis is summarized in the formula: $P/R = W/100$, $P$ being the water vapor pressure in millimeters of Hg, $R$ the units of obstructive resistance, and $W$ the heat input in watts. The latter is calculated at 1 watt per 1 ml. dried per hour. This formula can be expected to give only an overall indication of requirements, as it cannot take into consideration variations due to details of construction. Two of these have a great effect on the rate of flow of water vapor but are often neglected: (1) the position of the bottles in relation to the place of disposal of the water vapor and (2) the protective covering of the plasma against air contaminants. The bottles containing plasma to be dried should be placed with the opening down; the exit opening for the water vapor should be at the bottom of the vacuum chamber, and preferably the place of disposal of the water vapor should be below the point of origin. Obviously the ducts conveying the water vapor to the place of disposal should be as short as possible and of such diameter as to permit easy efflux of vapors.

A satisfactory protective covering is one made of two layers of cotton gauze, 40 mesh, arranged to make a bag over the opening of the bottle. It is important that the bag be sufficiently large to obtain a large filtering surface, so that the resistance to the flow of vapor is minimized. With this device, in itself simple to apply and economical, and slow final admission of air into the chamber through many layers of thick gauze, sterility of the plasma is readily achieved.

The drying cycle can be conveniently divided into two distinct phases: an initial one during which the bulk of the water is removed, and a later one during which a relatively small amount of water is slowly removed. The heat input during these two periods varies greatly, and its relation to heat loss must be carefully regulated to avoid excess cooling of the frozen plasma, resulting in a loss of efficiency, or excess heating, with consequent damage to the plasma. In the second phase the heat input becomes less critical, but the water vapor pressure must be sufficiently low to assure minimal residual moisture. During the final phase of drying the water vapor must pass through the layer of dried material, and the density of the latter determines in part the speed of diffusion. Plasma with high lipid content, which tends to rise to the inner surface of the hollow cylinder during shelling, requires a little longer to dry than plasma with lower lipid content. The slowing of water vapor diffusion is to a certain extent compensated for by the improved heat conductivity through thinner ice and the greater surface of evaporation.

### 3. *Methods of Supplying Heat*

With most systems of freeze-drying considerable heat must be applied to the frozen plasma to expedite drying, a sufficient quantity to maintain the temperature of the frozen plasma at a point just below the maximum safe temperature. Once this temperature has been determined for the apparatus in question, the matter of heat supply can be solved in a number of ways. With the manifold type of apparatus, the vessels containing frozen plasma can be immersed in a water bath maintained at the proper temperature; less efficient is the method of leaving them exposed to the temperature of the room. For the closed chamber type of apparatus, now most universally used for drying of plasma, heat can be conveyed by means of a water jacket, with the intermediary of copper sleeves surrounding each bottle, or by circulating warm water through the metal shelves supporting the bottles, with or without the aid of metal sleeves. Electrical sources of heat have also been used, including resistance heating, infra-red, high-frequency currents, and dielectric heating. These methods generally require a more complicated type of control, and some expose plasma to the danger of local overheating. For these reasons, although more rapid drying is sometimes obtained, these methods are not in general use for the drying of plasma.

### 4. *Pumps and Critical Evacuation Time*

A satisfactory vacuum must be maintained during the entire drying cycle. Ideally, a pump should be able to remove both the water vapor and the non-condensable gases, including those originally present, those dissolved in the frozen mass, and those due to minimal leakage in the apparatus. The steam jet type is the most satisfactory of these dual-service pumps, and it has been extensively used in large-scale commercial plasma production. Another system allows the water vapor to emulsify with the oil of the vacuum pump and removes the water from the oil by continuous centrifugation or by heating. This method has proved to be slow and not too practical (Flosdorf and Mudd, 1940).

In most cases the pump is not used directly to remove the water vapor. This is accomplished by means of chemical desiccants or low-temperature condensers interposed between the plasma and the vacuum pump. Any mechanical pump capable of attaining a vacuum of 500 microns Hg within the critical evacuation time and of maintaining a vacuum in the last phase of drying of at least 90 microns, and preferably less, can be considered satisfactory. Barrett and Beckett (1951) have pointed out that the use of pumps capable of attaining a pressure below that of the saturation vapor pressure of ice at the condenser temperature causes ice to resublime from the condenser and pass into the pump. Pressures of 1 to 5 microns are compatible with proper function when the condenser temperature is −55°C. or lower and the content of ice in the drying plasma is small.

The time required to attain a vacuum sufficient to ensure safe water vapor pressure (for plasma, about 500 microns) constitutes the critical evacuation time. This depends on the capacity of the pump, the volume of air to be exhausted, the thermal capacity of the frozen material, the safe water vapor pressure, etc. It must be determined for each system and for each load. When plasma is dried in fairly large amounts, the use of a refrigerated vacuum chamber to extend the critical evacuation time is generally not necessary.

### 5. *Removal of Water Vapor*

Chemical desiccants have long been used to remove water vapor from frozen material *in vacuo* (Leslie, 1811; Wollaston, 1813; Vansteenberghe, 1903). This method is limited at present, however, to drying small amounts of material and is therefore seldom used for plasma since on the larger scale very bulky equipment is required.

Low-temperature condensation is the method of choice for trapping water vapor for all types of systems, with the possible exception of the steam jet pumps for large-scale commercial applications. Solid carbon dioxide in ethanol or other solvents has been in use at least since 1906 (Bordas and d'Arsonval) and is still a popular refrigerant. It involves, however, greater expense, closer supervision, and bulkier apparatus than mechanical refrigeration.

The temperature of the condenser deserves some comments. Elser *et al.* (1935) pointed out that the loss of efficiency resulting from the change of the condenser temperature from −70° to −32°C. was only approximately 5%. The failure of the mechanical refrigeration system proposed by Elser was not due, as has generally been supposed, to too small a temperature differential between the substance being dried and the condensing surface. With low flow resistance we have constantly obtained good drying, with a residual moisture of less than 1% and with a maximum temperature differential of only 18° to 23°C. during the entire drying cycle. This differential was obtained with temperatures of −12°C. for the frozen plasma (the water jacket being at a temperature of 35° to 36°C.) and a temperature of the condensing surface of −30° to −35°C. The advantages in the employment of relatively high temperatures of water vapor condensation are, essentially, simplicity of operation and economy, since the heat-neutralizing capacity of a compressor falls rapidly as the temperature of condensation is lowered.

## VI. AN APPARATUS FOR FREEZE-DRYING PLASMA

This apparatus, illustrated diagrammatically in Fig. 1, was designed essentially for drying plasma and similar materials in their final containers. The daily capacity, when plasma is divided into 300-ml. units in the standard 400-ml. bottles, is 24 units or 7.2 liters. When 500 ml. of plasma is dried in the 650-ml. bottles, each loading consists of 15 bottles or 7.5 liters.

*The source of low temperature* is a two-stage, water-cooled compressor, with Freon 12 as refrigerant, and powered with a 1½ horsepower motor

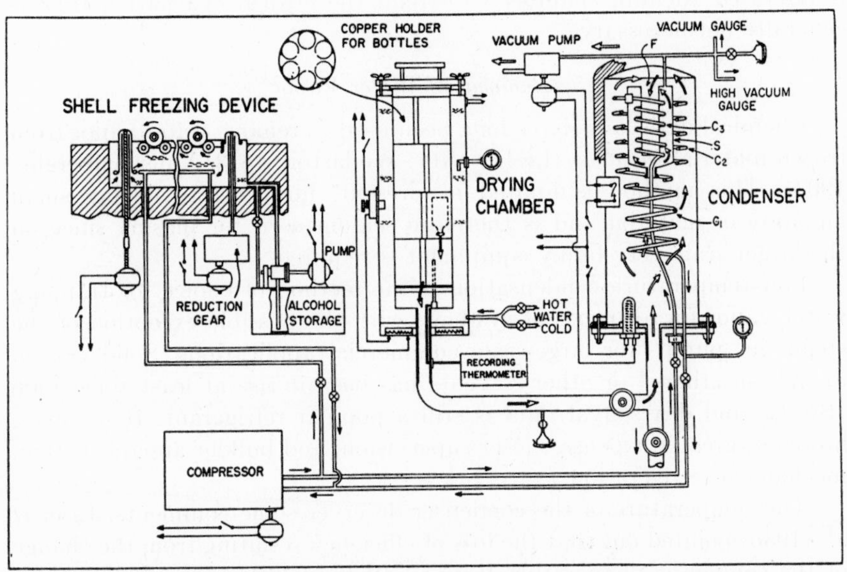


FIG. 1. Apparatus for shell-freezing and drying from the frozen state.

(General Electric Co.). A temperature-controlling device permits maintenance of the desired temperature in the shell-freezing bath. This refrigeration unit also cools the water vapor condenser. Valves permit the use of either unit separately or at the same time. Dial thermometers indicate the temperature of the cooling coil of the condenser and of the coolant in the shell freezing bath.

*The vacuum pump* is ½-horsepower rotary, oil-sealed (Cenco Megavac) with an oil trap. (The large model of the Welch Duo-Seal pump has been used with similar results.) Under optimal conditions it produces a vacuum of 0.1 micron and has a capacity of 600 liters of free air per minute. The pressure is shown by a Pirani-type gauge (Truvac gauge, model 12) and by a mechanical, dial-type gauge which gives rough readings from atmospheric pressure down to the range of the Pirani gauge.

*The shell-freezing bath* consists of a heavily insulated metal pan, cooled by a plate-type evaporator. This plate has at one extremity a round hole in which is fitted a motor-driven propeller, which maintains the coolant (usually alcohol) in rapid circulation around the plate. Motor-driven, rubber-tired rollers maintain the plasma bottles in very slow rotation (one full turn in 2 minutes) and can be so regulated that the bottles are immersed in the coolant to a depth of only 12 mm. The necks of the bottles protrude outside the metal border of the pan, to avoid freezing of plasma in the neck. The temperature of the coolant is automatically maintained at −30 to −35°C. A storage tank is provided for the coolant, when the shell-freezing bath is not in operation, and a small, electrically operated pump fills the shell-freezing pan to the desired level.

*The drying chamber* consists of a heavy brass cylinder (22.5 cm. in diameter and 70 cm. in height), surrounded by a water jacket. It is closed on top by a heavy steel lid, which rests on a rubber gasket. The lid may be tightened by threaded lugs and wing nuts. The opening for the connection to the condenser is in the middle of the base of the drying chamber. This constitutes an essential feature of the apparatus, for the gravity-wise motion accelerates the escape of water vapor from the drying chamber and its entrance into the low-pressure area of the condenser chamber. The exit is flush with the base itself and is 5 cm. in diameter. The connection to the condenser is a short copper pipe of the same diameter. The drying chamber is surrounded by a water jacket, formed by a cylinder of rustproof metal fixed to the flange of the inner chamber. The water jacket is 30 cm. in diameter and 90 cm. in overall length. It is provided with thermostatically controlled electric heater, fitted to the bottom and capable of maintaining the water at any desired temperature up to 80°C. Four copper baskets fit into the chamber, each consisting of an outer split cylinder of 24-ounce copper, approximately 22.5 cm. in diameter and 20 cm. in height. The lower border is turned in 12 mm. to strengthen the cylinder. This large cylinder contains a series of six split copper cylinders welded to the inner surface. These are 11.8 cm. high and are of the proper diameter to grip the plasma bottles tightly. The basket is completed by a transverse bar and springs, which maintain proper expansion of the outer cylinder, and by a series of copper wedges, which assist in increasing heat conduction as well as in keeping the bottles in contact with the copper shells. A recording thermometer (−10° to 80°C.) is provided for one of the copper shells of the lower basket, the bulb being fixed to the bottom of the drying chamber and in direct contact with two of the copper cylinders.

*The condenser* offers in its construction two essential features:

1. The large water-vapor inlet which is located in the lowest part of the copper condensing chamber.

2. The refrigerated coils which are so arranged that by means of properly placed cylindrical shields the water vapor is made to travel a long distance and come into contact with a large condensing surface. The last portion of the coil with which the vapor comes into contact is the coldest. This assures condensation of all of the water vapor. The total length of the refrigerated coil is 13 meters, and the inner diameter is 15.9 mm.

The water vapor enters the condenser from the bottom (Fig. 1). This is very important, because it permits slower diffusion of the water vapor and thus maximum condensation on the first set of coils with which the vapor comes into contact. Under ordinary conditions, the greater portion of the vapor is condensed on coil $C_1$. Some vapor escapes coil $C_1$ and reaches $C_2$. Here the vapor travels through a rather narrow space between the wall of the condenser and the cylindrical copper shield (S) placed inside $C_2$. If a trace of water vapor escapes $C_2$, it must travel through a narrow funnel-like tube (F) to reach $C_3$, which is enclosed in a copper box. The vacuum pump is connected to the condenser by means of an opening in the top of this box. The bulk of the water vapor is condensed on coil $C_1$, a smaller amount on coil $C_2$, and only a trace on coil $C_3$ (see Fig. 2). Under standard operating conditions, no water escapes to the vacuum pump. This has been determined by placing a copper U-tube, 5 cm. in diameter, in the vacuum line during experimental runs. The U-tube was immersed in a bath of solid carbon dioxide–alcohol at a temperature of $-70°$ to $-72°$C. At the end of the runs, no condensate was found in the U-tube.

The copper box (S in Fig. 1) is so constructed that the ice formed on $C_3$ will drain out when it is melted. This is accomplished by means of a self-sealing valve surrounding the coil as it enters the box from below. The valve consists of a short length of copper tube, insulated from the rest of the box, and approximately 2 mm. larger in diameter than the refrigerated coil passing through it. When the drying starts, water vapor very soon freezes around the refrigerated coil passing through the valve and so seals it. When the ice melts, the valve opens and allows water from coil $C_3$ to drain from the condenser.

The arrangement of coil $C_3$ just described is made in order to reduce the height of the condensing coil and chamber. If space is not an important factor, the construction can be simplified by placing coils $C_1$, $C_2$, and $C_3$ one on top of the other and reducing progressively the diameter of the condensing chamber, thus forcing the water vapor into contact with the coldest part of the condenser.

A dial thermometer shows the temperature of the portion of the coil of the condenser nearest to the expansion valve. This greatly assists in checking proper operation of the refrigeration compressor. An electric heater is provided in the condenser to melt the ice from the coils rapidly

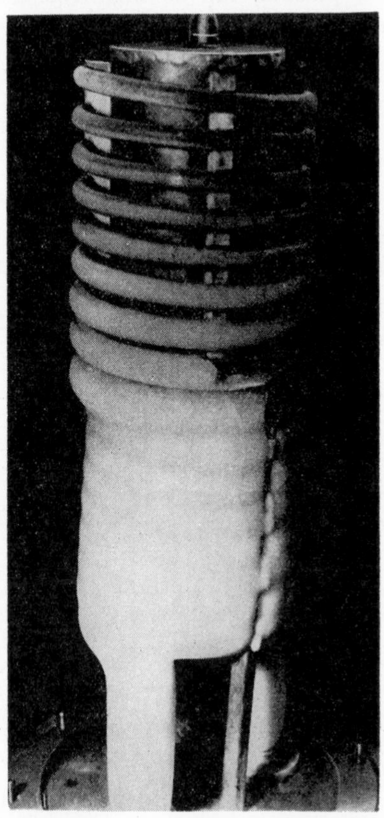

FIG. 2. Condensing coils. Note that the bulk of ice is formed on the lower coils near the point of entry of the water vapor.

at the end of each drying run. The melted ice is then drained from the condenser through the opening in the bottom. The Freon 12 gas should be pumped out of the coils before heat is applied in the condenser to melt the ice at the end of each run.

### 1. *Operation of the Freeze-Drying Apparatus*

Operation of the apparatus is relatively simple, the operator being assisted by the automatic features of the apparatus.

Twelve units, each containing 300 ml. of plasma, can be shell-frozen at −30° to −35°C. in 1 hour 15 minutes, using the precautions already mentioned under "Freezing of Plasma." Once the alcohol bath is cold, a second lot of twelve units of plasma can be shell-frozen in about 1 hour. In about 2 hours and 15 minutes, therefore, twenty-four bottles, each containing 300 ml. of plasma, can be shell-frozen. They must then be placed in the copper baskets and cooled to −20° to −25°C. in a standard freezing cabinet, where they can be stored for an indefinite period of

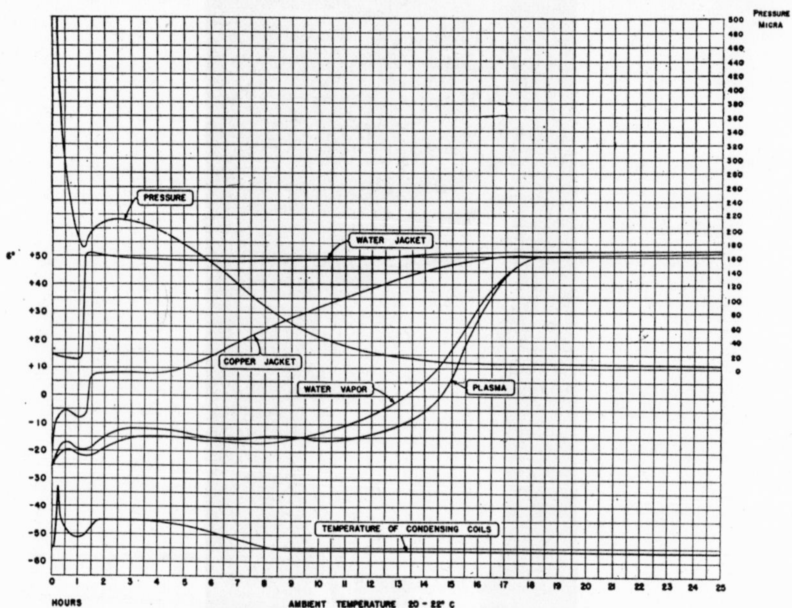


FIG. 3. Pressure and temperature records during drying of twenty-four 300-ml. units of plasma.

time.* At any time shortly before the drying the rubber stopper is replaced by a gauze cuff.

Before the start of the drying, the apparatus is tested for vacuum, proper temperature of condenser coils, etc. The baskets are rapidly placed in the drying chamber, which has been cooled to about 15°C. or less by circulating cold water in the jacket. The safe evacuation time with a full load, to a water vapor pressure of 500 microns, is about 15 minutes; actually it takes only about 12 minutes to attain this pressure. With a ¾-horsepower compressor, the condenser coils can be maintained at −35° to −40°C. without load, and at −30° to −35°C. while drying is

* Plasma properly frozen and stored in the frozen state at −20°C. or lower shows no demonstrable deterioration for 6 years. Even after 10 years of storage under these conditions the only change noted is a very slight decrease in prothrombin activity.

in progress. During the period of maximal condensation, the temperature may occasionally be a little higher. With a 1½-horsepower compressor, the coils can be maintained at lower temperatures, between −33° and −56°C. With these temperatures a residual moisture of well under 1% is always obtained. Figure 3 indicates the relationship of pressure and plasma temperature during a typical drying run.

The bulk of the water, more than 90%, is removed during the first 10 hours; the remaining amount requires approximately 8 more hours, during which the temperature of the plasma gradually rises until it is within 1°C. of the temperature of the water bath. This indicates that all the ice has sublimed. It is safe to remove the plasma 2 or 3 hours after this point is reached. Actually in the routine procedure, the temperature of the plasma is not recorded, but as a measure of the progress of drying the temperature of the copper shell surrounding the bottle is obtained on a round graph form.

In the routine process for freeze-drying plasma with the apparatus described,* advantage is taken of the period after the fourteenth hour of the drying cycle, when the refrigeration unit can be used for operating the water vapor condenser as well as the shell-freezing bath.

Under such conditions the output of the plant in 24 hours is 7.2 liters of plasma in twenty-four units of 300 ml. each.

## VII. STABILITY OF PLASMA IN THE DRY STATE

Random specimens of plasma dried from the frozen state, as well as selected specimens, have been stored for periods up to 10 years in evacuated glass bottles, closed with pure amber rubber gum stoppers. Some of the bottles were sealed in tin cans (Strumia *et al.*, 1952), and this appears to be the best overall method of packing (Strumia *et al.*, 1942).

At yearly intervals observations were made on residual moisture, solution time, pH, turbidity, prothrombin content, viscosity, albumin and globulin content, and complement content. Studies of the electrophoretic pattern were also made. Most of the essential properties of the plasma are preserved for at least 5 years; after this time the prothrombin activity drops progressively, but the plasma is otherwise satisfactory for at least 10 years. Results of clinical observations have paralleled those obtained from the *in vitro* studies.

## VIII. FREEZE-DRYING OF OTHER BLOOD PRODUCTS

The technique of freeze-drying has been extended to the preservation of other blood products, including normal human serum, modified globin from human red cells (Strumia and Sample, 1951), suspensions of human

* Precision Scientific Company, Chicago, Illinois.

erythrocytes for local application, and guinea pig serum as a source of complement. The technique used was that described in detail for plasma; it resulted in all cases in a product readily soluble and with all the essential properties of the original material.

Masucci (1946), summarizing his long experience with freeze-drying of biological products, confirms the excellent results with serum, but with antibody globulins, unless diluted to 5 or 6% prior to desiccation, a product was obtained with an excessively long solution time.

## REFERENCES

Allen, J. G., Sykes, C., Enerson, D. M., and Moulder, P. V. 1950. Homologous Serum Jaundice and Its Relationship to Methods of Plasma Storage. *J. Lab. Clin. Med.* **36,** 796–797.

Barrett, A. S. D., and Beckett, L. G. 1951. Aspects of the Design of Freeze-Drying Apparatus, in *Freezing and Drying.* Edited by R. J. C. Harris. The Institute of Biology, London. Pp. 41–49.

Bordas, F., and d'Arsonval, 1906. Les Basses Températures et l'Analyse Chimique. *Compt. rend.* **142,** 1058–1059.

Bradish, C. J., Brain, C. M., and McFarlane, A. S. 1947. Vacuum Sublimation of Ice in Bulk. *Nature* **159,** 28–29.

Buckley, E. S., Gibson, J. G., and Walter, C. 1950. The Use of Ion-Exchange Resins to Prevent the Coagulation of Whole Blood. Separation of the Formed Elements, the Protein, Carbohydrate, Lipid, Steroid, Peptide and Other Components of Plasma. *Bull. Harvard Univ. Lab.* Sect. **3.**

Carman, P. C. 1948. Molecular Distillation and Sublimation. *Trans. Faraday Soc.* **44,** 529–536.

Cohn, E. J. 1941. The Properties and Functions of the Plasma Proteins, with a Consideration of the Methods for Their Separation and Purification. *Chem. Revs.* **28,** 395–417.

Cohn, E. J. 1947. The Separation of Blood into Fractions of Therapeutic Value. *Ann. Internal Med.* **26,** 341–352.

Cohn, E. J., Gurd, F. R. N., Surgenor, D. M., Barnes, B. A., Brown, R. K., Devonaux, G., Gillespie, J. M., Kahnt, F. W., Lever, W. F., Liu, C. H., Mittelman, D., Monton, R. F., Schmid, K., and Aroma, E. 1950. A System for the Separation of the Components of Human Blood: Quantitative Procedures for the Separation of the Protein Components of Human Plasma. *J. Am. Chem. Soc.* **72,** 465–474.

Elser, W. J., Thomas, B. A., and Steffen, G. I. 1935. Desiccation of Sera and Other Biological Products (Including Microorganisms) in the Frozen State, with the Preservation of the Original Qualities of Products so Treated. *J. Immunol.* **28,** 433–473.

Flosdorf, E. W. 1949. *Freeze-Drying.* Reinhold Publishing Corp., New York.

Flosdorf, E. W., and Mudd, S. 1940. The "Desivac" Process for Drying from the Frozen State. *J. Am. Med. Assoc.* **115,** 1095–1097.

Greaves, R. I. N. 1946. The Preservation of Proteins by Drying, with Special Reference to the Production of Dried Human Serum and Plasma for Transfusion. *Med. Research Council (Brit.) Spec. Rept. Ser.* No. **258.**

Greaves, R. I. N., and Adair, M. E. 1939. High Vacuum Condensation Drying of Proteins from the Frozen Stat · *J Hyg* **39,** 413–445.

Janeway, C. A. 1947. Other Uses of Plasma Fractions with Particular Reference to Serum Albumin. *Ann. Internal Med.* **26,** 368–376.

Leslie, J. 1811. Methode Nouvelle de Produire et d'Entretenir la Congélation. *Ann. chim. et phys.* **78,** 177–182.

Masucci, P. 1946. Application of "Lyophile Technique" to Biologic Products: Sera, Antisera and Antibody Globulin. *J. Lab. Clin. Med.* **31,** 340–345.

Proesher, F. 1951. Anti-coagulant Properties of Ethylene-bis-Iminodiacetic Acid. *Proc. Soc. Exptl. Biol. Med.* **76,** 619–620.

Strumia, M. M. 1942. The Role of Low Temperature in the Preservation of Plasma. *Refrig. Eng.* **50,** 154.

Strumia, M. M., Blake, A. D., and McGraw, J. J. 1947. An Acid-Citrate-Dextrose Solution with Low Water Volume and Low Dextrose Concentration. *J. Clin. Invest.* **26,** 678–685.

Strumia, M. M., and McGraw, J. J. 1943. A Method and Apparatus for Shell-Freezing and Rapid Drying of Plasma and Other Products from the Frozen State by Low Temperature Water Vapor Condensation *in Vacuo. J. Lab. Clin. Med.* **28,** 1140–1155.

Strumia, M. M., and McGraw, J. J. 1949. *Blood and Plasma Transfusions.* F. A. Davis Company, Philadelphia. Pp. 278–281.

Strumia, M. M., McGraw, J. J., and Heggestad, G. E. 1952. Preservation of Dried and Frozen Plasma over a Ten-Year Period. *Am. J. Clin. Pathol.* **22,** 313–321.

Strumia, M. M., McGraw, J. J., and Reichel, J. 1941. Freezing of Plasma and Preservation in the Frozen State. *Am. J. Clin. Pathol.* **11,** 388–401.

Strumia, M. M., Newhouser, L. R., Kendrick, D. B., and McGraw, J. J. 1942. Development of Equipment for Administration of Dried Plasma in the Armed Forces. *War Med.* **2,** 102–113.

Strumia, M. M., and Sample, A. B. 1951. Modified Globin I. Method for Preparation from Human Erythrocytes. *J. Lab. Clin. Med.* **37,** 959–968.

Vansteenberghe, P. 1903. Procedé de conservation du virus rabique à l'etat sec. *Compt. rend. soc. biol.* **55,** 1646.

Wollaston, W. H. 1813. On a Method of Freezing at a Distance. *Trans. Roy. Soc. (London)* **103,** 71–74.

CHAPTER 5

# The Freeze-Drying of Antibiotics

J. H. SINGER*

*Glaxo Laboratories Ltd., Greenford, England*



## I. INTRODUCTION

Antibiotics have been defined as substances produced by living microorganisms and inhibiting the growth of other microorganisms. Penicillin, the first of them to be isolated, was discovered by Fleming in 1929, but its clinical significance was not realized until the early part of World War II when the work of Chain and colleagues (1940) focused attention on its possibilities. This led to the organization of large-scale clinical trials and later to intensive activity, both in Great Britain and in the United States, in the production of the material in large quantities. Commercial production of penicillin was first done by surface culture, the product being isolated as a relatively crude and very unstable aqueous solution of the sodium salt. Material required for parenteral administration was produced by freeze-drying the required quantity of solution in the final container, which was subsequently sealed.

It was fortunate that, by the time large-scale production of penicillin became an urgent necessity, freeze-drying had already been developed from a laboratory technique to a practicable commercial operation, particularly for the preservation of blood plasma; for in many respects the freeze-drying problems associated with both products are similar, and indeed the design of the equipment employed for penicillin solutions in

* Deceased 1953.

the initial stages was largely based on that already in use for serum drying. Had this state of affairs not existed, the isolation of penicillin and its presentation in a sterile form on a large scale would probably have been delayed for a long time just when it was most urgently required.

Penicillin is now isolated in crystalline form by other means and without freeze-drying, although similar equipment is commonly employed for removing the last traces of moisture. The product is filled into the final containers by dry subdivision of the sterile bulk, an operation that presented great difficulty in the earlier days of its development, but one for which efficient equipment has since become available. This procedure has been widely adopted for large-scale production of the more recently discovered antibiotic substances such as streptomycin and chloramphenicol, although some derivatives of the former are still isolated by freeze-drying to sterile bulk before being filled dry into vials. Freeze-drying has also been reported as practicable for the preparation of bacitracin (Anker *et al.*, 1948) and circulin (Nelson *et al.*, 1950).

Although now mainly of historical interest, the freeze-drying of penicillin in individual containers has been the subject of several publications (Flosdorf and Mudd, 1945a, b); a detailed description is included because the scale of the operation made it one of the largest industrial applications of the process to pharmaceutical products and the equipment and methods developed may well find useful application in other fields.

## II. DRYING IN INDIVIDUAL CONTAINERS

### 1. *Early Developments*

Early commercially produced penicillin was dried by methods that had already been developed on a laboratory scale for other purposes, and the final container was usually a sealed glass ampoule. The solution in these ampoules was shell-frozen by rotating in a refrigerated liquid bath, and the ampoules were then transferred to a manifold connected to a suitable condenser and vacuum system for drying. The heat necessary for the sublimation of the ice was provided from the atmosphere of the room in which the apparatus was installed; when drying was complete, the ampoules were removed from the manifold and sealed in the usual manner. Surprisingly large numbers of ampoules of penicillin were dried in this way both in the United States and in Great Britain, and numerous devices were produced to assist the process, particularly the shell-freezing, when large quantities of ampoules were involved.

Condensation of the water vapor from the drying manifolds was usually accomplished with Dry Ice as a refrigerant, and many attempts were made to develop equipment for reducing to a minimum the wastage of this relatively expensive material. The so-called "pig" of Wyckoff and Lagsdin (1944) embodied a central vacuum-insulated Dry Ice container and was designed to reduce the distance between evaporating and condensing surfaces to a minimum, although this was no great advantage with ampoules because their narrow necks formed the principal resistance to the flow of water vapor. The device was unable to accommodate a large quantity of ice on its condensing surface, and later types of manifold for drying were usually of sufficient diameter to avoid undue obstruction to vapor flow but connected to separate Dry Ice condensers of larger capacity with adequate insulation to prevent loss by direct adsorption of heat from the atmosphere. Though short-lived as commercial equipment, the small manifold drier with shell-freezing is still valuable in the laboratory when small quantities of new antibiotics are isolated for the first time. It has the advantage of being able to accommodate a wide variety of different sizes and shapes of container at the same time.

The Cryochem equipment, which had previously been developed in the United States for the small-scale production of blood serum in hospitals and similar institutions and for the production of stable vaccines (Flosdorf and Mudd, 1938), was also applied to the drying of penicillin solutions. In this system the water vapor was absorbed by a chemical desiccant, calcium sulfate, which was subsequently regenerated and used again. For small-scale operations the plant gave excellent results, and it was employed by the Federal Food and Drug Administration in the United States for testing and for the preparation of penicillin standards (Welsh *et al.*, 1944). It was particularly useful in those places where Dry Ice was unobtainable, and it avoided the difficulties that frequently occurred with the earlier types of mechanically refrigerated low-temperature condensers. Its disadvantage was the large quantities of desiccant required; this had to be periodically regenerated, thus adding materially to the initial cost of the equipment and presenting a considerable problem when the scale of operations increased. Except for very small installations it has now almost entirely given place to the mechanically refrigerated condenser.

### 2. *Design of Suitable Containers*

With the growing demand for penicillin, the difficulties of sealing large quantities of all-glass ampoules became apparent and, together with the obvious limitations to the use of manifolds to which they were individually attached, led manufacturers to seek a more suitable design of container. This ultimately took the form of a glass vial closed with a rubber plug, which was secured by an aluminium seal placed over the neck of the vial, after insertion of the plug, and spun on. A hole in the aluminium seal exposed an area of the rubber plug for insertion of a hypodermic needle and was either covered with a detachable dust cap or provided with a center portion, formed during manufacture, that could be torn off by the user. Besides facilitating large-scale freeze-drying and packaging, this container has generally been preferred by the medical profession to the single-dose sealed ampoule because, after reconstitution of the dry solid by the addition of solvent injected through the rubber plug, it can be used as either a single- or a multiple-dose container. Since about 1944 its use has become almost universal both in the United States where it originated and in Britain, and it is still extensively employed not only for antibiotics but also for other injectable products, whether frozen-dried in the vial or dry-filled from sterile bulk.

Frozen-dried penicillin is hygroscopic (Carr and Riddick, 1947), and most of the initial difficulties with rubber-plugged vials arose from the need to provide a moistureproof seal. Plugs manufactured from the rubber mixes previously used for closing vials of vaccines and other liquid injection products were found to pass moisture vapor to an extent that allowed rapid absorption by the frozen-dried solid, and much work in conjunction with rubber manufacturers was carried out in the attempt to produce a rubber mix suitable for making a stopper that was sufficiently elastic to permit the easy penetration of a hypodermic needle and reclosure and yet was also sufficiently impermeable to moisture vapor to enable penicillin to be stored for long periods in adverse humidity and temperature conditions. Starkweather and Walker had shown in 1937 that most rubber compositions are in some degree permeable to moisture but that this permeability is influenced by the addition of certain other substances. Flosdorf and Webster (1938) also examined the composition of various rubber closures for use with frozen-dried powders and concluded that neoprene showed no marked advantage over rubber as a barrier to moisture vapor. The results they obtained and the composition of the mixes examined have been further discussed and tabulated by Flosdorf (1949).

Stoppers finally developed in Britain for sealing penicillin vials contain in addition to the rubber about 50% of an inert filler and varying quantities (up to about 5%) of paraffin wax. These have been used in vast quantities in containers for frozen-dried penicillin and other antibiotics and have given satisfactory results under temperate conditions of storage over periods extending to several years. Under the extreme conditions of storage sometimes encountered in tropical climates, even these rubber stoppers are not entirely satisfactory as a moistureproof closure for antibiotics and other hygroscopic powders that deteriorate on absorption of moisture. Further work is required to discover a completely satisfactory solution to this problem without recourse to highly expensive forms of external packaging.

## III. EQUIPMENT FOR LARGE-SCALE DRYING OF PENICILLIN IN INDIVIDUAL CONTAINERS

Three main problems must be solved in the design of equipment for large-scale freeze-drying in individual containers. These are:

1. The handling of large numbers of individual small vials during the processes of washing, sterilization, filling, prefreezing, drying, and subsequent sealing, with reasonable economy of time and labor.
2. The maintenance of sterility of the contents throughout the process and the need to ensure that the dry solid does not absorb moisture between the conclusion of the drying operation and the final sealing of the vial.
3. Production of the necessary conditions of temperature and pressure for prefreezing the solution and for sublimation of the water from the frozen state at a temperature sufficiently low to avoid frothing and other undesirable phenomena.

Unlike blood plasma, which is usually dried in relatively small numbers of containers, each containing several hundred milliliters of solution, penicillin has to be dried in very large numbers of small containers, each containing usually less than 1 or 2 ml. of solution. It was the need to handle many thousands, and even millions, of these small containers that gave rise to most of the innovations in plants constructed for drying penicillin as compared with plants already in operation for other purposes. The introduction of the rubber-plugged vials as the final container in place of the glass ampoule greatly facilitated the design of the necessary equipment, because the vials are much easier to handle than ampoules and the difficult operation of final sealing in a flame is avoided.

To simplify the handling problem, 100 to 150 vials were usually washed and then placed in metal trays in which they remained until they were removed for final sealing at the end of the process. The tray of vials was fitted with a metal lid and sterilized by dry heat for a sufficient time to ensure that the vials themselves were maintained at a temperature of not less than 150°C. for 1 hour. Higher temperatures, in the region of 250°C., were sometimes employed to ensure the destruction of pyrogenic substances as well as bacteria, but there is no necessity for sterilizing temperatures above 150°C. if the final stage of washing is carried out with pyrogen-free, distilled water, thus avoiding the disadvantages of increasing the time required for the vials to cool after removal from the ovens and increasing the proportion of the vials likely to break during the heating period.

### 1. *Filling*

After sterilization and subsequent cooling to room temperature the trays of vials were transferred to a suitable closed room or cubicle where aseptic conditions were maintained during the filling operation. The bulk solution of penicillin previously sterilized by filtration was then transferred in accurately measured quantities to the individual vials.

The filling equipment was designed so that the vials could be filled without removal from the trays in which they were sterilized; Fig. 1

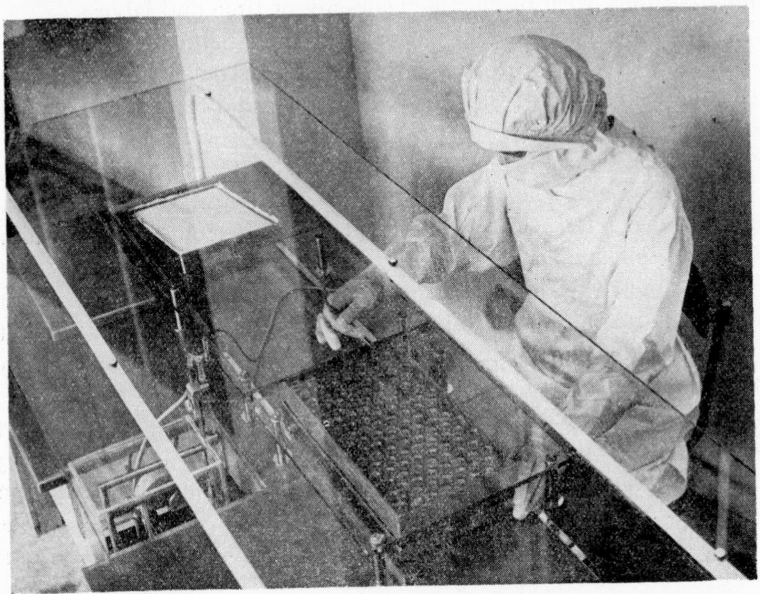

FIG. 1. Equipment for filling vials with solution prior to prefreezing.

shows a typical arrangement of this type. The tray of sterile vials with the lid removed was placed under a close-fitting glass plate and pushed forward until the first row was exposed to the operator, who filled them one at a time by means of a wandering lead from an automatic measuring pump which could be adjusted to deliver the required volume at successive intervals. When a row of vials had been filled, the tray was pushed forward to expose the next row, those already filled passing under a second glass plate which covered them until all the vials in the tray had been filled. The tray was then covered with a suitable lid, removed from the far end of the apparatus, and replaced by the next tray of empty vials.

By this comparatively simple system a single operator was able to fill 3000 or more vials an hour without difficulty and it therefore sufficed for any but the largest installations. For filling very large quantities, fully automatic machines were devised capable of filling a whole row of vials at a time and automatically advancing the tray from one row to the next. Figure 2 shows a typical machine of this type, capable of filling vials at a speed of 6 per second, or about 20,000 per hour. These machines had the disadvantage of requiring the vials to be accurately arranged in rows, and it was necessary to use with them specially designed trays containing a honeycomb or grid that orientated the vials in a suitable manner, adding

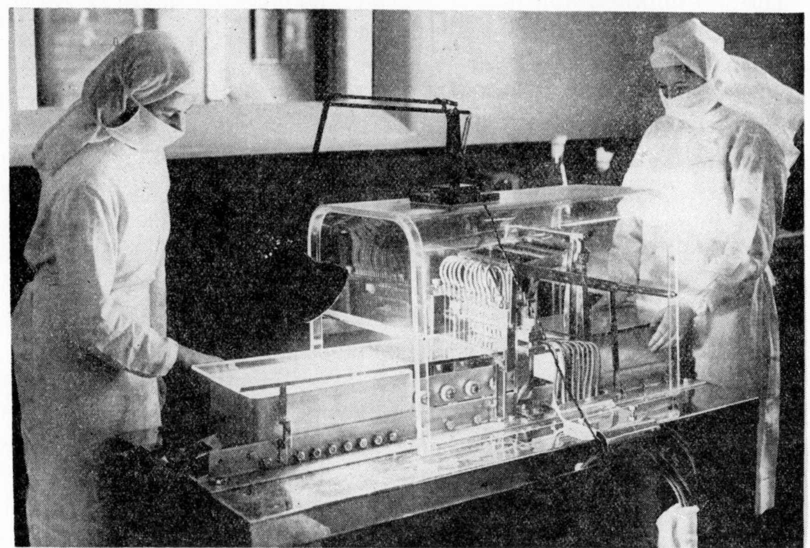

FIG. 2. High-speed automatic machine for filling vials.

considerably to the capital cost of the installation. The use of these machines by several manufacturers both in Britain and in the United States is some indication of the enormous scale on which penicillin was frozen-dried for parenteral use.

### 2. *Maintenance of Sterility*

After the vials have been filled, the maintenance of sterility of the contents becomes much more difficult. It was quite practicable for the metal lids used during sterilization of the vials to remain on the trays during prefreezing, but it was necessary for them to be removed during the actual drying operation to permit free flow of water vapor from the frozen solution to the condenser.

Flosdorf and Mudd, who had, as early as 1935, considered the problems of commercially applying freeze-drying to individual containers, carried out the prefreezing operation with the necks of the containers closed by plugs of cotton wool, so that any air entering as a result of contraction of the air inside them during the freezing operation was filtered free from bacteria. It was necessary to remove the plugs of cotton wool during the drying operation, but at this stage the outward flow of vapor from the necks of the containers prevented the ingress of bacteria and the containers were finally sealed without removal from the manifold on which they were dried.

This was impracticable on a large scale, and methods had to be devised to overcome the difficulties without involving the individual handling of the vials. Some manufacturers employed a tray with a close-fitting metal lid during prefreezing and subsequently removed the lid after the trays had been loaded into the drying chambers, which were scrubbed out with an antiseptic solution. This system relied on the current of vapor passing outward from the necks of the vials during drying to prevent the ingress of bacteria. At the conclusion of the operation air was readmitted to the chamber through a suitable sterilizing filter. The method had the disadvantage of a considerable risk of contamination during loading and unloading and during the period before the chamber was exhausted to the point at which sublimation began.

An alternative arrangement, which overcame the risk of infection during loading and unloading, was to place a loose-fitting metal cap on the neck of each vial, the caps being formed in such a way that water vapor could pass underneath them during drying. This system involved the sterilizing and individual handling of large numbers of small caps at several stages of the process, which was a considerable disadvantage on a large scale.

A simple and effective method of maintaining sterility of the material at all stages was an adaption of the method introduced by Greaves (1946) and first employed for serum drying in the M.R.C. serum unit at Cambridge. He used the cotton filter material employed during the war in gas masks as a closure for the necks of the bottles, which were then effectively sealed against the ingress of bacteria although water vapor could freely pass the barrier during the drying operation. This procedure was adapted to penicillin vials by the construction of trays that could be fitted with a plain metal lid for dry heat sterilization and storage up to the time of filling, subsequently being replaced by another lid consisting of a frame that had been sterilized separately and in which a piece of the filter material was fitted. This second lid remained in position through the operations of prefreezing and drying and was removed only when the vials were finally closed with a rubber plug and sealed.

This arrangement provided satisfactory conditions for the maintenance of sterility by placing the vials in a bacteriologically closed system, and it avoided the necessity for sterilizing the inside of the drying chambers and for special precautions when air was readmitted after drying. It was, however, somewhat expensive in labor and material; the cotton fabric did not survive repeated sterilization and also had a tendency to shed fibers that were liable to find their way into the vials. A search was therefore made for an alternative method of achieving the same result. This was accomplished with a plain metal lid that was placed on the trays when they were filled with washed vials before sterilization and temporarily removed during filling. It remained in place during freezing and loading into the drying units, but when the chambers had been evacuated to below 1000 microns the lids on all the trays were raised simultaneously by hydraulic control from outside the unit. They remained open during drying and were then closed by the same means at the end of the run, before air was readmitted to the chamber.

This solved the problem of cotton fibers entering the vials and at the same time saved both the material and the labor costs associated with the use of the fabric. The cost of installing the hydraulic lid-lifting gear was recovered in a few months, and the sterilizing and filling operations were simplified. Initial tests showed no difficulty in maintaining sterility if the lids were raised after the chamber was evacuated and lowered again before air was readmitted. As a general precaution, however, the air was always admitted slowly through a sterilizing filter, and the inside surfaces of the chambers were thoroughly cleaned with an antiseptic solution before each drying run.

### 3. *Prefreezing*

Before being dried the solution had to be prefrozen and cooled to a temperature sufficiently low for the frozen material to be transferred to the drying chambers and for these to be evacuated before the surface layer could melt. The conditions for prefreezing solutions of crude sodium penicillin were not particularly critical as long as the temperature was low enough and was not allowed to rise above −25°C. before drying began. The usual method was to prefreeze in cabinets at −50°C. and not to remove the vials until they had cooled to this temperature. This provided an adequate margin of safety for transfer to the drying chambers. In later types of equipment, in which prefreezing and drying were carried out in the same chamber, it was not necessary to cool the solution to so low a temperature.

It was also desirable that the solution should freeze as rapidly as possible, because then the crystals of frozen solid were small and there was less tendency for a layer of concentrated solution to form on the surface. Such a layer would not remain frozen during drying and would give rise to frothing, which resulted in the final product having an inelegant appearance or even having lost a considerable amount of material through the neck of the vial. Some crude solutions of the sodium salt of penicillin were particularly troublesome in this respect, owing to the presence of the sodium salts of other organic acids, some of which formed eutectic solutions with a much lower freezing point than solutions of sodium penicillin. That is why, in the early stages of development, facilities were frequently provided for freezing and drying at much lower temperatures than were later required when improved fermentation and extraction methods yielded a product of greater purity.

Shell-freezing in a refrigerated liquid bath was employed to some extent for large-scale production, but it had the disadvantages, first, of requiring individual handling of the vials and, second, that small quantities of solvent from the bath remained on the outside and subsequently passed into the vacuum pumping system of the drying equipment, where its presence was undesirable.

Since the sodium salt of penicillin could be isolated in solution at a concentration sufficiently high to permit the quantity required in the vial to be dried from a volume of 1 or 2 ml., it was unnecessary to shell-freeze and satisfactory results were obtained by freezing the solution as a plug or layer on the bottom of the vial standing on its base in the normal manner. This had the advantage that it allowed the vials to remain in their trays after filling, and in many large-scale installations prefreezing was carried out by placing the trays of filled vials in suitably designed refrigerated chambers until the solution was frozen and the frozen solid cooled to the required temperature. These were usually so constructed that the trays of vials could be stacked or placed on shelves in such a way that a blast of cold air from an internal fan circulated between them and thus greatly increased the rate at which heat was removed. The chambers themselves were so constructed that the circulating air on its return path to the suction side of the fan passed over a battery of coils cooled either by direct expansion of a refrigerant gas or by circulation of a suitable secondary refrigerant through them.

This system followed the general principle employed by Greaves (1942) for prefreezing blood serum and plasma except that in this method the air stream was directed on to the bottle itself, which was spun on its vertical axis to produce a shell of frozen material. By this method supercooling of the solution could be induced, followed by rapid freezing, which produced crystals of the desired small size. With small vials of penicillin solution in metal trays closed to maintain sterility it was impossible for the air stream to impinge directly on the containers, and freezing was consequently slower, especially as the contact and hence the heat transfer between the base of a glass vial and a metal tray is very poor. In practice, however, some supercooling did occur and a fairly rapid prefreeze to a satisfactory type of solid resulted.

An alternative and later method of prefreezing was to place the trays of vials on refrigerated shelves of box formation with suitable internal baffles to ensure proper distribution of the circulated refrigerant or on plain metal shelves with a refrigerated coil brazed or welded to the undersurface. Shelf freezing was preferable to freezing in a recirculated air stream, and particularly so for bulk freezing in trays, since the rate of freezing when the liquid to be frozen is in direct contact with the metal tray is much greater than in any other method. When the liquid was contained in vials the advantages in rate of freezing were not so great because of the poor contact between the base of the vials and the bottom of the metal tray. Glass vials frequently have a small ridge on their base, originating from the mold in which they are blown, and the contact between them and the tray can be very poor. It was usually necessary with quantities of 1 or 2 ml. of penicillin solution in each vial to allow for either method an overall prefreezing time of not less than 3 hours to ensure that the solution in all the vials was completely frozen.

The shelf method of prefreezing, however, permitted the design of a plant in which both prefreezing and drying operations could be carried out in one unit. In a small unit of this type, arranged so that after prefreezing the trays of vials can be transferred to the upper drying shelves, the lower shelves can then be used as the condenser during drying. This unit is particularly convenient and compact for outputs of the order of two or three thousand vials a day.

### 4. *Drying*

During drying it was necessary for the temperature of the frozen solid to remain below −25°C. Above this temperature partial separation of a eutectic solution was liable to occur, which caused frothing of the material in the vials and a resulting unsightly appearance. It was also difficult to remove the last traces of moisture from material that had frothed even to a small extent, and this had an important bearing on the stability of the final product.

In order to achieve satisfactory stability it was necessary that the residual moisture of the dried solid should be below 1% and that it should remain below this during the useful life of the product. In former days, when crude solutions were dried on manifolds and the temperature of the dry solid at the end of the operation was that of the room in which the apparatus was situated, it was frequently difficult to achieve a sufficiently low figure for residual moisture, and the final traces were then removed by secondary desiccation over phosphorus pentoxide. It was considered inadvisable to apply heat during the final stages of drying owing to the extreme instability of the penicillin in the presence of the impurities that were then present.

With improvements in production the stability of the material during the final stages of drying improved. By the time that the use of manifolds had given place to the direct drying of vials in large chambers it was possible to supply not only the latent heat of evaporation of the ice to the shelves on which the trays were placed but also to raise the temperature at the end of the drying cycle so that the residual moisture content could be reduced to below 1% in a single drying operation without the need for secondary desiccation. Ultimately it was found practicable to allow the temperature to rise to 40°C. at the conclusion of the drying cycle and still to obtain a satisfactory product; even if the temperature reached 50°C. in the final stages there was no evidence of appreciable loss of potency. The conditions required for drying crude solutions of penicillin were studied in detail by Sherwood during the early part of the last war, and his work, unpublished at the time, has subsequently been reported by Flosdorf (1949). The sublimation of ice from penicillin solutions has also been further studied by Carman (1948).

Crystalline sodium penicillin isolated by other means is much more stable than the earlier product produced by the freeze-drying of relatively crude solutions of the sodium salt; for example, it can be heated to 100°C. for considerable periods without loss of potency. This is in part due to the absence of impurities but also to the fact that freeze-drying from solution yields the substance in an amorphous form in which it is less stable than in the crystalline state. This phenomenon is of general occurrence and can be a serious disadvantage in the use of freeze-drying as a method of isolation.

A variety of different types of drying chambers were developed for drying penicillin solution in vials. A large rectangular chamber was widely employed, particularly in the United States. This was provided with shelves heated by the circulation of hot water, and the chambers were frequently designed to withstand an internal pressure of 15 lb. per square inch of steam so that they could be steam-sterilized when necessary. Figure 3 shows several chambers of this type installed for drying on a large scale. Each chamber is connected through independent vacuum valves to two manifolds, which pass outside the drying room in which aseptic conditions of low humidity are maintained. The smaller manifold is used for initial evacuation of the chambers. When the pressure has been reduced to the required value, the chambers are connected to the larger manifold through which the water vapor passes to the condenser. Alternative designs of drying chambers also employed were cylindrical, with the condenser incorporated within the chamber or connected directly to it.

FIG. 3. Large freeze-drying plant employing rectangular chambers. (Courtesy of British American Research Ltd.)

Whatever the type of chamber, the heat required for sublimation of the ice was usually supplied to the shelves either by circulation of hot water through them or by electrical heaters attached to the underside. Hot water circulation had the advantage of low cost as a source of heat for large installations, but in vial drying the volume of water to be evaporated was comparatively small and the cost of providing the latent heat of evaporation was therefore much less important than for bulk drying operations in which much larger volumes were evaporated in similar equipment. Further, the drying cycle itself was short, rarely exceeding 6 to 8 hours, and for maximum utilization of the plant, which was usually operated on 24-hour shifts, it was an advantage to reduce to a minimum the time between unloading one charge and loading the next.

In these circumstances electrical heating with resistance elements under the trays had the advantage that less heat remained to be dissipated from the shelves at the conclusion of a run and a further charge of frozen material could be placed upon them without risk of the temperature's rising above the required point before an adequate vacuum had been achieved in the chamber. Electrical heaters are also suitable for accurately controlling the total heat applied to the evaporating material, for the maximum shelf temperature can be limited by means of a suitable thermostat.

A considerable amount of experimental and development work was carried out on the use of infra-red radiation (Reavell, 1944) and on the application of dielectric heating (Brown *et al.*, 1946) to the freeze-drying of penicillin solution, and equipment was installed and operated on a pilot plant scale. In general, however, the disadvantages, particularly the high cost of the equipment, were such that the simpler methods of heating were usually preferred for industrial use, and dielectric heating, although attractive in theory because it can provide heat where it is required, i.e., at the evaporating surface of the ice rather than through the vial and the mass of frozen solid, gives rise to considerable practical difficulties when applied in a chamber operating under vacuum.

Except for the Cryochem system and in certain special circumstances when the availability of large quantities of steam made it possible to employ multistage ejectors for the direct pumping of water vapor, most installations employed a low-temperature condenser to remove the water vapor produced by the evaporation of the ice in the frozen solution and to maintain a suitably low vapor pressure within the chamber so that sublimation could proceed.

Before adequate experience was gained of the problem involved, condensers were frequently produced to operate at very low temperatures, sometimes as low as $-100°C.$, and these require specially designed and expensive refrigeration equipment. With a well-designed plant having the minimum obstruction to the flow of vapor from the evaporating to the condensing surface, the required temperature of the frozen solution in the vials could be maintained with a condenser at $-50°C.$, and this temperature could be achieved by the use of standard refrigeration equipment at considerably less cost.

The simplest types of condenser were either coils enclosed in a suitable lagged vessel or modified shell and tube condensers. These were defrosted with hot water or by other means after one or more of the drying runs, a comparatively simple and rapid operation. Sometimes condensers were

FIG. 4. Scraper condenser with flooded refrigeration system, installed for the large-scale drying of penicillin. (Courtesy of British American Research Ltd.)

installed in duplicate so that one could be defrosted while the second was in operation.

An alternative type designed to maintain a clean condensing surface and capable of handling large quantities of ice has been described by Morse (1947) and was employed on some of the larger installations (Fig. 4). The water vapor is condensed on the inner surface of a jacketed cylindrical condenser from which the ice is continuously scraped by a system of rotating blades driven by an external electric motor and a shaft passing through a specially designed high-vacuum gland. The ice detached from the condensing surface by the scraper blades falls into a large, similarly jacketed vessel, from which it can subsequently be readily removed. The jackets of both the condenser and this vessel are operated as a flooded refrigeration system designed to maintain a temperature of −70°F. at the condensing surface.

The advantage claimed for this system was the continuous removal of ice from the condensing surface and therefore more efficient condensation at all stages of the drying cycle. Its advantages were more apparent on very large systems and bulk drying operations when it was required to handle large volumes of water; for drying in vials, satisfactory results could be obtained with the simpler types of condenser at considerably less cost.

### 5. *Vacuum Pumping*

For initial evacuation of the drying chambers and removal of air that leaked into the system and of non-condensable gases evolved during drying, rotary, oil-sealed, mechanical vacuum pumps were usually employed. They needed to be large enough to evacuate the chambers to about 100 microns before the temperature of the frozen material rose to a point at which partial melting occurred. Owing to the relatively high water vapor pressures (200 to 300 microns) existing in the chamber during drying, there was no advantage to be gained by using pumping equipment capable of attaining very low pressures, and at the end of the drying cycle, when the last traces of moisture were being removed, a residual pressure of 50 microns was adequate.

This could be achieved by a large, single-stage, rotary pump, but the pumping speed of a single-stage pump falls off rapidly below about 100 microns and a more efficient arrangement employed on several plants was a large, single-stage pump backed by a smaller pump of the same type with a relief valve between them. This opened during the initial evacuation of the air from the drying chamber and closed automatically as soon as the volume of exhaust air from the main pump was within the capacity of the backing pump. The system functioned as a two-stage pump during the actual drying operation, giving a better performance than a single-stage pump in the later stages when a residual pressure of 50 microns was required.

An alternative and better pumping system became available later, when special types of oil diffusion pump were developed to operate efficiently at relatively much higher pressures than the previously existing types. These booster pumps, as they were usually called, when backed by a single-stage mechanical pump of appropriate size, increased its pumping speed by about five times at pressures in the region of 50 microns. This large increase in capacity at low pressure was particularly useful because small air leaks in the system were then of less significance in their effect on the residual vacuum and hence on the final moisture content of the dried penicillin.

When diffusion pumps were used it was necessary to provide a separate vacuum manifold and mechanical pump for the initial evacuation of the chambers, which were changed over to the high-vacuum system by means of suitable valves when the pressure had been reduced to about 200 microns.

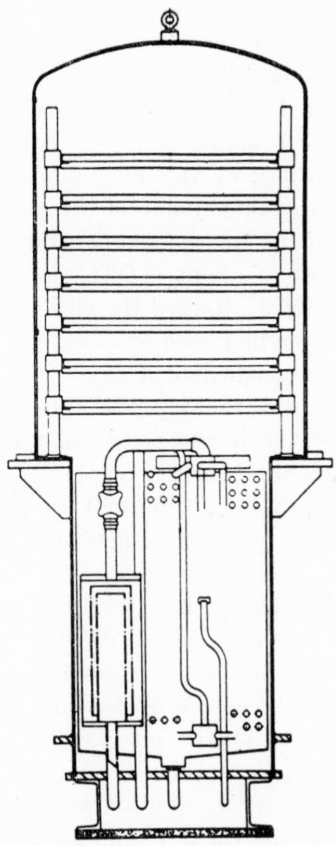

FIG. 5. Vial drying unit. Refrigeration by direct expansion.

Figure 5 shows the construction of a drying unit employed successfully in Great Britain for producing substantial quantities of penicillin in vials (Singer, 1946). It was originally designed for a comparatively small output, but with increasing demand additional units were constructed until finally eight were in continuous operation. Each unit consisted of a cylindrical uninsulated vacuum chamber constructed in two halves. The bottom half contained the condensing coil, the expansion valve, and the heat exchanger, arranged so that the valve was easily accessible with the chamber open. The shelves, which carried the heaters and supported the trays of bottles during drying, were permanently mounted on this half of the chamber, and all electrical and other connections were brought into it through the rim.

The top half of the chamber formed a large bell located in relation to the bottom by guides and lowered on to it after the unit had been loaded. Each chamber was mounted on the same base as its refrigerator—a four-cylinder, single-stage compressor operating on Freon 22 and capable of maintaining the condensing coil at −50°C. under full load. Placement of the expansion valve and the heat exchanger inside the vacuum chamber removed the necessity of bringing the cold condensing coil into contact with the uninsulated casing; by this means heat losses were minimized and undesirable frosting of the outside of the unit was avoided.

With the units in operation the temperature, measured toward the end of the coil, remained at about −50°C. for the greater part of the drying run and fell to −60°C. toward the end when substantially all the water in the frozen solution had been evaporated. The lower temperature of the condenser at the conclusion of drying assisted in removing the final traces of moisture from the dry penicillin. By heating the vials to 40°C. at the end of the run, it was possible to dispense with secondary desiccation and to reduce the moisture content to below 1.0% on the dry solid, which was sufficiently low for normal use and storage.

Each unit was capable of condensing about 30 liters of water in 36 hours at −50°C., but when loaded with trays of vials the volume of water in the chamber was much smaller, about 4 liters, and the drying time was reduced to 5 hours, so that four drying runs could be completed within 24 hours. The units were constructed to hold a charge of approximately 2700 vials in 21 trays of 130 each. With four drying runs in 24 hours this produced a daily output of just over 10,000 vials per unit, or about 80,000 vials a day from all eight units in operation together.

Whatever the type of drying equipment, it was essential to avoid the absorption of moisture by the dry solid in the vials during the operations of unloading the drying chambers and finally closing the vials with a rubber plug and seal. The quantity of frozen-dried material present in the smaller vials containing 100,000 units of penicillin was less than 100 mg.; hence in working to a moisture limit of 1% it was necessary to avoid subsequent absorption even of fractions of a milligram of moisture from the atmosphere.

This could be accomplished by rapid transfer of the vials to specially constructed cabinets where the plugs were inserted by hand. These were fed with filtered sterile air at 10% relative humidity from a specially designed activated alumina or silica gel drying plant. The area in which the drying chambers were situated was also air-conditioned to 35% relative humidity. It was, however, usually necessary to carry out the plugging and sealing operation during a normal 8-hour day, whereas the drying plant operated on shifts throughout the whole 24 hours, and, to provide a buffer between the two operations, secondary desiccators were frequently employed. These were simple chambers provided with shelves in which the trays of dried vials could be stored under vacuum over a small quantity of phosphorus pentoxide until required.

FIG. 6. Apparatus used for the bulk-drying of penicillin in the early days of its manufacture.

## IV. BULK DRYING

In the early days of penicillin manufacture material for pharmaceutical preparations and other purposes for which it was required in bulk was dried in glass apparatus using Dry Ice as refrigerant or on manifolds provided with some form of mechanically refrigerated condenser. Figure 6 shows one type of apparatus used for the purpose in Great Britain. It consisted fundamentally of a flask with a ground-glass neck into which was fitted an inverted thimble condenser filled with Dry Ice. This simple apparatus was capable of efficiently drying penicillin, but the obvious limitation on the size of both flask and condenser meant that each unit could handle only a small quantity at a time. With the increase in demand for bulk material, it became necessary to build up this glass apparatus by multiplication of the units, which were connected in banks of ten through a common manifold to a small, two-stage, mechanical pump capable of maintaining the residual air pressure in the system at about 50 microns Hg.

Each flask had a capacity of about 600 ml. of solution, which was shell-frozen on its inner surface in a bath of Dry Ice and alcohol, so that each bank of ten flask and condenser units held about 6 liters of solution which could be dried in 24 hours. The heat necessary for evaporating the ice in the frozen solution was absorbed from the atmosphere through the walls of the flasks, the rate of heat transfer and hence of drying being controlled to some extent by mounting electric heaters under them and surrounding each flask by a cylindrical jacket. Raising the temperature of the air immediately surrounding the flasks at the conclusion of the drying cycle also assisted final drying, and material with a residual moisture content of 1% or lower could be obtained without difficulty. At one period, before a more permanent plant could be made available, eight banks or eighty flask units of this type were in continuous service in one laboratory and over a period of about 2 years produced a substantial proportion of Britain's wartime penicillin output before being superseded. A similar type of bulk drying equipment was employed in the United States, but here stainless steel containers were used and provision was made for the water vapor to be carried by a common manifold from the drying canisters to a single, large condenser.

In the later stages of development, before the production of penicillin as a crystalline salt by other methods, bulk material was frequently dried in the chambers employed for drying the solution in vials and under similar conditions, with stainless steel trays to contain the solution.

### 1. *Streptomycin*

The advent of streptomycin gave rise to a somewhat different series of problems. Owing to the much larger quantity required in each vial, compared with penicillin, it proved more convenient to dry the solution in bulk, with subsequent sterile subdivision of the dry material, than to dry in the final containers. This was facilitated by the fact that by the time streptomycin was manufactured on a commercial scale suitable equipment for dry filling under aseptic conditions, not available in the early days of penicillin production, had been developed. Streptomycin, either as the calcium chloride complex or as the sulfate, and dihydrostreptomycin sulfate are produced as aqueous solutions containing about 40% of solid, from which the dry salts are isolated by freeze-drying, usually in stainless steel trays filled with solutions to a depth of approxiately 2 cm. A satisfactory product is obtained if the frozen solution is aintained at a temperature of −25°C. during the initial stages of dryng, and these conditions were readily obtainable with the equipment lready designed for drying penicillin.

The large rectangular type of drying chamber with refrigerated helves, in which bulk solution could be frozen *in situ*, was particularly

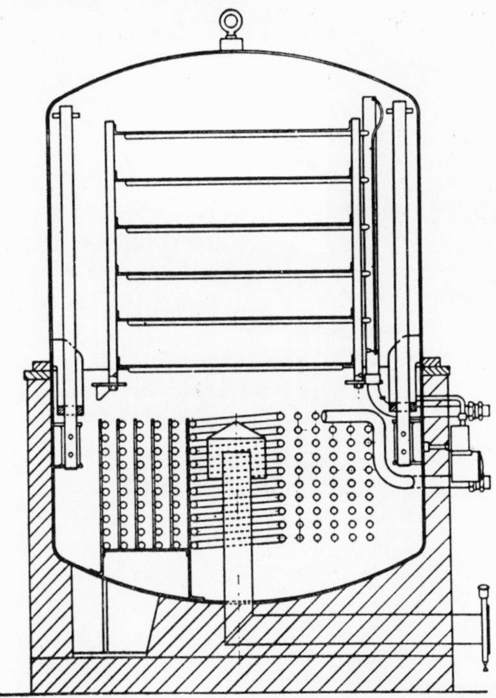

Fig. 7. Bulk-drying unit. Prefreezing and condensing by circulation of a secondary efrigerant.

suitable. Figure 7 shows the general design of a cylindrical type of drier somewhat similar to that illustrated in Fig. 5 and in fact produced in the light of previous experience obtained with the earlier unit. Figure 8 shows the plant at one stage in the cycle of operations. It was constructed specifically for bulk drying of streptomycin solutions and was designed to obviate the necessity for handling shallow trays of liquid by combining the operations of freezing and drying in one unit.

The refrigeration and vacuum pumping equipments were also removed from the drying room to a separate plant room outside and this involved considerable revision of the design of the plant. Five drying units are employed, each holding 36 trays with approximately 2 liters of solution per tray, or a total charge of about 72 liters. When they are all in operation, the plant is capable of drying over 300 liters of solution in a 48-hour cycle.

The vertical cylinder type of chamber was retained because experience had shown that it was easier and cheaper to manufacture than the oven

FIG. 8. Bulk-drying plant for streptomycin, showing one unit open, with drying trays in position.

type and was convenient to load, at the same time providing a satisfactory unobstructed path for the flow of water vapor between the evaporating and the condensing surfaces. The chamber was modified by an increase in diameter and a reduction in height to permit easier access from floor level and was constructed in nickel-clad mild steel, polished on the inside. The top half, as before, serves simply as a cover and is suspended on a wire cable passing over a pulley on the ceiling to a counterbalance weight in the plant area outside. This allows the units to be opened and closed by hand without effort.

The bottom half contains the condensing coil with the vacuum pipe, suitably baffled, in the center. The shelf units that carry the trays are also mounted on this half, and each shelf carries on its underside a serpentine coil for the circulation of refrigerant and an electrical heater of the cable type. Electrical and refrigerant connections are taken out through the back of the unit and pass through the wall of the drying room to the plant area. On this system it is necessary for the refrigerant pipes to pass through the metal shell, and the bottom half of each unit is therefore suitably lagged, the lagging being enclosed in an outer metal sheath.

With freezing and drying combined in the same unit the use of direct expansion refrigerators is impracticable and refrigeration is therefore provided by an indirect two-stage compressor system operating on Freon 22. Two low- and one high-stage compressor of the same type are employed, a fourth compressor being arranged in such a manner that it can be brought into operation at once as a replacement for either high or low stage in the event of trouble. For the same reason the expansion valves are duplicated and can be changed while the plant is operating.

The compressors have a heat extraction capacity of 36,000 Btu per hour at −55°C., which is applied to cooling a tank containing 500 gallons of a eutectic solution of methanol in water (approximately 70% methanol). This secondary refrigerant is pumped to the freezing and condensing coils in the units through lagged pipes that run along the outer wall of the drying room. With a circulation of approximately 1000 gallons per hour, the condensing coils can be maintained at −50°C. or slightly below, and there is a negligible temperature gradient between the ends of the coil. The refrigerators are designed to absorb the total heat load of four units drying and one freezing, while the 500 gallons of refrigerant in the storage tank provide a buffer against sudden temperature fluctuations.

The vacuum system consists of a roughing manifold 3 in. in diameter, with a single-stage pump at each end, and a high-vacuum manifold 6 in. in diameter for maintaining the vacuum in the chambers during drying. This is provided with a 6-in. diffusion booster pump backed by a single-stage mechanical pump at each end, but on both manifolds only one pump is normally in operation, the second serving as a standby in case of mechanical failure and to permit routine maintenance while the plant is in operation. Both manifolds are situated on the outside of the drying room wall and are connected to the individual units by 3 in. branches passing through the wall and provided with valves inside the drying room, so that each unit can be connected to either as required.

The plant is operated in the following manner. The stainless steel drying trays and lids, mirror-polished on the inside, are washed and rinsed with pyrogen-free filtered distilled water. They are then loaded into a rack holding 36 trays, the charge for one drying unit, and sterilized in a vacuum autoclave, which is mounted in the wall between the washing and drying rooms and provided with a door at either end. After autoclaving the trays are removed in the drying room, air-conditioned to provide a clean sterile atmosphere at 35% relative humidity, and loaded into the appropriate unit.

FIG. 9. Bulk-drying plant. Charging the trays with solution prior to freezing.

They are then charged with solution under aseptic conditions by an operator using a machine that automatically delivers the correct quantity to each tray (Fig. 9). During filling, the lid of the tray is raised at one corner to allow the filling jet to enter and then replaced to engage with the hydraulic control, which will subsequently lift it while drying is in progress.

When all the trays have been filled the bell is lowered, and the solution is frozen by allowing refrigerant to flow through the shelf coils. This takes about 3 hours and is recorded by a resistance thermometer in contact with the side of one tray. Before the actual freezing of any individual tray takes place, supercooling occurs in the particle-free solution, which remains liquid for some time. The trays do not all freeze at exactly the same time, and a considerable additional period is required for further cooling to −30°C. after freezing. Because of this, separation of concentrated solution on the surface of the frozen layer was expected, but this has not in fact occurred and a homogeneous frozen mass is produced.

When the temperature of the frozen solution has fallen to −30°C., the unit is exhausted. As soon as the pressure in the chamber falls below 200 microns, it is connected to the high-vacuum manifold with the remaining units at various stages of their drying cycles. Circulation of refrigerant to the shelves is then stopped, the lids of the trays are opened by means of the hydraulic control, and the heaters are switched on.

The heat input is adjusted to give an overall drying time of 40 hours. Drying takes place at a temperature of −28°C. in the initial stages, but toward the end of the run, when the final traces of moisture are being removed, the dry solid is allowed to rise to 40°C.

When drying has been completed, the tray lids are lowered, air is readmitted to the chambers, and the trays of dry solid are removed for further processing. The condensing coil in the drying unit is then defrosted by means of a hose connected to the hot water supply, and the surplus water is pumped out from the drier base. The whole unit is finally cleaned, and the shelves and the inside of the chamber are wiped down with antiseptic as a general precaution. It is then ready for the next run.

The design and method of operation of these units has served to reduce the labor and time required between runs to a minimum. No more than two operators are required in the drying room at any time, and the 48-hour cycle makes it possible to complete all the necessary operations within the normal working day. Shift working is necessary in the plant room where an engineer is on duty throughout the 24 hours.

In the development of any new antibiotic substances that may require to be isolated by freeze-drying from solution, it seems probable that bulk drying followed by dry subdivision of the sterile powder into the final container will generally be the preferred method on a commercial scale. A greater degree of flexibility in both design and size of the final pack can be achieved than by "vial drying," and material is also made equally available for other pharmaceutical operations.

---

The author wishes to thank British-American Research Ltd. for permission to publish Figs. 3 and 4.

## REFERENCES

Anker, H. S., Johnson, B. A., Goldberg, J., and Melany, F. L. 1948. Bacitracin: Methods of Production. *J. Bacteriol.* **55**, 249–255.

Brown, C. H., Bierworth, R. A., and Hayler, C. N. 1946. Radio Frequency Dehydration of Penicillin Solutions. *Proc. I.R.E.* **34,** 58–65 w.

Carman, P. C. 1948. Molecular Distillation and Sublimation Including Sublimation of Ice from Penicillin Solutions at −20°C. to −30°C. *Trans. Faraday Soc.* **44,** 529–536.

Carr, C., and Riddick, J. A. 1947. Hygroscopicity of Penicillin Salts. *Ind. Eng. Chem.* **39,** 1021–1023.

Chain, E., Florey, H. W., Gardner, A. D., Heatley, N. C., Jennings, M. A., Orr Ewing, J., and Sanders, A. C. 1940. Penicillin as a Chemotherapeutic Agent. *Lancet* **ii,** 226–228.

Flosdorf, E. W. 1949. *Freeze-Drying.* Reinhold Publishing Corp., New York.

Flosdorf, E. W., and Mudd, S. 1935. Procedure and Apparatus for Preservation in "Lyophile" Form of Serum and other Biological Substances. *J. Immunol.* **29,** 389–425.

Flosdorf, E. W., and Mudd, S. 1938. An Improved Procedure and Apparatus for Preservation of Sera, Microorganisms and Other Substances—the "Cryochem" Process. *J. Immunol.* **34,** 469–490.

Flosdorf, E. W., and Mudd, S. 1945a. Drying Penicillin by Sublimation in the United States and Canada. *Brit. Med. J.* **i,** 216–218.

Flosdorf, E. W., and Mudd, S. 1945b. Drying Penicillin. *Am. J. Med. Sci.* **209,** 694–695.

Flosdorf, E. W., and Webster, G. W. 1938. Neoprene and Rubber Stoppers for "Lyophile" Serum Containers. *India Rubber World* **98,** 33–37.

Greaves, R. I. N. 1942. The Freezing of Human Serum and Plasma in Medical Research Council Transfusion Bottles before Drying by Sublimation from the Frozen State. *J. Hyg.* **41,** 489–495.

Greaves, R. I. N. 1946. Preservation of Proteins by Drying. *Med. Research Council (Brit.) Spec. Rept. Ser.* No. **258.**

Morse, R. S. 1947. High Vacuum Technology. *Ind. Eng. Chem.* **39,** 1064.

Nelson, H. A., DeBoar, C., and DeVries, W. H. 1950. Production of Circulin. *Ind. Eng. Chem.* **42,** 1259–1262.

Reavell, J. A. 1944. Sublimation of Penicillin Solutions using Infra-red Heating. *Ind. Chemist* **20,** 54.

Singer, J. H. 1946–7. Application of Freeze-Drying to Penicillin Production. *Proc. Inst. Refrig. (London)* **42,** 167–175.

Starkweather, H. W., and Walker, H. W. 1937. Water Resistance of Neoprene. *Ind. Eng. Chem.* **29,** 1380–1384.

Welsh, H., Grove, D. C., Davis, R. P., and Hunter, A. C. 1944. The Relative Toxicity of Six Salts of Penicillin. *Proc. Soc. Exptl. Biol. Med.* **55,** 246–248.

Wyckoff, R. W. G., and Lagsdin, J. B. 1944. A Simple Outfit for Drying Plasma from the Frozen State. *Am. J. Clin. Pathol.* **8,** 10–16.

CHAPTER 6

# The Freeze-Drying of Mother's Milk

G. G. A. MASTENBROEK

*Head of the Lactarium, Netherlands Red Cross, The Netherlands*



## I. INTRODUCTION

"Il est presque universellement reconnu que l'alimentation artificielle ne peut pas toujours remplacer le lait de femme."

This experience, put into words by Freudenberg, has led to the establishment of lactaria in many countries, and the oldest organized lactarium was founded in Boston, many years ago.

A lactarium is faced with special difficulties in the preservation and transportation of mother's milk. In most cases, for example, it is necessary to sterilize the milk, and, conceivably, in that process many of the valuable ingredients of the milk will get lost.

Very weak infants are often completely dependent on mother's milk for their nutrition and, in fact, on mother's milk in its most natural form. Attempts have often been made to preserve the milk by fractionated pasteurization, but this long heat treatment undoubtedly does little to improve the quality of the milk.

Another method is to deep-freeze the milk. The objection to this is that it is difficult to convey such milk to the consumer and, moreover, the functioning of the deep-freezer has to be frequently and conscientiously supervised. Milk has been known to thaw and refreeze unperceived and, thus spoiled, to be distributed.

The safest method of preservation is to dry the milk. In Germany, where a chain of lactaria existed, this was done for many years in small vacuum drum driers. This drying, however, was performed at too high a temperature, and the milk did not quite fulfil the requirements.

## II. COLLECTION OF THE MILK

In the Netherlands, a National Lactarium was founded on Januar 1, 1947, by the Netherlands Red Cross, assisted by some other societie Mother's milk is collected in various towns and villages and is stored i sterile bottles in deep-freezers until a sufficient quantity is available t send to the Central Laboratory at Amsterdam. The Netherlands Railwa gives free transportation to the insulated containers.

On arrival in the Central Laboratory, the bottles are thawed an tested routinely for bacterial contamination. The bacteriological supe vision of the *dry* powder is in the hands of the Amsterdam Health Servic

FIG. 1. Shell-freezing of bottles with milk.

Further tests are made to determine whether the milk has been adulte ated with cow's milk. The young mothers make a free gift of their milk t the Red Cross, and such adulteration occurs rarely, arising, perhap from an excess of social feeling!

In the test for added cow's milk 1 ml. of the sample to be tested i mixed with 1 ml. 8 *N* sulfuric acid and 8 ml. water and left at roo temperature for 5 hours. Flocculation occurs if adulteration with cow milk has taken place, and as little as 5% of cow's milk in mother's mil will be brought to light by this reaction. This method is more reliab than the fluorescence method and less expensive than methods involvin the use of antisera.

The tested milk samples are then mixed in order to obtain an averag composition. As is generally known, the composition of the milk change gradually during the lactation period. The milk is collected from man donors, and thus an average composition of the milk will result, althoug it must be recognized that most women have a surplus of milk in th beginning of the lactation period, and this they donate to the Lactarium. As lactation proceeds, the young mother will often find that she has just sufficient milk for her own baby, and the Red Cross asks for milk only if a mother has a surplus.

The mixed milk is then transferred to blood transfusion bottles, each containing about 400 ml.

The Lactarium's Central Laboratory is, of course, unaware of the state of health of the donors, who live all over the country, and the milk has now to be pasteurized at 67°C. for 30 minutes. Such a pasteurization procedure suffices to free the milk from pathogenic bacteria, provided that standard Anglo-Dutch blood transfusion bottles are used. The bottles are then cooled in running water and frozen quickly to −40°C. (Fig. 1).

The pasteurization kills most of the vegetative organisms and, after the subsequent sudden fall in temperature, practically no new bacterial growth occurs. The milk is further hardened for at least another 24 hours at −40°C. in order to obtain the most suitable ice crystals for the primary drying process.

## III. THE DRYING PLANT

In the Central Laboratory of the Blood Transfusion Service, the Netherlands Red Cross had at its disposal a freeze-drying installation for the drying of blood plasma. The obvious thing to do was to find out whether freeze-drying could be easily applied to the preservation of mother's milk too. After investigation, it became apparent that no serious difficulties were likely to arise.

The installation was designed by the staff of the Central Laboratory of the Blood Transfusion Service in the years 1940–1945, during the German occupation. Several types of apparatus were constructed. The final installation, however, completed after the war, consists of three primary and three secondary driers, a refrigerator unit, vacuum pumps, etc.

For plasma, the drying capacity is 120 liters daily. Each drier unit consists of a vertical tube of stainless steel with 96 apertures to which bottles containing the material to be dried can be attached. This tube is then placed on a stainless steel container surrounding a cooling coil, the temperature of which is maintained at −40° to −50°C. The entire apparatus may then be evacuated. In order to accelerate the drying process, a hood of a transparent plastic material is placed over the vertical tube with the bottles (Fig. 2). Hot water is conducted along the inside of this hood, and the bottles are suspended in an atmosphere saturated with hot water vapor. The vapor condenses on the cold surface of the bottles, transferring the heat of condensation and thus accelerating the sublimation. A bottle which is not drying quickly is warmer, as less heat is being withdrawn from it, and, consequently, such a bottle will condense less vapor. In view of this, a bottle will not thaw if the temperature of the water-vapor atmosphere (usually between 25° and 55°C.) has been correctly adjusted. In this way a fully automatic heat regulation is obtained.

When the primary drying of the substance has been completed, the entire bottle assembly is transferred to a second stainless steel container in which, instead of a refrigerated cooling coil, there are plates containing

FIG. 2. Primary and secondary driers.

phosphorus pentoxide. The whole apparatus is again evacuated. The primary and secondary drying both take 20 to 24 hours, with bottles containing approximately 400 ml. of plasma or mother's milk.

For the secondary drying of mother's milk, a somewhat different technique may be adopted. The mother's milk is predried in blood-transfusion bottles (with all possible sterility precautions), and the powder is then removed from these bottles and transferred into smaller bottles. These are the definitive packing, and they each contain 12.5 grams of powder, the equivalent of 100 ml. of milk.

In order to ensure that the final product is completely dry, these small bottles are secondarily dried in a modified drier. This consists of a round, stainless steel rack with adaptors to receive some 400 of the small bottles containing the primarily dried mother's milk. The rack is attached to the tank containing the phosphorus pentoxide, and a hood of stainless steel hermetically seals the rack to the tank. The entire installation is now evacuated and kept in vacuum for 20 to 24 hours. As soon as the apparatus is opened, the bottles are rapidly corked and sealed with plastic.

## IV. PROPERTIES AND ADVANTAGES OF DRIED MILK

The experience of the Netherlands Red Cross over a period of five years has shown that powdered mother's milk can be kept safely for years and that it will not turn rancid or otherwise change its taste. In all probability this is due, first, to the fact that the powder is extremely dry and, second, to the fact that the milk has never had any contact with metals. The powder will readily dissolve in water and is ready for use immediately. One of the immediate advantages of dried mother's milk is that a more concentrated milk can be prepared by dissolving the powder in less water. Such concentrated milk may often be fed with advantage to babies with particular diseases.

Prior to the year 1947 in which the Lactarium of the Netherlands Red Cross came officially into operation, extensive tests had been made with powdered mother's milk in two different university clinics in the Netherlands. These tests showed that reconstituted frozen-dried mother's milk was practically equivalent to fresh mother's milk.

The concentration of vitamins A and B in the dried milk were the same as that usually found in fresh mother's milk, but the vitamin C content was reduced practically to zero. It is probable that the milk loses its vitamin C content during transportation in half-filled bottles which must be severely shaken *en route* to the Lactarium. The vitamin C can easily be restored by adding the vitamin to the dissolved powder, either in the form of orange juice or as the synthetic product.

Wegelin (Thesis, Utrecht 1952) compared the whey from frozen-dried mother's milk with that from fresh mother's milk. Cream was separated by centrifugation and the casein removed by precipitation with acid in the presence of calcium ions and rennin. The whey was dialyzed and concentrated by freeze-drying. Ninety-six per cent of the total protein content of the powder appeared in the cream-free liquid. However, only 58% of the total protein content of the powder was found in the whey. According to the literature, this should have been about 70%. The loss was probably a result of slight denaturation of the milk proteins during pasteurization.

Electrophoretic investigation of fresh and frozen-dried mother's milk (at pH 6 to 8, I.S. = 0.15) gave the results shown in Table 1. It is important to bear in mind, however, that the tests were not made with fresh and frozen-dried mother's milk from the same sample. The fresh milk was obtained from a few women attending the lying-in hospital and was taken in the early stages of lactation. The dried powder came from a larger number of women who, on the average, had certainly progressed further into the lactation period.

The mobilities of the different fractions were found to be much the same in both cases, and the small differences which appear are undoubtedly a result of the pasteurization process and what has been observed previously regarding the period of lactation.

TABLE 1
ELECTROPHORETIC COMPOSITION OF WHEY FROM MOTHER'S MILK

| | Fresh | | | | Frozen-dried | | | |
|---|---|---|---|---|---|---|---|---|
| | Mobility, $10^{-5}$ cm.$^2$ v$^{-1}$ sec.$^{-1}$ | | Concentration, % | | Mobility, $10^{-5}$ cm.$^2$ v$^{-1}$ sec.$^{-1}$ | | Concentration, % | |
| Component | Asc. | Desc. | Asc. | Desc. | Asc. | Desc. | Asc. | Desc. |
| A | 6.0 | 5.4 | 9.8 | 11.2 | 5.6 | 5.5 | 21 | 20 |
| $B_1$ | 4.0 | — | 20 | — | } 4.0 | 4.3 | 29 | 25 |
| $B_2$ | 2.9 | — | 38 | — | | | | |
| $B_1 + B_2$ | — | 3.6 | — | 42 | — | — | — | — |
| C | 1.2 | 1.6 | 32 | 47 | 2.1 | 2.2 | 42 | 48 |

For the past two years, each batch of mother's milk delivered has been accompanied by a questionnaire, for the attention of the responsible physician. One hundred and fifty completed forms were returned. These, without exception, reported favorable results with the powdered mother's milk, and not a single complaint regarding the product has yet been received. In the five years of its existence, the Netherlands Lactarium has distributed about 100,000 bottles, each containing the equivalent of 100 ml. of fresh milk. A steadily increasing demand, which can hardly be met, proves that the method described produces a mother's milk which fully meets all requirements.

## V. CONCLUSIONS

The cost of the scheme to the Netherlands Red Cross has been considerable. The milk is supplied on a medical prescription only, and contributions from the children's parents have to be sought, scaled according to their ability to pay.

The Lactarium has deep-freezers at its disposal in various big towns and is also experienced in the transport of cooled materials, and it has occupied itself since 1952 with the organization of a bone-graft service for surgical purposes. The material, derived from calf bone, is also preserved and despatched by the Lactarium, the service being sponsored by the Netherlands Red Cross.

Attempts have been made to freeze-dry such bone for grafting, paralleling the similar experiments in the United States for the preservation of bone, cartilage, skin, and artery (Strong, 1953; Billingham, this volume, p. 253).

It is hoped that such a sharing of the resources of the Lactarium will help to reduce the overhead expenses which devolve at present upon the milk product.

## REFERENCE

Strong, W. R. 1953. The Tissue Bank. Its Operation and Management, in *Preservation of Normal Tissues for Transplantation.* Ciba Foundation Symposium. In press.

CHAPTER 7

# The Freeze-Drying of Foodstuffs*

R. GANE

*Low Temperature Station for Research in Biochemistry and Biophysics, University of Cambridge and Department of Scientific and Industrial Research, Cambridge, England*



## I. INTRODUCTION

Freeze-drying, as a method of food processing, can be expected to combine the advantages of both freezing and dehydration. It is, however, a comparatively new process and as yet undeveloped in food technology. The aim of quick freezing, and also of dehydration, is to arrest all forms of deterioration to which biological material is inherently susceptible and thereby retain the characteristic properties of the foodstuff.

Quick-freezing achieves this by a rapid reduction of temperature to a level at which changes due to chemical and enzymatic activity are so slowed down as to be negligible and at which the growth of microorganisms ceases. Temperatures for freezing may be as low as −40°F. and, for storage, between 14° and −20°F., and the size and disposition of the ice crystals must not impair the structure of the tissue.

The same ends are sought in dehydration through the removal of water, although the resultant product usually needs protective packing to keep it dry. The temperature for storing dry products is not so critical, but they may have to be specially prepared if they are to be stored at 90° to 100°F. for a long time. The reduction in weight on drying depends on the foodstuff and may vary from 75% for eggs to 90% for cabbage.

For freeze-drying of foods to be worthwhile, the product must be superior to that obtained by either freezing or dehydration alone, and theoretically this should be possible. Obviously, if the material to be frozen-dried is prefrozen by any of the recognized methods of quick-freezing, it will start at the same level of quality as a quick-frozen food

* This review was written as part of the program of the Food Investigation Organization of the Department of Scientific and Industrial Research.

and the subsequent drying operation is unlikely to improve its initial quality. If, however, freezing occurs in the drier by the evaporation of water at a low pressure, it will be much more rapid than under atmospheric pressure, particularly with permeable tissues. For example, reducing the pressure to 0.77 mm. Hg, which is well within the range and capacity of the pumping systems used in freeze-drying plants, will, by itself, lower the temperature to 4°F. (−20°C.). In continuously operating plants handling pastes and fluids which can readily be introduced into the evacuated chamber, freezing can be extremely rapid; but in a batchwise operation there must be a time lag before freezing commences, depending on the rate at which the chamber is exhausted. Even so, however, the rate of freezing is likely to be rapid and the size and distribution of ice crystals, although differing in different frozen tissues, is therefore generally more uniform in vacuum-frozen material than in similar material quick-frozen by the usual methods.

An extreme example is the ultrarapid freezing achieved when tissues intended for histological examination are immersed in *iso*pentane at the temperature of liquid nitrogen. Such a method is both impracticable and unnecessary, however, in the freezing of foodstuffs, and the small ice crystals so obtained could be prevented from enlarging only by storing at very low temperatures.

Apart from the size and disposition of the ice crystals, we have to consider chemical changes which may occur while the material is within a certain critical range of temperature. For example, the quality of frozen fish is materially affected by differences in the length of time taken for its temperature to fall from −1° to −5°C., i.e., in the region of the plateau on the cooling curve (Food Investigation Leaflet No. 11) during which time a considerable portion of the water is frozen out. The same phenomena occur in the freezing of meat and poultry, but the effects are not significant with the latter since the thawed tissue does not "drip."

A factor which influences the rate of drying is that, during freezing, there is a separating out of water within the tissues. When ice crystals are formed outside the cells, which usually occurs, drying is likely to be facilitated because the path for the escape of vapor is more free.

The conditions under which the foodstuff is frozen prior to freeze-drying will influence the degree of rehydration of which the dehydrated product is capable. The ease and speed of rehydration, being one of the outstanding features of frozen-dried foods, is especially marked with powders that are readily wettable and with porous tissues which permit entry of liquid water. Most dehydrated plant tissues, on soaking, do not take up as much water as was removed during dehydration, since the cells lose the ability to form and retain a vacuole;* those approaching nearest to their original size and water content are those that have their cells filled with starch which swells on hydration.

The temperature at which the foodstuff is dried will affect both the rate of drying and the structure of the dehydrated product. True freeze-drying is achieved only at temperatures below the cryohydric (eutectic) temperature of the soluble constituents. When liquids are dried at temperatures above their cryohydric temperature, ice first evaporates until only the liquid phase remains, and, on further drying, foam formation occurs with a considerable increase in volume. Cryohydrates are formed by fruit juices at about −25°C. (Heiss and Schachinger, 1951) and by solutes from coffee at about −10°C. (Gane, 1946). With meat, all the water is frozen at −37.5°C. (Moran, 1934), although a lower temperature has been postulated (Heiss, 1933). Tests show that tissues need not be dried below the cryohydric temperature since very little shrinkage occurs, and it was found that peas could be dried and a satisfactory product obtained at a relatively high temperature (Ede, 1949). Space in a vacuum drier should be minimal because the vessels are costly to produce and exhaustion of unnecessary space needs to be avoided.

The bulk density of frozen-dried products is necessarily low, and consequently frozen-dried tissues are very fragile, needing careful handling and special packing if they are to retain their shape and appearance. Containers used for packing must be hermetically sealed both to prevent ingress of water vapor and to retain the chemically inert atmosphere, usually nitrogen, which is necessary to prevent adverse oxidative reactions (Barker *et al.*, 1946).

Freeze-drying is expensive, requiring costly equipment for a relatively low output in comparison with other methods; hence its applications in the dehydration of foods may be limited. Its special merits are that it dehydrates any foodstuffs with little or no change in the chemical constituents, reduces the water content to lower values than are normally attained by other means, and produces no effects due to overheating or cooking. Foods ordinarily preferred and consumed in the raw state, such as juices, milk, and fruits, would need to be reconstituted with cold water to obtain a satisfactory product. Liquids can be so reconstituted, but freeze-drying of berries and other fruits, and vegetable tissues generally, is not so satisfactory because soluble constituents tend to leach out on soaking and the tissues do not completely regain their original plumpness and firmness. Preconcentration of liquids prior to freeze-drying makes for considerably higher outputs from the drier, and this principle has been adopted commercially (Burton, 1947).

* Having no osmotic pressure and no turgor pressure.

When fluid and even solid foodstuffs are frozen-dried, there may be a loss of the volatile constituents, depending on their properties, such as vapor pressure and their ability to be adsorbed as the material dries, and on characteristics of the drying plant, such as the temperature difference between the evaporating and condensing surfaces, the duration of drying, and the volume of vapor pumped from the chamber during the drying period. Materials containing bicarbonates lose carbon dioxide during freeze-drying; hence the pH of reconstituted dried whole egg, both spray-dried and frozen-dried, may be high compared with that of fresh whole egg (Brooks and Hawthorne, 1943).

Drying with heated air (Food Investigation Special Report No. 53; Gane, 1950) does not usually reduce the water content below a value in equilibrium with 30% relative humidity unless the air is specially dried—as with bin-finishers. Even with "in-can" desiccants (Howard, 1945), further drying proceeds rather slowly, presumably owing to the denseness of the dried tissue and the resultant low rate of diffusion of the water vapor. Frozen-dried tissues, being porous, show relatively little resistance to the movement and escape of water and, under the special conditions in the drier, drying can be prolonged until the moisture content is in equilibrium with the pressure of water vapor at the temperature of the condenser. Although such extremes of dryness are necessary for pharmaceutical products and blood serum, they are not needed for foodstuffs, and the practical minimum water content has yet to be determined for most of the dried foods, particularly under adverse storage conditions, e.g., at tropical temperatures.

## II. FREEZE-DRYING EQUIPMENT

While considerable effort has been expended on the design and performance of plants for the dehydration of pharmaceutical preparations, the problems associated with the drying of foodstuffs have not been examined in great detail. Equipment built for the preparation of frozen-dried foods (Meyer and Stoltz, 1946; Gane, 1951) in laboratories cannot be considered as a prototype for a large-scale plant; they have merely served the purpose of producing products for assay. Pilot plants, built by the specialist firms, have been used to define the most efficient means of vacuum drying (e.g., Hellier, 1949). No doubt a bulk-drying plant as used for pharmaceutical preparations (Flosdorf, 1949) could also be used for foodstuffs and, since these do not need stringent aseptic conditions and very low temperatures, the running costs would be lower; some simplification of design would also be feasible, and this would reduce the capital outlay.

In a freeze-drying plant, apart from the vacuum vessels, there are three major features, namely the drying stages, the means of supplying heat to them, and the method of removing or condensing water vapor. The most compact arrangement is one in which the material is dried on trays in a cabinet with hollow shelves which can be heated, or cooled, by the circulation of fluid. The foodstuffs may be either prefrozen or frozen on the trays in the drier; in the latter case the fluid circulated through the shelves needs to be at a lower temperature during freezing than during drying. Frothing can be serious during evacuation of the cabinet while the material is being frozen, and any advantage of an increase in the rate of freezing due to rapid evaporation may be negatived by the disadvantages due to foaming, leading to splashing and overflow from the trays. *In vacuo,* heat transfer from the shelves to the trays is by conduction and radiation; the former is desirable but it is difficult to ensure that there is good thermal contact between the trays and shelves. As drying proceeds, ice recedes into the center of the mass, being sublimed both from the exposed surface and from the underside adjacent to the heating surface; heat, therefore, has to be transferred through dry material which, unfortunately, acts as a thermal insulator. One method which overcomes the difficulty of conduction through the dry material (McFarlane, 1942) is to freeze the liquid to be dried onto a coil of piping, building up a layer approximately ½ in. thick, and then to place the coil in the drying chamber. By controlling the temperature of the fluid circulated through the coil, with which the frozen layer is in good thermal contact, ice recedes inwards from the exposed surface as drying proceeds. Heat is thus conducted through frozen material and not, as in tray-drying, through the dry material.

The alternative to tray-drying is to use a continuous belt that passes through freezing and drying zones. Although such an arrangement is not so compact as a cabinet tray-drier, it has certain advantages; it permits control of the time spent in the zones and of the thickness of the film and, by irradiation of the exposed surface, it overcomes some of the difficulties of heat transfer through the belt (Schwartz, 1948).

The use of "waste" heat (Kidd, 1941) from the compression stage of the refrigerating machine is not usually adopted in freeze-drying, although it is a vital part of the low-temperature evaporative process for the concentration of orange juice (Anon. 1949; Cloud, 1950; Schwartz and Penn, 1948).

The methods to be adopted for the removal of water vapor depend on the size of the plant and the pressures involved. In laboratory units, a desiccant, phosphorus pentoxide or anhydrous calcium sulfate, is very convenient. In larger equipment, working at pressures of 0.1 to 4 mm. Hg, a refrigerated brine (either a solution of lithium chloride or calcium chloride) is used to absorb the water vapor, and the diluted brine is concentrated externally, cooled, and returned to the drier. The efficiency of a liquid absorber is maintained at any desired value by varying the concentration and temperature of the brine and, by spraying the brine, a large and continually renewed surface is available for absorption. Rigid condensing surfaces, whether pipes or plates, become less efficient as the thickness of the ice deposit increases, the rate of loss of efficiency depending on the form and density of the ice mass. In batchwise operations the condensers can be defrosted during the unloading and recharging of the cabinets and, in systems with multiple cabinets and condensers, they may be taken out of the circuit as required. Where one condenser serves several cabinets it must be kept in operation, and a very ingenious method has been devised (Morse, 1947) whereby the ice is deposited on the inside of a refrigerated cylinder and is removed mechanically by rotating scrapers. Although liquid absorbers offer some mechanical advantages over "dry" condensing systems, they are not necessarily more efficient thermally (Plank, 1947).

## III. GENERAL CONCLUSIONS

The high water content and relative cheapness of most foodstuffs preclude the economic use of freeze-drying as a means of dehydration, except in those cases where priority and special needs would justify it, e.g., the preparation of powdered orange juice for the United States Armed Forces.

The major factor retarding the rate of drying is the low thermal conductivity of the dry tissue. Increasing the rate of heat transfer in the drying material by resistance or dielectric heating has only limited application.

Speeding up the process to such an extent that it ceases to be freeze-drying (Flosdorf, 1946) is hardly a solution, since some of the special features of the process are lost. Similarly, subdividing tissues, as by chopping vegetables and grinding meat to facilitate drying, limits the products to use in soup, stews, and the like. Actually, the process is capable of drying pieces of a size suitable for normal dishes and should be used in this way.

It may be that the process could better be used as one stage in the dehydration process, either as a preliminary treatment to render tissue porous so that subsequent drying by heated air could proceed rapidly, or, alternatively, as a final stage to achieve the required water content safely.

## REFERENCES

Anon. 1949. Frozen Concentrated Citrus Juice Contributes New Know-How. *Food Inds.* **21**, 905.

Barker, J., Gane, R., and Mapson, L. W. 1946. The Quality of Green Peas Dried in the Frozen State. *Food Manuf.* **21,** 345–348.

Brooks, J., and Hawthorne, J. R. 1943. Dried Egg. V. The pH of Reconstituted Dried Egg. *J. Soc. Chem. Ind. (London)* **62,** 181–185.

Burton, L. V. 1947. High Vacuum Techniques Utilized for Drying Orange Juice. *Food Inds.* **19,** 617–622.

Cloud, H. R. 1950. Advances in Evaporation Freezing Made by Minute-Maid Plant. *Food Inds.* **22,** 1891–1894.

Ede, A. J. 1949. The Low-Temperature Vacuum Drying Process as Applied to Green Peas. Part II. *J. Soc. Chem. Ind. (London)* **68,** 336–340.

Flosdorf, E. W. 1946. Process and Product of Dehydrating Foodstuffs. U. S. Pat. 2,400,748.

Flosdorf, E. W. 1949. *Freeze-Drying.* Reinhold Publishing Corp., New York.

Food Investigation Leaflet No. 11. 1950. *The Freezing and Cold-Storage of Fish.* H. M. Stationery Office, London.

Food Investigation Special Report No. 53. 1948. *The Physics of Drying in Heated Air with Particular Reference to Fruit and Vegetables.* H. M. Stationery Office, London.

Gane, R. 1946. The Concentration of Coffee Extracts by Freezing. *Food Manuf.* **21,** 519–524.

Gane, R. 1950. The Water Relations of Some Dried Fruits, Vegetables and Plant Products. *J. Sci. Food Agr.* **2,** 42–46.

Gane, R. 1951. Freeze-Drying of Foodstuffs, in *Freezing and Drying.* Edited by R. J. C. Harris. The Institute of Biology, London. Pp. 31–39.

Heiss, R. 1933. Untersuchungen über den Kältebedarf und die angefrorenen Wassermengen beim schnellen und beim langsamen Gefrieren von Lebensmitteln. *Z. ges. Kälte-Ind.* **40,** 97–104.

Heiss, R., and Schachinger, L. 1951. Fundamentals of Freeze-Concentration of Liquids. *Food Technol.* **5,** 211–218.

Hellier, E. G. 1949. High Vac Belt Dryer Improves Product, Cuts Costs. *Food Inds.* **21,** 1191–1193.

Howard, L. B. 1945. Desiccants Improve Dry Packs. *Food Packer* **26,** No. **4,** 31.

Kidd, F. 1941. Improvements in and Relating to the Low Temperature Treatment for the Preservation of Perishable Foods and Other Materials. Brit. Pat. 539,477.

McFarlane, A. S. 1942–3. The Drying of Foodstuffs in the Frozen State. *Proc. Brit. Assoc. Refrig.* **39,** 69–78.

Meyer, J. C., and Stoltz, E. 1946. The Freeze-Drying of Foods—A Look into the Future. *Farm Research* **12,** Farm Research Reprint No. 61. New York State Agricultural Experiment Station, Geneva, N.Y.

Moran, T. 1934. The Eutectic of Muscle. *Rept. Food Invest. Board,* H. M. Stationery Office, London.

Morse, R. S. 1947. High Vacuum Technology. *Ind. Eng. Chem.* **39,** 1064.

Plank, R. 1947. Die Gefriertrocknung. *Angew. Chem.* **19B,** 36–38.

Schwartz, H. W. 1948. Dehydration of Heat-Sensitive Materials. *Ind. Eng. Chem.* **40,** 2028–2033.

Schwartz, H. W., and Penn, F. E. 1948. Production of Orange Juice Concentrate and Powder. *Ind. Eng. Chem.* **40,** 938–944.

CHAPTER 8

# The Preservation of Media for the Culture of Bacteria and Tissues

DUNCAN C. HETHERINGTON

*Duke University Medical School, Durham, North Carolina*



## I. INTRODUCTION

It will be possible to delete the word "bacteria" almost immediately from the discussion of frozen-dried media. Careful inquiry into and a wide search of the literature has been unrewarded by any reference to drying by sublimation from the frozen state as a means of preserving media for the cultivation of bacteria. Commercial houses have for many years been purveying dehydrated media and organic salt mixtures from which nutrient broths could be prepared quite simply for growing countless strains of microorganisms. There is no indication that during the desiccation freezing temperatures were employed. On rare occasions frozen-dried extracts, rich in coenzymes and glutamine, have been prepared. These are added to broths or to other media for enrichment in order to coax certain exacting strains of gonococci and *Bact. influenzae* to proliferate (personal communication*). Lately, however, most of these accelerators are prepared more economically in the fluid state. Micro-

* The author wishes to express his appreciation to Dr. C. W. Christensen of the Difco Laboratories for furnishing information about some of the frozen-dried preparations.

organisms, on the whole, have never been so demanding of their media as have cultured cells.

Other chapters in this book deal with the historical aspects of freeze-drying, details of techniques and the application of these to the preservation of microorganisms, proteins, antibiotics, vaccines, and food.

The stability of frozen-dried materials, particularly when sealed *in vacuo* in all-glass containers, is remarkable. Guinea pig complement, which is rated as one of the most notoriously delicate of biological substances, has retained almost full activity after 5 years in storage (Flosdorf *et al.*, 1945). The effect of freeze-drying upon the chemical constitution of the dried materials has been most fully investigated on proteins. Correctly processed to an optimum degree of dryness where the moisture content is 0.05% or less, most proteins will remain unaltered for years. Fats, as such, are not altered by the actual process of freezing and subsequent drying, but they may undergo slow oxidation and become rancid if not stored in complete absence of oxygen (Flosdorf, 1949).

Lipoproteins may undergo some denaturation during processing (Cohn, 1945), which alters their solubility during reconstitution; they tend to dissolve very slowly and may produce cloudy solutions. On the other hand, an occasional protein—gelatin, for example, which dissolves only slowly and poorly without the application of heat—will, when frozen-dried from a solution, dissolve immediately when water is added to the dried powder. Antigenic properties of proteins have remained unchanged for long periods of time; enzymes, hormones, and vitamins have been maintained unimpaired without any loss of their properties either during freeze-drying or following subsequent long storage (Flosdorf, 1949).

## II. FROZEN-DRIED TISSUE CULTURE MEDIA

As long ago as 1936, Gey and Gey, in one of their papers dealing with the maintenance of animal cells in continuous culture, made the first reference to the use of "lyophilized" media in tissue culture. Their experience with the materials which they had processed was apparently not sufficiently satisfactory to warrant their continued preparation. Hetherington and Craig (1939, 1940) and Hetherington (1944), who had been attempting to evaluate the effects of certain substances upon the growth of chick heart explants *in vitro*, were impressed with the variability from time to time of the responses of the experimental and control cultures alike, effects which could be accredited to the batch variations in the media being used, although a constant routine was followed in their preparation. They experimented in the production of frozen-dried embryo extract, chicken plasma, and serum, and found the preparations to be quite satisfactory from most standpoints and particularly useful in comparative types of experiment. Sufficient material could be prepared so that an entire set of experiments could be executed with the same basic media. As well as stabilizing the media, considerable time was liberated which would otherwise have been taken up in the continuous and repetitive preparation of fresh stocks. This time factor is of considerable value in small and understaffed laboratories: the less time spent in routine, the more time may be spent upon investigations.

There is practically no literature available dealing only with tissue culture media dried from the frozen state. Accidentally one discovers in reading a report of some experiments that the authors used, for one purpose or another, frozen-dried media or some special ingredient so prepared—an incident not to be deduced from the title of the report. Peacock and Shukoff (1940) mention in a very brief notice that desiccated chick embryos kept under refrigeration at 4°C. could be used satisfactorily for making embryo extract. Shukoff (1942) further indicated that embryo extract made from these desiccated embryos, which had been stored in a refrigerator for a period of 2½ years, produced growth stimulation of tissues in culture comparing favorably with that occurring in control cultures planted with extracts from fresh embryos. No mention was made, however, of the mode of desiccation employed. Davidson and Waymouth (1945) and Waymouth and Davidson (1945) prepared defatted tissue extracts (*v.* Hewitt, 1927) and plasma for some special studies on nucleoproteins of fibroblasts in culture. They stated that defatted extracts were further improved by being dried from the frozen state. A method for the preparation of sterile proteins in the "lyophilized" state has been reported by Railton *et al.* (1941). Although these proteins were not used in connection with the preparation of media, the technique might be applicable in some instances.

## III. COMMERCIAL PRODUCTION OF MEDIA

One of the first projects of the Tissue Culture Association (previously the Tissue Culture Commission, 1946–1949) was to investigate the kinds of media needed by tissue culture workers and to consider the possibility of having these prepared at some central laboratory for later distribution. A questionnaire to tissue "culturists" brought requests for chicken plasma, embryo extract, human placental cord serum, and horse serum as the media most commonly used apart from the salines and ultrafiltrates. With the cooperation of the Difco Laboratories of Detroit, Michigan, and the "Testing Laboratory," aided by generous grants and directed through the Tissue Culture Association, methods were worked out for the commercial production of frozen-dried chicken plasma, human placental cord serum, horse serum, chick embryo extract, and beef embryo extract. These products are available and have been found to be satisfactory for use in the growth of tissues and cells by all the usual methods.

There is at the present time no way by which one may determine the extent to which "lyophilized" media are being employed by laboratories where the tissue culture technique is being utilized for the elucidation of various problems. Some small laboratories, by report, rely exclusively upon commercially prepared media and seem to be quite satisfied with them. Still others have voiced various complaints about one or another of the products. The most persistent complaint (apart from the one relating to the general high cost of the materials) is that of the delayed clotting time of the reconstituted plasma. This will be mentioned again later. Some of the earlier complaints were real and led to alterations in the processing of the medium in question such that the final product was much more satisfactory. Slight modifications of the reconstituting fluids have resulted in lowering the pH to optimum levels, and in the case of reconstituted plasma the delayed clotting time has been largely corrected.

The production of media in large quantities commercially has introduced alterations in the processing differing from the methods first devised by Hetherington and Craig (1939, 1940). The media made by Difco, after careful, aseptic preparation, are placed in their final containers before freeze-drying. The vials are then cooled slowly to 0°C. and the contents frozen rapidly to −50°C. by Dry Ice. They are then placed in the desiccators which are evacuated to pressures between 10 and 300 microns Hg for 24 hours. During the first part of the drying the pressure is 300 microns, and as drying progresses it diminishes to 10 microns. After desiccation is completed, the vacuum is released aseptically with dry air, and the vials are suitably rubber-stoppered and protected by metal covers and caps. All products are stored at −10°C. until supplied on order.

### 1. *Embryo Extracts*

a. Chick

An embryo extract is prepared from selected 11-day-old chick embryos from incubated eggs of healthy and virus-free stocks of birds. The embryos are ground in all-glass homogenizers kept sufficiently well chilled to avoid a rise in temperature of the homogenate. The pulp is centrifuged, and the supernatant bottled in measured quantities for drying. This material constitutes a pure embryo extract or juice which may be reconstituted to original volume with sterile, triple-distilled water to produce a 100% embryo extract. This in turn may be further diluted to any concentration desired by adding the requisite amounts of one of the chosen balanced salines.

b. Beef

A beef embryo extract is also prepared in a similar manner and in similar concentrations. The laboratory procedure for its production before freeze-drying has been outlined by the Geys (1936). In commercial production, embryos of 60 to 90 days of age from disease-free cows constitute the source of this growth-promoting stimulant.

### 2. *Embryo Powders*

In addition to 100% embryo extracts, frozen-dried chick and beef embryo powders have been prepared in the "lyophile" state. Embryo extracts of any desired strength may be made by adding to a unit of powder the correct amount of a balanced saline. After the powder has steeped for a suitable length of time, the solution is centrifuged at 2500 to 3000 r.p.m. to sediment all the particulate matter. The supernatant may be stored in the refrigerator until needed, but storage should not exceed a week since the extract undergoes rather rapid loss of growth-promoting power if allowed to stand for longer periods.

### 3. *Plasma*

Chicken plasma is prepared and packaged as a frozen-dried product, usually in 5-ml. ampoules. Blood is drawn aseptically by the most convenient method from disease-free cockerels 4 to 8 months of age. The birds have been fasted for 24 hours but allowed free access to water before being bled. Only enough heparin is added to stabilize the plasma during the numerous stages of processing. The pooled plasma, freed of cells, is flasked and dried from the frozen state. The product may be reconstituted in several ways. The proper amount of sterile, triple-distilled water is added, and the contents of the flask or vial slowly rotated to fold in the dry powder. About half an hour is required to complete solution. The reconstituted plasma is found to be alkaline owing to the removal of carbon dioxide during the vacuum drying, but it may be brought to the proper pH by transferring the liquid to a lightly stoppered sterile tube and allowing the solution to equilibrate slowly in air or more rapidly by placing the tube in an atmosphere of carbon dioxide. Better reconstitution is accomplished with specially prepared water saturated with carbon dioxide. If no other means are at hand, simple blowing of alveolar air through the fluid by way of a sterile cotton-plugged pipette will bring the pH down satisfactorily.

If the pH is not adjusted, the clotting time of the plasma, after addition of the tissue explants and embryo extract, may be unduly prolonged. It has been recommended that the embryo extract used in the clotting of the plasma be reconstituted with a saline containing a moderate quantity of calcium ions. As previously mentioned, most complaints about the frozen-dried culture media centered about the delayed clotting time of the plasmas. This abnormality is probably a result of a summation of several factors.

Unless one takes great care in the bleeding of chickens to prevent the entry of tissue juices into the blood while it is being drawn and, in addition, uses specially prepared and chilled receptacles, the blood will clot rather rapidly. Addition of a small quantity of heparin will stabilize the blood sufficiently to prevent clotting during various manipulations; however, one may easily exceed the minimal amount required to prevent sudden clotting. It has been observed during studies on the freeze-drying of blood plasma for use in the armed forces and the Red Cross and also from analyses of the protein fractions of various products that the clotting mechanisms are often altered. Lipoproteins (Cohn *et al.*, 1946) suffer slight denaturation during freeze-drying, which results in slow and poor solution when the dry powders are being rehydrated. Certain of the thromboplastins are lipoproteins (Cohn *et al.*, 1944; Edsall *et al.*, 1944), and these deteriorate rapidly in plasma stored in the liquid state but much less rapidly in frozen plasma (Taylor *et al.*, 1944).

It is not surprising, therefore, that frozen-dried plasma is slow to clot: the heparin content, the absence of carbon dioxide in sufficient concentration, the slightly denatured lipoproteins, the decrease of thromboplastins, and the rather low calcium content of reconstituting salines—all these factors, any one of which could militate against normal clotting times, combined constitute an insult. On occasion this delayed ability of the plasma to form a clot can be beneficial, particularly during planting of cultures in roller tubes, because it allows the operator to orient the tissue fragments before they become too tightly fastened to the tube wall.

### 4. *Sera*

#### a. Human Placental Cord Serum

This constituent of culture media is often used in feeding solutions for the maintenance of cultures in continuous growth. A laboratory method for the collection of the serum has been described by the Geys (1936); and a method for its freeze-drying by Hetherington (1944). Commercially the product is prepared from the pooled plasma extracted from placentas of 25 or more Wasserman-negative women. Asepsis is maintained in so far as possible throughout all the procedures of collection of the blood, its clotting and extrusion of the serum, and the removal of the cells. The final serum, which should not show any evidence of hemolysis, is sterilized by passage through an ultra-fine, sintered, Pyrex-glass filter before drying from the frozen state.

b. Horse Serum

This is more easily obtained and more widely used in tissue culture work than the human cord serum. It has been prepared commercially from the blood of fasted, healthy, lean geldings and dried by vacuum sublimation observing the same aseptic precautions as in the preparation of human cord serum.

### 5. *Packaging and Storage of Frozen-Dried Products*

The various methods of final packaging of frozen-dried products and the effects of temperature and humidity upon the contents have been discussed by Flosdorf (1949) and elsewhere in this volume. The best insurance against deterioration of correctly frozen-dried materials is to seal them *in vacuo* in (preferably) all-Pyrex-glass containers. So sealed, high humidity of the storage atmosphere cannot affect the contents as it will do in time if the processed flasks are plugged by rubber stoppers or closed by metal clamped rubber tubing, even though these are additionally protected by plastic coatings. The lipid contents of material sealed *in vacuo* are not prone to become rancid, nor are the proteins so liable to deterioration even when the external temperature is as high as 48°C.

At the present time only the most commonly used media are being prepared commercially by freeze-drying and are currently packaged in small vials or ampoules sealed with rubber stoppers. As greater demand develops for frozen-dried media and the value of the products becomes more widely appreciated, a greater variety of substances will be processed and the currently high cost of production should decrease proportionately.

## REFERENCES

Cohn, E. J. 1945. The Chemical Separation and the Clinical Appraisal of the Components of the Blood. *Medicine* **24,** 333–338.

Cohn, E. J., Oncley, J. L., Strong, L. E., Hughes, W. L., and Armstrong, S. H. 1944. Chemical, Clinical and Immunological Studies on the Products of Human Plasma Fractionation. I. The Characterization of the Protein Fractions of Human Plasma. *J. Clin. Invest.* **23,** 417–432.

Cohn, E. J., Strong, L. E., Hughes, W. L., Mulford, D. J., Ashworth, J. N., Melin, M., and Taylor, H. L. 1946. Preparation and Properties of Serum and Plasma Proteins. IV. A System for the Separation into Fractions of the Protein and Lipoprotein Components of Biological Tissues and Fluids. *J. Am. Chem. Soc.* **68,** 459–475.

Davidson, J. N., and Waymouth, C. 1945. The Nucleoprotein Content of Fibroblasts growing *in Vitro*. 2. The Effect of Tissue Extracts. *Biochem. J.* **39,** 188–199.

Edsall, J. T., Ferry, R. M., and Armstrong, S. H. 1944. Chemical, Clinical and Immunological Studies on the Products of Human Plasma Fractionation. XV. The Proteins Concerned in the Blood Coagulation Mechanism. *J. Clin. Invest.* **23,** 557–565.

Flosdorf, E. W. 1949. *Freeze-Drying*. Reinhold Publishing Corp., New York.

Flosdorf, E. W., Hull, L. W., and Mudd, S. 1945. Drying by Sublimation. *J. Immunol.* **50,** 21–54.

Gey, G. O., and Gey, M. K. 1936. The Maintenance of Human Normal Cells and Tumor Cells in Continuous Culture. I. Preliminary Report: Cultivation of Mesoblastic Tumor and Normal Tissue and Notes on Methods of Cultivation. *Am. J. Cancer* **27,** 45–76.

Hetherington, D. C. 1944. Frozen-Dried Serum as a Medium Constituent for Tissue Cultures. *Proc. Soc. Exptl. Biol. Med.* **57,** 196–197.

Hetherington, D. C., and Craig, J. S. 1939. Effect of Frozen-Dried Plasma and Frozen-Dried Embryo Juice on Tissue Cultures. *Proc. Soc. Exptl. Biol. Med.* **42,** 831–834.

Hetherington, D. C., and Craig, J. S. 1940. Tissue Culture Growth Stimulants from Ground Frozen-Dried Chick Embryos. *Proc. Soc. Exptl. Biol. Med.* **44,** 282–285.

Hewitt, L. F. 1927. Optical Rotatory Power and Dispersion of Proteins. *Biochem. J.* **21,** 216.

Peacock, P. R., and Shukoff, R. I. 1940. Use of Desiccated Chick Embryo in Tissue Culture Technique. *Nature* **146,** 30–31.

Railton, I. R., Cunningham, B., and Kirk, P. L. 1941. The Preparation of Sterile Proteins in the "Lyophile" State. *Science* **94,** 469–470.

Shukoff, R. I. 1942. Use of Desiccated Chick Embryo in Tissue Culture Technique. *Nature* **150,** 461.

Taylor, F. H. L., Lonzer, E. L., Davidson, C. S., Tagnon, H. J., and Newhouser, L. R. 1944. Preservation of Normal Human Plasma in the Liquid State. II. Comparative *in vitro* Studies on the Physiologic Activity of Labile Constituents of Liquid and Frozen Plasma. *J. Clin. Invest.* **23,** 351–356.

Waymouth, C., and Davidson, J. N. 1945. A Simplified Plasma Coagulum for Tissue Culture. *Biochem. J.* **39,** xxii–xxiii.

CHAPTER 9

# The Preservation of Viruses

R. J. C. HARRIS

*Research Fellow, British Empire Cancer Campaign, Institute of Cancer Research, London, England*



## I. INTRODUCTION

It has been known for more than fifty years that vaccinal pulp could be preserved in a virulent state by drying *in vacuo* at room temperature over calcium chloride or sulfuric acid (*v.* Fasquelle and Barbier, 1950). In 1909 Shackell published the first clearly recorded use of vacuum sublimation for the drying of biological material. In this process the material was first frozen in a salt-ice mixture and then dried in a desiccator over sulfuric acid. Complement, antisera, rabies virus, and blood were dried in this way. Two years later Harris and Shackell (1911) reported the preservation of rabies virus in desiccates of rabid brain by the same method.

A specimen of bovine origin, prepared in 1916 and stored at room temperature, was still virulent when reconstituted thirty years later (Fasquelle and Barbier, 1950).

The overall procedure for drying and preserving viruses from the frozen state may be divided into four major steps.

1. Preparation of a suitable suspension.
2. Freezing of the suspension.
3. Withdrawal of the ice by sublimation.
4. Storage of the dry product.

## II. OPTIMUM SUSPENDING MEDIA FOR VIRUSES

It is well known that viruses become increasingly unstable in suspensions with decreasing protein content, e.g., yellow fever virus (Bauer and Pickels, 1940). For this reason dilutions are usually made in a serum- or broth-containing medium. Adams (1948) has shown that in the *E. coli* phage series $T_1$–$T_7$ the increased inactivation with increased dilution is an interface phenomenon (*v.a.* Kriss and Roukina, 1948). Dilute, buffered saline suspensions of $T_7$ phage were totally inactivated at 26°C. by gentle shaking for 35 minutes. In the absence of a gas phase in the shaking vessel, inactivation was negligible. Adams showed that as little as $0.01\gamma$ per milliliter of gelatin had some protective action, and the duration of the protection was found to be a function of the gelatin concentration, since the added protein was "denatured" by the shaking. Gum arabic and serum albumin had a similar action to that of gelatin but only in higher concentrations. It would appear probable, therefore, that one action at least of these protein adjuvants which appear to protect viruses in dilute suspensions is to "compete" with virus for the gas-liquid interface at which protein denaturation and virus destruction take place. The greater the success of this protein "competitor," the more stable will be the virus suspension. It follows, too, that the smaller viruses are inactivated more rapidly than the larger, and that the rate of inactivation is directly proportional to temperature, since thermal forces are responsible for bringing the virus particles to the interfaces. There is some evidence in support of these predictions.

Anderson (1944) discovered that dilution with sterile skim milk stabilized large organisms such as *R. prowazeki*, and infectivity was retained for some 48 hours. Other protein-containing media such as egg yolk or 10% guinea pig serum in Tyrode's solution were better diluents than Tyrode's solution or water alone. Bovarnick *et al.* (1950) recommended a diluent containing 0.1 to 1.0% bovine or human serum albumin, 0.218 *M* sucrose, 0.005 *M* glutamate, and a ratio of $K^+$ to $Na^+ > 1$ for the optimum preservation between 0°C. and room temperature of *R. prowazeki*, *R. tsutsugamuschi* (*orientalis*), and *Dermacentroxemus rickettsi*. The interesting suggestion was made that the glutamate had a stabilizing action by virtue of being a substrate for the organism.

Animal and human sera have been used as diluents and suspending media for a large number of different viruses, namely, yellow fever (Bauer and Mahoffy, 1930), St. Louis encephalitis (Brodie, 1935; Cook and Hudson, 1937), herpes simplex (Zinsser and Tang, 1929), and vaccinia (Goodpasture and Buddingh, 1936).

The presence of non-specific virus-inactivating substances in animal and human sera has led to the use of other media such as broth, gelatin (Behrens and Ferguson, 1935), skim milk (Duffy and Stanley, 1945), and bovine plasma albumin in buffered saline (Dick and Taylor, 1949). Dick and Taylor used an agitative method (McLimans, 1947) for producing inactivation of yellow fever and influenza viruses. Normal monkey and horse sera (10%) had good preservative properties under these conditions, but gum arabic (5%) and gelatin (1%) were not so good as bovine plasma albumin (0.2%).

## III. STABILITY OF VIRUSES TO FREEZING

Suspensions of virus-infected tissues or body fluids may generally be preserved by freezing to temperatures below −25°C. Below this temperature there is not likely to be an interstitial water phase, and the virus material will, in effect, be "dry." Thus Horsfall (1940) successfully stored human influenzal throat washings, PR8 influenza virus, and mouse pneumonitis and canine distemper viruses at −76°C., according to the procedure described for influenza-infected mouse lung and for yellow fever virus by Turner (Turner, 1938; Turner and Fleming, 1939). Burmester (1952) preserved crude extracts of fowl lymphoma tissue for over a year at this temperature. Higher storage temperatures, readily provided by mechanical refrigerators, of −20° to −25°C. have been found to be satisfactory for the preservation of unpurified suspensions of a number of different viruses, including lymphogranuloma venereum (Lépine *et al.*, 1948), Ntaya (Smithburn and Haddow, 1951), yellow fever, poliomyelitis, and Japanese B encephalitis (Melnick, 1946). Scherp *et al.* (1938) stored influenzal mouse lungs at −10°C. In general, the lower the temperature of storage, the better is the preservation. Rivers (1927) studied the resistance of a variety of biological materials, from bacteria to enzymes, to rapid freezing to −185°C., followed by rapid thawing to 16° to 18°C. In concentrated but unpurified suspensions, vaccinia, herpes, and phage were surprisingly resistant to this drastic procedure. It is interesting to note, however, that more dilute suspensions of the same viruses were less resistant and withstood fewer freezing-thawing cycles.

In the last few years more strictly quantitative assessments of the effects of freezing on viruses in different dilutions in different suspending media have been made. Olitsky *et al.* (1949) reported that 10% mouse brain suspensions of a number of neurotropic viruses (Eastern, Western, Russian, Far East, and Japanese B encephalitis, and Lansing and MEF poliomyelitis) in 1:1 normal rabbit serum:saline retained almost full infectivity for 9 months at −25°C. Influenza strains PR8A and Lee B and mumps virus (as 10% suspensions of infected allantoic fluid in 9:1

normal horse serum: saline) showed adequate but incomplete retention of infectivity under similar conditions, but, in every case, the fluid titers were greater than those in which *undiluted* infected allantoic fluids were frozen. Subsequently Olitsky and his colleagues (1950) found that 0.2% serum albumin or 2% bovine plasma albumin in buffered saline were satisfactory diluents for a very large number of neurotropic viruses stored between −20° and −25°C. for hemagglutination studies. Speck *et al.* (1951) studied the preservation of egg-adapted herpes simplex in different media at −70° and at −20°C. In animal tissues this virus is very stable, but in infected amniotic and allantoic fluids it becomes relatively unstable. At −70°C., over a period of 7 to 8 months, 10% suspensions were best preserved in skim milk or egg yolk. At −20°C., in the same media, adequate titers were retained to 4 months. At either temperature, salt-containing media alone were most unsuitable. The same virus, and also meningopneumonitis virus, was investigated by Allen *et al.* (1952), both for stability at −70° and −25°C., and also at +4°C. Similar results were obtained. For herpes simplex, 20% suspensions of infected chorioallantoic membranes could be preserved for 4 months at −70°C. in homologous yolk or allantoic fluid, or in skim milk or 10% normal rabbit serum. At −20°C. the normal rabbit serum was not so effective, and at +4°C. only yolk and skim milk were satisfactory. Meningopneumonitis virus showed the same properties, but a glutamate medium similar to that described by Bovarnick *et al.* (1950) was also useful at the subzero temperatures.

From a consideration of the data concerning dilution media which afford good protection against freezing, it would not appear to be too difficult to select a medium in which a particular virus could be suspended, frozen, and then the ice sublimed, with the retention of almost complete infectivity.

In the apparatus for freeze-drying in which the virus samples are "snap-frozen" by evaporation, the freezing point of the suspending medium will be a factor in successful drying and the medium may not be so important where the samples are rapidly shell-frozen before drying is started. There are, indeed, a number of problems involving the drying process which are over and above those involved in dilution and in freezing. It should not be assumed, therefore, that if a virus can be frozen in a particular medium then it can also be frozen-dried in the same medium.

## IV. DRYING FROZEN VIRUS SUSPENSIONS BY VACUUM SUBLIMATION

It has already been stated that virus-infected tissues and body fluids may be frozen to −25°C. or less with adequate preservation of virus activity. The advantages of drying such materials under these conditions are purely those of convenience of final handling, since it is easier to store material at 0° to +4°C. than at −25° to −75°C. In 1929 Sawyer *et al.* dried yellow fever virus in infected blood or liver, and since that time the same process has been widely employed for swine influenza (Shope, 1931), Rift Valley fever (Kitchen, 1934), mumps (Johnson and Goodpasture, 1934), influenza (Scherp *et al.*, 1938), filterable tumors (Knox, 1939; Hoffstadt and Tripi, 1946), lymphocytic choriomeningitis and St. Louis encephalitis (Wooley, 1939), measles (Hurst and Cooke, 1941), hog cholera (Munce and Reichel, 1943), sandfly fever (Sabin and Paul, 1944), lymphogranuloma (Durieux, 1944), Mengo encephalomyelitis (Dick, 1948), equine influenza (Jones *et al.*, 1948), Ntaya fever (Smithburn and Haddow, 1951), and fowl lymphomatosis (Burmester, 1952).

Plant viruses are much more stable and easily preserved than their animal counterparts, and it is scarcely surprising, therefore, that there is very little information about their resistance to freezing and drying. Tobacco mosaic virus is infective after drying, but most other plant viruses have been found to be inactivated (but see Dykstra and Du Buy, 1942). Some of the tobacco necrosis viruses withstand drying directly from sap, but purified preparations are inactivated. Tobacco mosaic virus shows marked changes in birefringence and serological behavior, and often when it is dried from the *frozen* state it is rendered largely insoluble and inactive (Bawden, 1950). This behavior may be related to the purely physical properties of the plant viruses, for it has been concluded from x-ray studies of tobacco mosaic virus that there is no water *within* the macromolecule, and yet the rods are normally associated with about their own weight of water, probably as a surrounding layer several molecules thick.

The satisfactory freeze-drying of more purified suspensions of animal and bacterial viruses requires more care than the drying of pieces of infected tissue, etc. Whereas the suspending medium is important, so are other factors, such as the temperature of the drying mass and the rate and extent of water withdrawal. These have been much less studied. So far as the storage of the dried product is concerned, at least two factors must be considered—water content of the product, and storage temperature.

### 1. *Influence of Suspending Medium on Survival*

The ideal medium would have the following properties:

1. Easily separable from the virus after reconstitution [or (3)].
2. "Bulky" but not "frothy" in the dry state.
3. Non-antigenic.

4. Non-hygroscopic, to avoid redistribution of water in the specimen during storage.
5. Lyophilic, for ease of reconstitution.
6. Antioxidant.

A consideration of some of these points led Rivers and Ward (1935) to select gum acacia (final concentration, 2.5%) for the preservation of vaccinia, and Campbell-Renton (1941) subsequently used 10% gum acacia for phage. Topping (1940) found that rickettsiae were difficult to dry in the tissue of origin but that sterile skim milk was a very good suspending medium. This medium was further simplified by Hornibrook (1950), who devised a non-antigenic protein-less solution which was better for yellow fever vaccine than saline or human serum. This solution contained substantially the dialyzable components of skim milk but had the disadvantage of giving a "frothy" product.

Broths or peptone media of one kind or another have been used successfully for many different viruses in a more or less "purified" state. In most cases the results have been expressed in terms of survival or non-survival (Beaudette *et al.*, 1948; Scherp *et al.*, 1938), and rarely quantitatively. However, Collier (1951) found that vaccinia elementary bodies could not be dried satisfactorily from suspension in water, weak buffers, or saline, whereas suspensions in 5% peptone or 10% normal horse serum gave good survival. Moreover, the preservative action of these protein- and peptone-containing media cannot be unrelated to the preservative action for vaccinia of digest broth (Amies, 1934) or of 1% peptone (Behrens and Ferguson, 1935), in the case of virus stored at 37°C. or at 5° to 10°C., respectively. Quantitative studies have also been made by Carr and Harris (1951) on the preservation of Rous sarcoma agent. Whereas crude virus preparations could be dried from suspension in water, more highly purified material could not. Dilute buffer and saline solutions were almost useless, although some agent survived. Dextrose and dextrose-broth mixtures were better than buffers alone, but the broth (Lemco) alone, undiluted, gave complete preservation of purified virus preparations, and these could be stored successfully at 0° to +2°C. for years. Investigation of intact protein media such as egg albumin or gelatin showed that these were difficult to reconstitute without virus aggregation occurring, but guinea pig serum and protein hydrolyzates gave good results (i.e., $>1\%$ recovery). Reducing agents such as BAL or cysteine had no significant protective action when incorporated into otherwise less efficient media.

It was subsequently found (Harris, 1951) that the protective effect of Lemco broth was a function of the polypeptide fraction, since a solution of the peptone component of the broth mixture containing the same concentration of polypeptide nitrogen (1 mg./ml.) had almost exactly the same protective effect. Moreover, inactivation of the Rous agent by freezing in the different media did not fully parallel the inactivation by freeze-drying in the same media. Thus, 5% dextrose is a good medium for preservation of Rous agent by freezing, but poor for preservation by freeze-drying.

These optimal media do not have a universal validity. Scherp *et al.* (1938) failed to influence the recovery of swine influenza virus (in saline extracts or suspensions of infected mouse lungs) by the use of addenda such as normal sera, gum acacia, Difco heart-brain infusion, or gastric mucin. Again, Pollard (1951a, b) found that poliomyelitis virus was exceedingly labile to freeze-drying, losing both infectivity and antigenicity. A variety of protective agents was tested (0.15% saline, 5% normal rabbit serum, 6% glucose, 12.5% lactose, 3% skim milk, 0.5% tryptophan, 5% gastric mucin, and thioglycollate broth). Of these, 0.15% saline gave the best results!

Schade has suggested (Schade and Caroline, 1943; Schade, 1945) that lipid antioxidants such as freshly prepared lecithin are good protective agents. Bacterial lysates were found to lose considerable amounts of phage after freeze-drying (count reduced from $1 \times 10^9$ to $1 \times 10^3$ particles per milliliter). Addition of Difco meat extract before freezing took the final count up to $1 \times 10^5$, and extracts of fresh brain, kidney, or pancreas gave complete protection. On the other hand, polysaccharides, and glycogen in particular, had the reverse effect and reduced the final count below $1 \times 10^3$.

### 2. *Influence of Sublimation Temperature and Rate of Water Removal on Survival*

One of the most satisfactory studies of the physical factors influencing survival of an organism during freeze-drying has been made for *Br. abortus* by Hutton *et al.* (1951). The medium used contained 0.1% Difco tryptose, 0.25% sodium chloride, 2.0% dextrose, 0.5% ascorbic acid (pH 6.5), 0.5% ammonia, and 0.5% thiourea. Survival counts showed that an elevation of the ice-film temperature in the drying material caused a progressive decrease in bacterial survival (50.8 ± 7.6% at −30°C. to 1.4 ± 0.9% at −10°C). Slow drying was preferable to fast, and recovery immediately after drying was correlated with final dryness (2% at 5% $H_2O$, and 80% at 1% $H_2O$). The storage at room temperature was also influenced by dryness, the wetter preparations being the less stable.

No similar study appears to have been made for viruses, and such a variety of home-made and commercial equipment has been used that it becomes very difficult to extract exact information on these aspects of the problem. Bauer and Pickels (1940) discovered that yellow fever virus could not be satisfactorily frozen-dried by the Flosdorf-Mudd procedure, and they suggested that the frozen material had actually thawed at some late stage in the drying cycle, exposing the virus to the deleterious effects of high salt concentration. The reason for thawing was held to be a diminution in evaporative cooling resulting from (a) the lowered vapor pressure of the more concentrated material and (b) the retarded diffusion of water molecules though an increasing thickness of exposed and partially dried preparation. When, in fact, the design of the freeze-drier was modified and the temperature of the drying material kept below the original freezing point throughout the drying cycle, the virus was adequately preserved. External cooling has also been used by Smadel *et al.* (1947) in the freeze-drying of formolized Japanese encephalitis virus (in buffered saline extracts of whole, infected chick embryos) and by Hilleman *et al.* (1951) for undiluted allantoic fluid infected with influenza virus (PR8, FM1, and Lee). Both procedures involved shell-freezing the virus suspensions in a solid carbon dioxide–alcohol bath. It is known that some broths, for example, do not dry well above −30°C., and in some cases it has been necessary to dry at −60°C. to obtain perfect desiccation (Greaves, 1946). It would probably be worth while, therefore, to attempt to dry labile viruses (such as poliomyelitis) at the lowest convenient temperature.

Burruss and Hargett (1947) found no difference in the subsequent heat stability and storage properties of aqueous-base 17-D yellow fever vaccine (Hargett *et al.*, 1943), if 1-ml. samples in ampoules were dried for about 3 hours with an external temperature of 23° to 25°C., or for 20 to 21 hours at −19° to −25°C., rising to 38° to 40°C. at the end of the cycle. Daubney (1951) has also found that for drying small aliquots (0.5 to 1.0 ml.) of living virus vaccines (such as rinderpest, Newcastle disease, and fowl plague) a room temperature of 23° to 25°C. provided sufficient heat for the drying material. When extra heat was put in from the sides of the chamber containing the ampoule carrier, it was important to ensure (a) uniform heat distribution throughout the ampoules and (b) a maximum temperature of 35° to 40°C.

### 3. *Contamination of the Freeze-Drying Equipment*

Cowan (1951) has described cross-infection in the vacuum chamber of a freeze-drier (using the centrifugal spin-freezing of Greaves) where a number of different bacterial cultures were being frozen-dried. It appeared that particles were discharged from individual tubes from a breakup of the surface film by the release of water vapor from frozen particles beneath the surface. It has also been shown (Stein and Rogers, 1950) that bacteria can be cultured from the condensate at the end of a freeze-drying cycle. In this case the apparatus was a modified Flosdorf-Mudd type employing long-necked, unplugged glass ampoules attached to the conventional "pig" and a solid carbon dioxide–alcohol chilled condenser. Five different virus preparations were similarly tested—Newcastle disease, vesicular stomatitis, equine infectious anemia, equine encephalitis, and hog cholera. In every case the frozen-dried products showed retention of virulence, but only Newcastle disease virus could be recovered from its condensate.

Thorne (1953) has also reported the carryover into the condenser of both caprinized and lapinized rinderpest viruses which were being frozen-dried as goat spleen pulp suspensions in wide-mouthed tubes covered with a single-layer lint sterility cap. The apparatus was similar in design to that used by Cowan, and Thorne considered that the major part of the carryover occurred during the evaporative freezing. However, no virus could be recovered from the walls of the desiccator chamber.

## V. STORAGE OF DRIED VIRUS PREPARATIONS

### 1. *Water Content*

It has generally been found that sealed dry preparations may be stored at room temperature for long periods without significant loss in titer, provided that the residual water content is less than 1% and that no redistribution of water has occurred. Daubney (1951) recorded water contents of 0.6 to 1.0% for rinderpest vaccine which had been secondarily dried over phosphorus pentoxide and sealed *in vacuo*. Some batches contained as little as 0.03 to 0.04%. Storage at −20° to −30°C. was necessary to ensure a minimal loss of titer over long periods (up to 27 months) for some of the more labile viruses. Scott and Brotherston (1952) claimed that lapinized rinderpest vaccines (final water contents 1.36%, 0.58%) retained "potency" at +4°C. for at least 3 months. Smadel *et al.* (1947) quoted residual water values of 0.15% to 1.46% (average 0.62%) for their Japanese encephalitis vaccine. This material retained "potency" for over 2 months at +5°C. The influenza antigens prepared by Hilleman *et al.* (1951) in the same way (primary drying only) contained between 0.21 and 1.68% water but could not be safely stored if the content was >0.9%.

### 2. *Storage Temperature*

Burruss and Hargett (1947) found that the potency of their yellow fever vaccine could be maintained at the required level for at least three years when the desiccated preparations were stored at −9° to −32°C. All the samples could be used (i.e., sufficient virus for immunization per routine dose) after 8 weeks at 37°C., and virus was still *detectable* after two years at this temperature. Lowering the storage temperature does, of course, minimize the possibility of water redistribution within the sample. This has been shown to occur in some frozen-dried materials, especially those such as apple juice or milk, which contain sugars (Gane, 1951). It has been suggested that one of the significant properties of these optimal suspending media may be that of holding an optimal amount of water in the sample and keeping it in the right places. It would appear to be desirable, in any event, to store frozen-dried virus preparations at the lowest practicable temperature.

## VI. GENERAL CONSIDERATIONS

It is frequently quite simple to preserve viruses in infected fluids (e.g., allantoic) or in homogenates of infected organs or tissues, and straightforward freezing and maintenance at −25°C. or less will usually suffice.

Where the virus is required in a more "purified" state, a wide range of potential suspending media is available. Most of these contain proteins or peptones or are carbohydrate in nature (such as gum acacia). Their function as protective agents both against freezing and against drying is probably not a simple one and may cover such factors as (a) colloidal stabilization, (b) provision of an optimum freezing point, (c) antioxidation, (d) ease of reconstitution, and (e) retention of optimal amounts of properly distributed water.

It may, in addition, be desirable that the medium should be nonantigenic or else readily separable from the virus after rehydration.

The temperature of the ice film in the drying material has been shown to be important in the drying of *Br. abortus* and may well be so for viruses. In apparatus in which external cooling of the bottles or ampoules is available, it may be possible to dry labile viruses from apparently unpromising suspending media (such as saline, buffers, or water) by suitably lowering the ice-film temperature and prolonging the drying cycle. Media which protect viruses against freezing and thawing may not, for this reason, be optimal media for freeze-drying the same viruses.

Some primary drying cycles, over refrigerated condensers or chemical desiccants, reduce the water content to 1% or less, which seems by general consent to be the upper limit for safe storage. It may be necessary, however, to prolong the drying for a second cycle over a desiccant such as phosphorus pentoxide, followed by sealing *in vacuo* or in *dried* nitrogen. Whatever the final water content, preparations should be stored at the lowest practicable temperature for maximum protection.

## REFERENCES

Adams, M. H. 1948. The Surface Inactivation of Bacterial Viruses and of Proteins. *J. Gen. Physiol.* **31,** 417–431.

Allen, E. G., Kaneda, B., Girardi, A. J., McNair Scott, T. F., and Sigel, M. M. 1952. Preservation of Viruses of the Psittacosis-Lymphogranuloma Venereum Group and Herpes Simplex under Various Conditions of Storage. *J. Bacteriol.* **63,** 369–376.

Amies, C. R. 1934. The Influence of Temperature on the Survival of Pure Suspensions of Elementary Bodies of Vaccinia. *Brit. J. Exptl. Pathol.* **15,** 180–185.

Anderson, C. R. 1944. Survival of *Rickettsia prowazeki* in Different Diluents. *J. Bacteriol.* **47,** 519–522.

Bauer, J. H., and Mahoffy, A. F. 1930. Studies on the Filterability of Yellow-Fever Virus. *Am. J. Hyg.* **12,** 175–195.

Bauer, J. H., and Pickels, E. G. 1940. Apparatus for Freezing and Drying Virus in Large Quantities under Uniform Conditions. *J. Exptl. Med.* **71,** 83–88.

Bawden, F. C. 1950. *Plant Viruses and Virus Diseases.* Chronica Botanica Co., Waltham, Mass. Pp. 195, 254, 255.

Beaudette, F. R., Hudson, C. B., Bivins, J. A., and Miller, B. R. 1948. The Viability of Dried Viruses of Avian Origin. *Am. J. Vet. Research* **9,** 190–194.

Behrens, C. A., and Ferguson, W. W. 1935. Preservation of Purified Suspensions of the Virus of Vaccinia. *J. Infectious Diseases* **56,** 84–88.

Bovarnick, M. R., Miller, J. C., and Snyder, J. C. 1950. Influence of Certain Salts, Amino Acids, Sugars and Proteins on the Stability of Rickettsiae. *J. Bacteriol.* **59,** 509–522.

Brodie, M. 1935. Route of Transmission of St. Louis Encephalitis Virus in Mice. *Proc. Soc. Exptl. Biol. Med.* **32,** 1647–1649.

Burmester, B. R. 1952. Studies in Fowl Lymphomatosis. *Ann. N. Y. Acad. Sci.* **54,** 992–1003.

Burruss, H. W., and Hargett, M. V. 1947. Yellow-Fever Vaccine Inactivation Studies. *Public Health Repts.* (*U.S.*) **62,** 940–956.

Campbell-Renton, M. L. 1941. Experiments on Drying and on Freezing Bacteriophage. *J. Pathol. Bacteriol.* **53,** 371–384.

Carr, J. G., and Harris, R. J. C. 1951. Preservation of the Agent of the Rous Sarcoma No. 1 by Freeze-Drying. *Brit. J. Cancer* **5,** 95–105.

Collier, L. H. 1951. The Preservation of Vaccinia Virus by Freeze-Drying, in *Freezing and Drying.* Edited by R. J. C. Harris. The Institute of Biology, London. Pp. 133–137.

Cook, E. A., and Hudson, N. P. 1937. The Preservation of the Virus of St. Louis Encephalitis. *J. Infectious Diseases* **61,** 289–292.

Cowan, S. T. 1951. Infection and Drying Techniques, in *Freezing and Drying.* Edited by R. J. C. Harris. The Institute of Biology, London. Pp. 127–132.

Daubney, R. 1951. The Freeze-Drying of Living Virus Vaccines for Veterinary Use, in *Freezing and Drying.* Edited by R. J. C. Harris, The Institute of Biology, London. Pp. 143–153.

Dick, G. W. A. 1948. Mengo Encephalomyelitis Virus: Pathogenicity for Animals and Physical Properties. *Brit. J. Exptl. Pathol.* **29,** 559–577.

Dick, G. W. A., and Taylor, R. M. 1949. Bovine Plasma Albumin in Buffered Saline Solution as a Diluent for Viruses. *J. Immunol.* **62,** 311–317.

Duffy, C. E., and Stanley, W. M. 1945. Studies on the Biochemical, Biophysical and Immunogenic Properties of Japanese B Type Encephalitis Virus and Vaccines. *J. Exptl. Med.* **82,** 385–410.

Durieux, C. 1944. Note on the Preservation of Lymphogranuloma Virus. *Compt. rend. soc. biol.* **139,** 759–761.

Dykstra, T. P., and Du Buy, H. G. 1942. Preserving Plant Viruses *in vitro* by Means of a Simplified Lyophile Apparatus. *Science* **96,** 189–190.

Fasquelle, R., and Barbier, P. 1950. Some Examples of the Preservation of the Vitality of Viruses and Bacteria by Freeze-Drying. *Compt. rend. soc. biol.* **144,** 1618–1621.

Gane, R. 1951. Freeze-Drying of Foodstuffs, in *Freezing and Drying.* Edited by R. J. C. Harris. The Institute of Biology, London. Pp. 31–39.

Goodpasture, E. W., and Buddingh, G. J. 1936. Protective Action of Rabbit Serum for Vaccinia Virus at High Temperatures. *Science* **84,** 66–67.

Greaves, R. I. N. 1946. The Preservation of Proteins by Drying, with Special Reference to the Production of Dried Human Serum and Plasma for Transfusion. *Med. Research Council (Brit.) Spec. Rept. Ser.* No. **258.**

Hargett, M. V., Burruss, H. W., and Donovan, S. 1943. Aqueous-Base Yellow-Fever Vaccine. *Public Health Repts. (U.S.)* **58,** 505–512.

Harris, R. J. C. 1951. Preservation and Properties of the Agent of Rous No. 1 Sarcoma. *29th Ann. Rept. Brit. Empire Cancer Campaign.* Pp. 304–306.

Harris, D. L., and Shackell, L. F. 1911. The Effect of Vacuum Desiccation upon the Virus of Rabies, with Remarks upon a New Method. *J. Am. Public Health Assoc.* **1,** 52.

Hilleman, M. R., Buescher, E. L., and Smadel, J. E. 1951. Preparation of Dried Antigen and Antiserum for the Agglutination-Inhibition Test for Virus Influenza. *Public Health Repts. (U.S.)* **66,** 1195–1203.

Hoffstadt, R. E., and Tripi, H. B. 1946. A Study of the Survival of Certain Strains of Viruses after Lyophilization and Prolonged Storage. *J. Infectious Diseases* **78,** 183–189.

Hornibrook, J. W. 1950. Useful Menstruum for Drying Organisms and Viruses. *J. Lab. Clin. Med.* **35,** 788–792.

Horsfall, F. L. 1940. A Low Temperature Cabinet for the Preservation of Viruses. *J. Bacteriol.* **40,** 559–568.

Hurst, E. W., and Cooke, B. 1941. Experimental Measles: Transmission of the Disease to Monkeys, Failure to Transmit Measles to Rabbits. Cultivation of the Virus on the Chorioallantoic Membrane. *Med. J. Australia* **28,** 323–329.

Hutton, R. S., Hilmoe, R. J., and Roberts, J. L. 1951. Some Physical Factors That Influence the Survival of *Brucella abortus* during Freeze-Drying. *J. Bacteriol.* **61,** 309–319.

Johnson, C. D., and Goodpasture, E. W. 1934. An Investigation of the Aetiology of Mumps. *J. Exptl. Med.* **59,** 1–20.

Jones, T. C., Gleiser, C. A., Maurer, F. D., Hale, M. W., and Roby, T. O. 1948. Transmission and Immunization Studies on Equine Influenza. *Am. J. Vet. Research* **9,** 243–253.

Kitchen, S. F. 1934. Laboratory Infections with Rift Valley Fever. *Am. J. Trop. Med.* **14,** 457–464.

Knox, R. 1939. Desiccation of Filterable Tumours and Other Biological Materials. *J. Pathol. Bacteriol.* **49,** 467–481.

Kriss, A. E., and Roukina, E. A. 1948. The Role of Protective Colloids for the Preservation of Bacteriophages from Denaturing Influences. *Mikrobiologiya* **17,** 24–251.

Lépine, P., Levaditi, J. C., and Reinié, L. 1948. Duration of the Antigenic Potency of the Virus of Lymphogranuloma Inguinale. *Ann. Inst. Pasteur* **74,** 140–142.

McLimans, W. F. 1947. The Inactivation of Equine Encephalitis Virus by Methodical Agitation. *J. Immunol.* **56,** 385–391.

Melnick, J. L. 1946. Storage of Mouse-Adapted Strains of Poliomyelitis Virus and of Japanese B Encephalitis Virus at Sub-Freezing Temperatures. *J. Infectious Diseases* **79,** 27–32.

Munce, T. W., and Reichel, J. 1943. The Preservation of Hog Cholera Virus by Desiccation under High Vacuum. *Am. J. Vet. Research* **4,** 270–275.

Olitsky, P. K., Casals, J., Walker, D. L., Ginsberg, H. S., and Horsfall, F. L. 1949. Preservation of Viruses in a Mechanical Refrigerator at −25°C. *J. Lab. Clin. Med.* **34,** 1023–1026.

Olitsky, P. K., Yoger, R. H., and Murphy, L. C. 1950. Preservation of Neurotropic Viruses. *U.S. Army Med. J.* **1,** 415–417.

Pollard, M. 1951a. Preparation of Specific Complement-Fixing Antigens with Lansing Poliomyelitis Virus. *Proc. Soc. Exptl. Biol. Med.* **78,** 388–392.

Pollard, M. 1951b. The Inactivation of Poliomyelitis Virus by Freeze-Drying. *Texas Repts. Biol. and Med.* **9,** 749–754.

Rivers, T. M. 1927. Effect of Repeated Freezing (−185°C.) and Thawing on Colon Bacilli, Virus III, Vaccine Virus, Herpes Virus, Bacteriophage, Complement and Trypsin. *J. Exptl. Med.* **45,** 11–21.

Rivers, T. M., and Ward, S. M. 1935. Jennerian Prophylaxis by Means of Intradermal Injections of Culture Vaccine Virus. *J. Exptl. Med.* **62,** 549–560.

Sabin, A. B., and Paul, J. R. 1944. Phlebotomus (Pappatasi or Sandfly) Fever. *J. Am. Med. Assoc.* **125,** 603–606, 693–699.

Sawyer, W. A., Lloyd, W. D. M., and Kitchen, S. F. 1929. The Preservation of Yellow Fever Virus. *J. Exptl. Med.* **50,** 1–13.

Schade, A. L. 1945. Note: Egg Yolk and Ovolecithin as Stabilizing Agents in Virus Lyophilization. *Am. Assoc. Advance. Science, Research Conf. on Cancer.* P. 58.

Schade, A. L., and Caroline, L. 1943. The Preparation of a Polyvalent Dysentery Bacteriophage in a Dry and Stable Form. *J. Bacteriol.* **46,** 463–473.

Scherp, H. W., Flosdorf, E. W., and Shaw, D. R. 1938. Survival of the Influenzal Virus under Various Conditions. *J. Immunol.* **34,** 447–454.

Scott, G. R., and Brotherston, J. G. 1952. The Viability and Potency of Freeze-Dried Lapinized Rinderpest Vaccine. *J. Comp. Pathol. Therap.* **62,** 108–115.

Shackell, L. F. 1909. An Improved Method of Desiccation, with Some Applications to Biological Problems. *Am. J. Physiol.* **24,** 325–340.

Shope, R. E. 1931. Swine Influenza. III. Filtration Experiments and Aetiology. *J. Exptl. Med.* **54,** 373–385.

Smadel, J. E., Randall, R., and Warren, J. 1947. Preparation of Japanese Encephalitis Vaccine. *Bull. U.S. Army Med. Dept.* **7,** 963–972.

Smithburn, K. C., and Haddow, A. J. 1951. Ntaya Virus. A Hitherto Unknown Agent Isolated from Mosquitoes Collected in Uganda. *Proc. Soc. Exptl. Biol. Med.* **77,** 130–133.

Speck, R. S., Jawetz, E., and Coleman, V. R. 1951. Studies on Herpes Simplex Virus. I. Stability and Preservation of Egg-Adapted Herpes Simplex. *J. Bacteriol.* **61,** 253–258.

Stein, C. D., and Rogers, H. 1950. Recovery of Viable Microorganisms and Viruses from Vapors Removed from Frozen Suspensions of Biologic Material during Lyophilization. *Am. J. Vet. Research* **11,** 339–344.

Thorne, A. L. C. 1953. Recovery of Caprinized and Lapinized Rinderpest Viruses from Condensed Water Vapor Removed during Desiccation. *Nature* **171,** 609.

Topping, N. 1940. The Preservation of the Infectious Agents of Some of the Rickettsioses. *Public Health Repts.* (*U.S.*) **55,** 545–547.

Turner, T. B. 1938. The Preservation of Virulent *Treponema Pallidum* and *Treponema Pertenue* in the Frozen State: With a Note on the Preservation of Filterable Viruses. *J. Exptl. Med.* **67,** 61–78.

Turner, T. B., and Fleming, W. L. 1939. Prolonged Maintenance of Spirochaetes and Filterable Viruses in the Frozen State. *J. Exptl. Med.* **70,** 629–637.

Wooley, J. G. 1939. The Preservation of Lymphocytic Choriomeningitis and St. Louis Encephalitis Viruses by Freezing and Drying *in Vacuo*. *Public Health Repts.* (*U.S.*) **54,** 1077–1079.

Zinsser, H., and Tang, F. F. 1929. Further Experiments on the Agent of Herpes *J. Immunol.* **17,** 343–355.

to assess the value of the large number of techniques which have been advocated. It is to be hoped that in all future work in this field some attempt will be made to produce quantitative results, even of the roughest kind.

## III. TECHNIQUE OF DRYING BACTERIA

The general theoretical principles involved in drying have been fully discussed in an earlier chapter, and there is no need to go into them in detail here. It is of some interest, however, to consider the very large number of differences in technical detail that have been introduced—so large a number that one may fairly say that, with a few exceptions, no two workers have used exactly the same technique.

The various methods may conveniently be divided into eight groups, in each of which some important points are common to all.

### 1. *Shackell's Method*

Shackell (1909) developed a method for prevention of hydrolysis of glycogen in liver which was being preserved by drying. Although he did not attempt to dry bacteria, his name should be mentioned, as he drew attention to the importance of freezing, and drying from the frozen state, as a means of preventing harmful concentrations of dissolved solids during the drying process. His material was frozen in an ice-salt mixture and dried in a desiccator under a vacuum obtained with a Geryk pump, the pressure being described as less than 1 mm. Hg. Sulfuric acid was used to absorb water vapor, and Shackell laid great stress on the need for occasional shaking of the desiccator to prevent undue dilution of the upper layers of the acid. Harris and Shackell (1911) followed the same method for drying brains and spinal cords for preservation of rabies virus, and they noted that the virus which was dried quickly from the frozen state maintained its virulence.

Hammer (1911) used a very similar method for drying *Bacterium coli*, *Staphylococcus aureus*, and *Pseudomonas pyocyanea*. Paper strips were soaked in broth cultures of these organisms and put in beakers into a desiccator over sulfuric acid. Two desiccators were used, one being frozen by standing in an ice-salt mixture and partially evacuated to a pressure of 18 mm. Hg. The other desiccator was left at atmospheric temperature and pressure. The air-desiccated cultures were dead in 2 to 4 days, whereas the vacuum-desiccated cultures showed much longer survival, *Bact. coli* being alive up to 57 days, *Staph. aureus* alive at 54 days, and *Ps. pyocyanea* alive at 17 days but dead at 23 days. These results are poor by present-day standards, but Hammer was only using a very moderate vacuum with rather inefficient freezing.

Rogers (1914) used almost the same method for preserving lactic acid bacteria in milk. He, like Shackell, was impressed by the danger of increasing the concentration of salts during drying and froze his milk cultures either in an ice-salt mixture or in a refrigerator. The frozen cultures were then dried over sulfuric acid in a vacuum produced by a Geryk pump, stated to be about 0.01 mm. Hg. He tried to get some quantitative survival rates by means of viable counts but found this to be difficult with the dried milk powder. Later, he estimated the survival by the acidity produced in sterile milk at 30°C. after 1 mg. of dried culture was added to 1 liter of milk. He applied his drying technique to pure cultures of *Lactobacillus bulgaricus* and also to "cultures occurring in Swiss cheese and cultures of the coli group." A note of disappointment may be detected in his conclusion, with regard to the possibility of preserving stock dried cultures in the laboratory: "It is apparent, however, that the ability to withstand this process varies with different organisms. It is also possible that varying results may be due to the inability of some organisms to give a luxuriant growth in the medium used. Whatever the cause may be, the number of failures to revive after long periods has been great enough to preclude an unconditional recommendation for this purpose."

All the methods so far mentioned in this group employed sulfuric acid as the desiccant, with a moderate vacuum and some method of freezing. Otten (1930, 1932) also used sulfuric acid, but a much higher vacuum, 0.01 mm. Hg or less, and he did not freeze the cultures except in so far as they may have frozen as a result of evaporation. Instead of drying in the medium in which the organisms were grown, Otten washed the growth off solid medium, after removing the water of condensation, and made concentrated suspensions in saline and, in some experiments, in water and broth. He considered that it was very important to use highly concentrated suspensions to obtain a high survival rate. His published results show survival rates of 2.5 to 5% for *Salmonella typhi* and 0.5% or less for *Shigella shigae*. *Vibrio cholerae* showed a survival of 0.005% "at the utmost," and pneumococci, gonococci, and meningococci below 0.1%. [These last figures have been quoted by Stamp (1947) as 0.05 and 1%, respectively, apparently through confusion between the symbols °/₀ and °/₀₀.] These survival rates given by Otten are presumably the results immediately after drying, and no results after storage are given, although he preserved his cultures, after drying, in a vacuum of 0.01 mm. Hg or less.

### 2. *Swift's Method*

Swift (1921) devised a method somewhat similar to Shackell's in which the desiccator contained glycerol which was chilled by standing in an ice-salt mixture. The tubes of bacterial suspension, prepared by concentrating broth cultures in the centrifuge, were prefrozen in ice-salt and then transferred to the cold glycerol in the desiccator, which contained a tray of phosphorus pentoxide to absorb water vapor. The pump used is not mentioned, but Swift says: "It is necessary to have a mechanical pump that will give a vacuum as low as 2 or 3 mm. Hg." Evacuation was continued "until the proper degree of vacuum has been obtained," when the pump was disconnected and the whole desiccator placed in the icebox until drying was complete, usually about 12 hours. At the end of this time the tubes were taken out, the cotton plugs were pushed down, and the tubes were sealed by running in melted paraffin wax. In a later paper (Swift, 1937) an elaboration of this method was described in which the glycerol in the desiccator was cooled by the addition of solid carbon dioxide. The tubes of bacterial suspension were quickly frozen in this, and their temperature lowered to about −79°C. The pump was then started, and after all the carbon dioxide had evaporated drying began. Phosphorus pentoxide was the desiccant. Again no exact details are given as to degree of vacuum, but Swift says: "A vacuum of less than 1 or 2 mm. of Hg is necessary for satisfactory results, and with a good set-up with a Hyvac pump a pressure of 30 to 50 microns is obtained." Presumably these lower pressures were usually employed. His suspensions at this time were prepared by centrifuging broth cultures, or by scraping growth off solid media and resuspending in broth or serum in a high concentration. The tubes were usually sealed in air with paraffin wax as in the earlier method, but Swift refers to the possibility of sealing *in vacuo* by attaching them to the pump. No quantitative results are given, but in 1937 he described cultures of hemolytic streptococci preserved in 1916–1917 (by his original method) which were still viable 20 years later. "Many other strains of haemolytic streptococci have been similarly stored in this laboratory within the past twelve years . . . these have been recovered at intervals and have consistently maintained their characteristics noted at the time of their original preservation. Pneumococci similarly preserved have kept their type specificity."

Elser *et al.* (1935) described a method in which they froze cultures in ice-salt at −18° to −20°C. The tubes were then loaded into a metal container kept at −4°C., which was put into a metal cylinder. This was evacuated, using either phosphorus pentoxide or a refrigerated condenser to absorb the water. After 3 hours, dry air was admitted, the tubes were taken out and constricted, put on a manifold connected to a pump, and sealed *in vacuo*. It is stated that meningococci and gonococci dried in this way were recovered after 18 years.

Roe (1936) adopted a method described as a combination of Swift's method and Brown's method (Brown, 1925, 1932) for drying spore-bearing anaerobes. Concentrated suspensions of very young cultures were made in sterile serum and dried on strips of filter paper *in vacuo* while frozen, with phosphorus pentoxide as desiccant. No mention is made of the temperature at which they were frozen or of the degree of vacuum. For storage, the paper strips were sealed *in vacuo* over calcium chloride in individual tubes, which were stored at a low temperature. The total drying time is not stated. Results are given by the "death or survival" method; after 1 year 98%, and after 2 years 96%, of the strains dried were still viable.

Morton and Pulaski (1938) dried a large number of different organisms by Swift's method, using ice-salt for freezing most of the cultures, but solid carbon dioxide in acetone for a few. Their results were fairly good for a few years, but some strains of *Salmonella* and *Vibrio metchnikovi* were dead after 37 months. Some other strains, including *Salmonella, Shigella, Staph. aureus, Strep. haemolyticus,* and *Strep. pneumoniae,* survived for 3 years but were dead at 57 months. (It should be noted that the results for *Vib. metchnikovi* quoted here from their Table 2 do not agree with the results given in their summary.) Many other strains survived for 50 to 60 months. Although these results are stated by the "death or survival" method, these authors make a plea for more detailed records. "One is appalled at the lack of critical data on the preservation of cultures by this method. Methods which have been in use for just a few years enjoy such claims as 'The cultures would probably keep indefinitely if the seals remained intact.' Only by quantitative studies, which have been lacking, will it be possible to venture a definite statement."

Stillman (1941) dried several types of *Strep. pneumoniae* by Swift's method, freezing in solid carbon dioxide. His results showed that, after storage for 3 years, only 57% of tubes were viable. In those that had survived, there was no loss of type-specific substance, and no drop in virulence for mice.

Proom and Hemmons (1949) reported the results of drying some 1500 strains of bacteria, using Swift's method with minor modifications. The freezing was similar to Swift's 1937 method, but the whole desiccator was placed on a metal box containing solid carbon dioxide contained in a lagged wooden box. It was thus kept cold without being in the refrigerator and could be continuously exhausted during drying. Evacuation was continued overnight, and the following morning the pump was disconnected and the desiccator was placed on the bench for 2 hours to warm up. Dry nitrogen was then run in, and the tubes were taken out, wiped, and labeled. After the cotton plugs were pushed half-way down, the tubes were put into another desiccator over phosphorus pentoxide and redried in high vacuum at room temperature for 7 days. Dry nitrogen was then run in, and the tubes were taken out and sealed in the blowpipe above the cotton plugs.

In a table, Proom and Hemmons give the results of drying 1273 different strains in broth suspensions. After storage for periods from 1 to 5 years, they give the number of batches from which one tube tested was either viable or non-viable, and, in the event of a single tube being found non-viable, the number of batches in which all tubes were non-viable. On the basis of these figures, they give a column showing the routine interval recommended before redrying any particular organism. For only two organisms, *Vibrio cholerae* and *Neisseria gonorrhoeae*, is this interval as short as 1 year. Most workers would agree that these two present the severest test of any, but it may be noted that, after 2 to 3 years' storage, Proom and Hemmons found two complete batches of each of these organisms to be non-viable. They also give a few quantitative results, showing the percentage survival of six different organisms immediately after drying in broth and saline, both at room temperature and at −78°C.

### 3. *Brown's Method*

This method, first described at a meeting of the Society of American Bacteriologists, was published only in abstract form (Brown, 1925). In a later paper (1932), also only an abstract, Brown described a modification of the technique. His suspensions for drying consisted of a loopful of culture mixed with blood or serum, on a piece of filter paper or a glass cover slip. At first these were dried in a desiccator, "partially evacuated," but later he used milk bottles, the rims of which had been carefully ground, covered with a ground-glass lid. The bottle, which contained calcium chloride, had its rim greased with wax, and the cover was put on loosely. During drying, it was put under a bell jar which was evacuated, and the bottle was sealed by suddenly admitting air to the bell jar, thus pressing the loose cover down on the waxed rim. Dried in this way and stored in the icebox *in vacuo*, 5 strains of hemolytic streptococci survived for 12 years, and 5 strains of pneumococci, 16 out of 17 strains of streptococci, and 5 strains of *Corynebacterium pyogenes* survived for 8 years. A few other organisms still showed survival for periods ranging from 4 to 7 years. In the 1925 paper he reports the death of gonococci 3 months after drying.

Brown's method of sealing his bottles, ingenious as it was, had the disadvantage that a small amount of air, and with it moisture, was admitted to the bottles. The calcium chloride in the bottle would absorb the moisture, but the air would remain. It will be noted that there was no freezing in this method. Whether such small volumes could have frozen by evaporation is doubtful, but this question is discussed more fully later.

Leifson (1936) developed a modification of Brown's method, which avoided the entry of air during sealing. He used a rectangular glass jar, with a ground lid rather larger than the top of the jar. This was perforated near one edge, and a tube through which the jar was evacuated was sealed over this hole with wax. When it was desired to seal the jar, it was only necessary to slide the lid to one side, so that the hole was brought outside the edge of the jar. All joints were of course carefully greased. The only other modification from Brown's method was that the bacterial suspensions were dried on glass beads as well as on filter paper. He used calcium chloride "or some other drying agent," and his vacuum was stated to be about 0.01 mm. Hg. Leifson dried three different organisms, *Salm. typhi*, *Vib. cholerae*, and *N. meningitidis*, comparing the survival times in five different suspending media. His results will be discussed later.

Harris and Lange (1933) adopted Brown's milk bottle technique for drying *Mycobacteria*, with the single modification that they dispensed with the filter paper strips and transferred some of the growth from 4-week-old cultures directly to the inside of glass vials. After 11 months of storage in the icebox, all their cultures were viable. Two strains, one human and one bovine, of *Myco. tuberculosis* were tested on animals and were found to have survived without any apparent loss of virulence.

Frobisher *et al.* (1947) devised a method which was essentially the same as Brown's, except that their bacterial suspensions in sterile rabbit's blood were mixed with sand in the drying tubes. Instead of the milk bottle, they used a Mason fruit jar; the lid was sealed on with a ring of plasticine, which was perforated nearly horizontally with a needle, leaving a small hole about 0.5 mm. in diameter. When air was admitted suddenly at the end of evacuation, the lid was forced down and the hole closed. These workers dried a large number of organisms by this method and reported some long-term survivals, e.g., 38 out of 42 strains of beta hemolytic streptococci alive after 18 years, 18 out of 20 strains of *H. bronchisepticus* (*Br. bronchiseptica*) viable after 9 years, 24 strains of staphylococci all viable after 9 years, and 15 of these which were retested after 19 years also all viable. Other good results up to 7 years were reported with pneumococci, *Salm. typhi*, other *Salmonella*, and *Shigella*. On the other hand, *Br. melitensis* and *suis*, pathogenic *Neisseria*, *H. pertussis*, and *H. influenzae* were not viable at the end of 1 year.

Two other groups of workers have used methods which have something in common with Brown's technique. Stark and Herrington (1931) dried with calcium chloride or phosphorus pentoxide as desiccant. Their paper is unfortunately published only in abstract form, but the volumes of suspension must have been very small, since they state that apparent dryness was obtained in less than 3 minutes. The cultures are said to have been stored under dry conditions. Their results are stated quantitatively and show 66% viability of streptococci after 97 days, but only 2 to 3% viability of *Staph. albus*, *Bact. coli*, and *Lactobacillus acidophilus* after the same period. Rayner (1943) described a method of drying single drops of blood-broth cultures on Cellophane squares in a Petri dish placed in a desiccator over calcium chloride. A Hyvac pump was used, and Rayner states that "the cultures quickly freeze and dry within 20 minutes." After standing overnight in the exhausted desiccator the Cellophane squares were transferred to test tubes which were constricted, evacuated on the pump, and sealed *in vacuo*. No detailed results are given, but Rayner states that "It is possible to dry the gonococcus, the meningococcus and *Haemophilus pertussis* successfully in this way."

### 4. *Flosdorf and Mudd's Method*

Flosdorf and Mudd (1935) gave a very complete account of the technical details of a method of drying, the chief points of which were prefreezing of the tubes in solid carbon dioxide in Methyl Cellosolve and removal of the water vapor by one or more condensers cooled with solid carbon dioxide. The tubes to be dried were attached to the manifold after freezing, or, in some cases, were frozen after attachment to the manifold. With a good pump, the rate of evaporation was such that a low temperature was maintained during the early stages of drying, and the temperature gradually rose as drying approached completion. When dry, the tubes were sealed off *in vacuo* on the manifold, and there was no need to admit air or other gas at any stage. This original method was known as the "lyophile" process. In a later paper (Flosdorf and Mudd, 1938) they described a modification of the process, in which the cold condensers were replaced by a chemical desiccant, and for this they used a preparation of anhydrous calcium sulfate known as Drierite. This technique was known as the Cryochem process. If it was desired to avoid the use of solid carbon dioxide entirely, they recommended holding the tubes at a somewhat reduced pressure for a time to allow the escape of all dissolved gases. The pressure could then be lowered rapidly without any danger of frothing, and the contents of the tubes would freeze by evaporation. In their two papers, Flosdorf and Mudd state that bacteria have been successfully dried by these methods, although no details or results are given, but in a paper by Flosdorf and Kimball (1940) the successful drying of *Haemophilus pertussis* by the Cryochem process is described. Suspensions of these organisms dried in skim milk remained alive with all original characteristics of phase I for over 2 years.

Other authors have also reported results with the "lyophile" or Cryochem processes. Siler (1936) dried strains of *Salm. typhi* for preservation for preparation of vaccine, using the "lyophile" process. Growth was scraped off agar cultures and suspended in veal infusion peptone broth at pH 7.4. After 5 to 6 hours' drying, the tubes were sealed *in vacuo* and stored at about 5°C. Siler states that "up to the present" (i.e., from January to October, 1935) "no change of any kind has been detected in the strains preserved in this way." Naylor and Smith (1946), in an investigation into the most suitable conditions for drying, used the "lyophile" process for some of their experiments, but during drying their ampoules were held below the freezing point of the suspension by means of solid carbon dioxide. The actual temperature at which they were held is not stated, but if they were kept at the temperature of solid carbon dioxide it is hard to see how any drying could take place, since the vapor pressure of the ice in the condensers would be equal to that of the contents of the ampoules. The organism used by Naylor and Smith was *Serratia marcescens* (*Chromobacterium prodigiosum*). Stamp (1947) also records one experiment with the same organism dried by the "lyophile" process and gives a survival rate of about 30%.

Knox (1939) describes a modification of Flosdorf and Mudd's apparatus designed to reduce the length of the manifold and so reduce the obstruction to the flow of water vapor to the condensers. He did not use this apparatus himself for bacterial drying, but Glover (1946) used it for experiments on drying *Mycobacterium tuberculosis*. Suspensions were prepared in distilled water, physiological saline, and inactivated bovine serum, freeze-dried by Knox's method, and stored at −4°C. Duplicate samples of the saline suspensions were stored at −76°C. without drying. Attempts to estimate survival were made by culture on glycerol egg agar and also by inoculation of tenfold falling dilutions into guinea pigs or hamsters. All surviving animals were killed after 4 months and examined for tuberculous lesions. Glover concluded that, although the undried suspensions stored at −76°C. showed no appreciable loss after 180 days, freeze-dried material sustained an immediate loss of activity after drying, estimated at 100- to 1000-fold, but thereafter it remained stable.

Hornibrook (1949) described a process which bears some resemblance to Flosdorf and Mudd's methods but differs in that sulfuric acid is the desiccant. This change was made in order that the final water content might be controlled by varying the concentration of the acid. A manifold of Pyrex glass was arranged with its side tubes attached near its upper surface and of such a size that the manifold itself could contain 100 ml. of acid. The ampoules of suspension were attached to the manifold and then frozen in a bath of alcohol containing solid carbon dioxide. The pump was then turned on, and the freezing bath was removed when the pressure had fallen to about 0.5 mm. Hg. In some experiments, snap-freezing after degassing was used instead of prefreezing in the cold bath. Two essential precautions were emphasized: the acid must be agitated by occasional tilting of the manifold to prevent dilution of the upper layer, and the glass must be perfectly clean since sulfuric acid, although not volatile at ordinary temperatures, may react with certain salts, e.g., sodium chloride, to form volatile acids. Hornibrook gives diagrams showing the concentration of acid required to achieve a definite moisture content in the dried product. With suspensions of *Vib. cholerae* in skim milk dried in this apparatus, three runs gave survival rates of 1.3, 0.05, and 0.5%. Two runs with a normal "lyophile" apparatus with cold condensers gave survival rates of 0.4 and 0.05%.

### 5. *Potter's Method*

Potter (1935, 1937, 1939) carried out a number of experiments with *Mycobacterium tuberculosis*, including avian, bovine, and human types. These were designed to study the effect of oxygen deprivation, but since they involved rather severe desiccation they should be mentioned here. No drying chamber was used, the tubes, containing bacteria scraped from the surface of a solid medium, being sealed direct to the vacuum line of a high-grade mercury pump. The pump was run for periods of time varying from 12 to 60 hours. In one experiment phosphorus pentoxide was the desiccant; in some of the experiments the tubes were "gettered" with magnesium, and in one case with cesium azide, to remove the last traces of oxygen. The vacuum was between $10^{-5}$ and $10^{-6}$ mm. Hg. After storage in the dark for periods from 1 to 12 months, all tubes were viable when tested by animal inoculation, and almost all when tested by culture. In the one experiment in which the tubes were "gettered" with cesium azide (Potter, 1939), they were stored after sealing for 10 months at 37°C. and were viable after this severe treatment.

### 6. *Sordelli's Method*

This method is described by St. John-Brookes and Rhodes (1936) and by Rhodes (1950). They attribute it to Professor A. Sordelli of Buenos Aires but can give no reference to any previously published description. It is perhaps the simplest of any so far described. A loopful of sterile horse serum is put on the inner wall of a small sterile test tube, and a loopful of growth from a culture on a suitable solid medium is emulsified in the serum. This small tube is plugged with cotton and put into a slightly wider and much longer tube which contains a little phosphorus pentoxide at the bottom. The outer tube is constricted near its upper end and attached direct to a tube connected to a Hyvac pump for exhaustion. When the vacuum is satisfactory, usually in 2 to 3 minutes, the tube is sealed off *in vacuo* at the constriction and stored in the dark at room temperature.

Results are given only on a death or survival basis, expressed as a fraction of which the numerator is the number of cultures viable and the denominator the number tested in any given period. At less than 1 year after drying, the more sensitive organisms show a surprising number of non-viable cultures, some viability figures given being *Vibrio* 56/74, *Neisseria* 62/69, and *Haemophilus* 191/237. Fisher (1950), in a succeeding paper, gives some viable counts for four different organisms before and after drying.

Campbell-Renton (1942) carried out a series of experiments on many strains of *Vib. cholerae,* using a technique that bore some resemblance to Sordelli's except that, in order to dry a number of identical tubes at once, the initial drying was done in a desiccator over phosphorus pentoxide, evacuated for 30 minutes. A single drop of a 24-hour peptone-water culture was put into each tube, and freezing, by evaporation, is said to have occurred in 4 to 5 minutes. Five hours later the tubes were taken out of the desiccator and put into larger tubes containing a little phosphorus pentoxide as in Sordelli's method. These tubes were constricted, evacuated singly on the pump for about 3 minutes, and sealed *in vacuo.* All the cultures were counted before drying and at intervals during storage, and the survival rates for different strains ranged from 5.1 to 0.01% after 24 hours, and from 0.7% to zero after 4 years. Only 4 out of 15 strains tested were nonviable after 4 years.

### 7. *Stamp's Method*

Stamp (1947) described a method which differed greatly from all others in that his cultures were dried slowly at a pressure of 100 to 300 mm. Hg. Single drops of thick suspensions in a suitable fluid were put on pieces of sterile waxed filter paper and dried in a desiccator over phosphorus pentoxide for 2 to 3 days at room temperature. Air was then admitted, the waxed papers taken out, and the disks of dried suspension were carefully scraped off, transferred to a suitable sterile plugged container, and stored in a desiccator over phosphorus pentoxide "usually at a low pressure." During the first 2 years of Stamp's investigation the desiccators were stored at room temperature, about 18° to 21°C.; after this they were stored in a cool cellar at a somewhat lower temperature.

This method was followed for investigating the most suitable suspending medium for the bacteria during drying, and Stamp gives very full quantitative results. The drops used for drying were all delivered with a pipette calibrated to deliver 36 drops per milliliter under controlled conditions. Since the suspensions were dried at a relatively high pressure, it is clear that no freezing occurred, and they were dried from the liquid state. The drying process must also have been slow, and, as it was carried out at room temperature, there may have been time for some growth to occur with some organisms during the early stages of the drying process. Stamp himself was aware of this danger, and says, in his comments on an experiment to compare the survival after drying by his method and by the "lyophile" process: "The higher survival rates obtained with *Chromobacterium prodigiosum* by the slower drying process might in part be accounted for by some degree of growth during drying. Tests with *Chr. prodigiosum* in nutrient gelatin showed that with the concentration employed ($10^{10}$ organisms per ml.) the count might increase slightly during the first 3 hr. of drying. The maximum increase obtained was 30%, but it was usually less than this figure. In the presence of ascorbic acid this increase was never found to occur. The factor of growth therefore did not appear to play any substantial part in the results obtained." That such growth can occur with somewhat less concentrated suspensions has been shown by Fry and Greaves (1951). They dried a suspension of a paracolon bacillus containing $1.6 \times 10^8$ organisms per milliliter by Stamp's technique and examined samples at intervals during the drying. There was a steady rise in the viable count at first, and by 9 hours it showed an eightfold increase. After this there was a slow fall, but by 9 days the viable count was still more than double the predrying count. Such a dramatic rise is unlikely to have occurred in Stamp's experiments with more concentrated suspensions, but the possibility that some of his survival rates represent the balance between growth and death must be borne in mind. His results will be discussed later in the section dealing with the choice of the suspending medium.

Naylor and Smith (1946) also used Stamp's method for some of their work in an investigation of the most suitable suspending medium. Their results will be discussed later.

### 8. *Greaves' Method*

This method, known as the centrifugal vacuum freezing method, was devised by Greaves (1944) in order to obtain a snap-freeze by evaporative cooling without previous degassing. The tubes or ampoules are mounted in a disk so drilled that the tubes are inclined inwards at the top at an angle of 5° from the vertical. The disk is rotated by a small electric motor, and the contained suspension is spread up the side of the tube in the form of a wedge. Greaves states that a speed of 1450 r.p.m. with a minimal radius of 1 in. was more than adequate to inhibit the formation of bubbles in liquids *in vacuo*. In practice, the tubes are loaded into the disk, the drying chamber is closed, and the spinner motor is started. The pump is then switched on, and when the pressure, as indicated by a suitable gauge, has fallen low enough to ensure that the snap-freeze has occurred (0.1 mm. Hg is a safe pressure for this) the spinner motor is turned off. It is important not to keep this motor running for too long if it is mounted inside the drying chamber, as it cannot easily get rid of its heat *in vacuo* and may burn out. Water vapor is absorbed either by trays of phosphorus

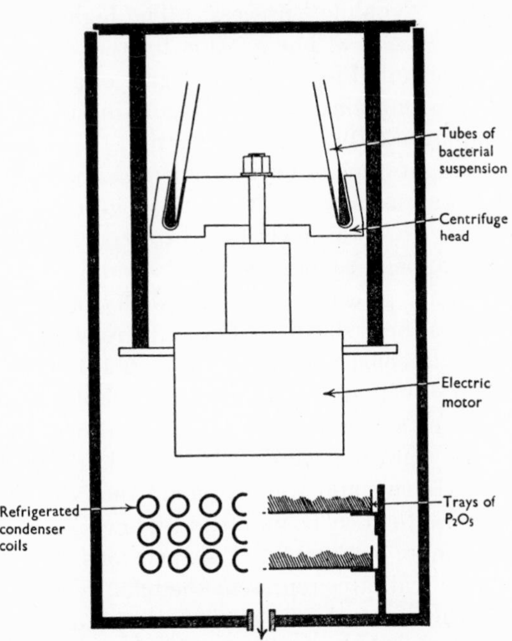


FIG. 1. Diagram of the apparatus used for drying multiple tubes by the centrifugal vacuum freezing method, using either a refrigerated coil condenser or a chemical desiccant. (Fry and Greaves, 1951.)

pentoxide at the bottom of the drying chamber or by a refrigerated coil cooled to about −40°C. Figure 1 shows an early model of this apparatus in diagrammatic form, and Fig. 2 shows a small commercially produced laboratory model, in which the drying chamber consists of a glass bell jar. This method of drying has been described by Fry and Greaves (1951), who give a large number of quantitative results obtained in many experiments with a limited range of organisms. As this work, like Stamp's, was carried out mainly to determine the best suspending medium, it will be discussed later.

Fry and Greaves also described another technique which they used in a few experiments, in which the suspensions were prefrozen by liquid air and dried *in vacuo* with a liquid air condenser to absorb water. Four 0.005-ml. drops of a suspension were placed on a narrow strip of Cellophane, and a large number of such strips were mounted in a metal Petri dish in such a way that they were held firmly but could be easily detached

Fig. 2. A small apparatus for drying by the centrifugal vacuum freezing method. W. Edwards & Co. (London) Ltd.

with forceps. This dish was floated on liquid air in a larger dish, which was suspended in the drying chamber. At the bottom of the chamber were one or two trays containing phosphorus pentoxide. Projecting downwards from the lid of the drying chamber was a metal cylinder, closed at the lower end, which was about an inch above the tray containing the Cellophane strips. This apparatus, made to fit in the drying chamber of Fig. 1, is shown diagrammatically in Fig. 3. As soon as the chamber was closed, the cylinder was filled with liquid air and the pump was started. When the liquid air in the dish had boiled away, the chamber was rapidly evacuated to less than $10^{-4}$ mm. Hg and drying by sublimation started. After about an hour, by which time drying of these small drops was complete, no more liquid air was added to the cylinder, and the ice on the cylinder was allowed to sublime over into the phosphorus pentoxide. After about 6 hours the whole process was complete, but it was found to be useless to take out the Cellophane strips in the laboratory, as the drops

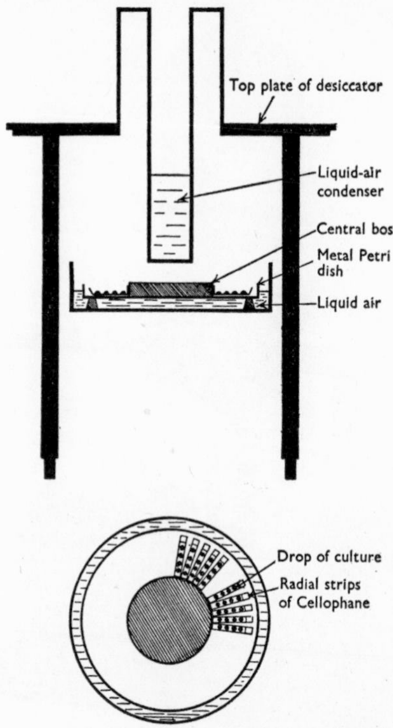


FIG. 3. Diagram of an apparatus used for drying cultures on Cellophane strips with a liquid air condenser. (Fry and Greaves, 1951.)

of dried suspension were so hygroscopic that they quickly liquefied in moist air. To overcome this, the drying chamber was opened in the relatively dry air of a refrigerator room at −25°C., and the Cellophane strips were transferred individually to small glass tubes which were closed with a paraffined cork. These tubes were then constricted in the usual way, put on a manifold attached to a pump, and evacuated, with a phosphorus pentoxide trap, for about an hour and then sealed *in vacuo*. This method of drying at a very low temperature proved useful in finding suitable suspending media for very sensitive organisms, especially *N. gonorrhoeae* and *Vib. cholerae*, and very good survival rates were obtained, both immediately and after long storage. The method was clearly not suitable for routine work, but with the information gained from a limited number of these low-temperature experiments it was found possible to dry the more delicate organisms successfully by the ordinary centrifugal vacuum-freezing method.

## IV. FACTORS INFLUENCING SURVIVAL

The foregoing pages give some account of the technical details of many of the common methods in use at the present day for preservation of bacteria by drying. From this information, together with the published results, it should be possible to form some opinion on the factors which are essential to ensure a good survival. Unfortunately only a small proportion of authors have published quantitative results by which the value of their technique may be assessed. For example, a statement that after 3 years' storage of dried cultures of pneumococci only 57% of tubes were viable (Stillman, 1941) only tells us that we should have a slightly better than even chance of finding any single tube viable—a poor prospect if the cultures were valuable. On the other hand, the statement that a particular strain of *Salmonella typhi* showed a survival rate of 75% 2 to 3 days after drying, 34.7% after 2 years' storage, and 21.8% after 4 years' storage (Stamp, 1947) gives a clear picture of how this strain is dying off on storage, and an assurance that it will remain viable for many years more.

In spite of this lack of clear-cut results, it is worth considering the numerous factors which may influence survival, to see how much information can be obtained under each heading.

### 1. *The Nature of the Organism*

All workers who have used a variety of organisms are agreed that some are far more sensitive to drying than others. Stark and Herrington (1931) state that streptococci dried by their method showed 66% viability, but *Staph. albus*, *Bact. coli*, and *Lact. acidophilus* showed only 2 to 3% viability. Brown (1925) reported death of gonococci in 3 months, while in a later paper (Brown, 1932) he described survival of streptococci and pneumococci for many years. Stamp's results show similar great differences in viability, as also do those of Fry and Greaves (1951), who showed that two strains of hemolytic streptococci (groups B and E) showed very high survival rates of 100 and 72% after about a year, *Staph. aureus*, *Salmonella typhi-murium*, and *Bact. coli* gave much lower survival rates, between 10 and 30%, and *Vib. cholerae* and *N. gonorrhoeae* showed a survival of the order of 1% or much lower, according to other variable conditions that were imposed upon them. The long tables published by Proom and Hemmons (1949) and by Rhodes (1950) which include large numbers of different genera, show the same effect, although their results are given only in the form of numbers of cultures viable after different times of storage. Fisher (1950), in a short quantitative table, gives the following death rates immediately after drying by Sordelli's method: *Bact. coli* 37%, *Strep. pneumoniae* 18%, *Vib. cholerae* 99%, and *N. gonorrhoeae* 92%.

Taking all these results, and many others to be found in the literature, it is clear that, of the more common organisms, most of the streptococci, especially *Strep. pyogenes*, are very resistant to drying. Staphylococci, in spite of Stark and Herrington's figures quoted above, also generally appear to be very resistant. *Bacterium*, *Salmonella*, *Shigella*, and *Brucella* are four genera which, although moderately resistant, are much more sensitive than the streptococci. *Neisseria*, especially *N. gonorrhoeae*, *Haemophilus influenzae*, and *Vib. cholerae*, are among the most sensitive organisms and provide the most severe test for any drying technique. These facts must be taken into account when considering the value of any technique, since a method by which *Strep. pyogenes* can be kept alive is not necessarily a good one except for this particular organism, although a method by which it cannot be preserved is sure to be a bad method. Any technique which is satisfactory for the more sensitive organisms, on the other hand, is likely to be good for all.

### 2. *The Suspending Medium*

A large number of different media have been used for making the bacterial suspension before drying, inactivated serum and broth being the two most common. Generally, no explanation is given as to why a particular medium was chosen, and only a few workers have attempted controlled experiments with more than one medium.

Harris and Lange (1933) and Potter (1935, 1937, 1939), when drying *Mycobacteria*, used no suspending medium, but transferred growth scraped off solid cultures directly to the glass tubes for drying. Potter states that this was done without washing, but care was taken not to include particles of the medium. These workers all found survival of *Myco. tuberculosis* for periods of 6 to 12 months when tested culturally or by animal inoculation, but the proportion of viable to dead organisms is not known. The only comparable experiments with the same organisms are those of Glover (1946), who suspended *Myco. tuberculosis* in serum, distilled water, and physiological saline. His conclusions, based mainly on animal inoculations, was that there was a considerable immediate loss of activity, estimated at 100- to 1000-fold, in all three media, and that "the type of substrate used for suspending the bacilli before conservation seemed to be immaterial."

Otten (1932) was one of the first of the earlier workers to use more than one suspending medium. His work is particularly important since he used *Vibrio cholerae* as one of the test organisms. Drying this in physiological saline, he obtained a survival rate of 0.005%, but he says that his survival rates were higher after drying in distilled water, and higher still in meat extract. In another paper (Otten, 1930) he showed that a bacterial suspension diluted with a *thick* suspension of dead bacteria had a much higher survival rate than one similarly diluted with saline. On the basis of this finding, he obtained greatly improved survival of *H. pertussis*, *Past. pestis*, and *N. meningitidis* after drying when mixed with a thick suspension of killed staphylococci. Otten concluded that the protein of dead bacteria, or that in the meat extract, acted as a protective colloid, making the withdrawal of water a less violent process but not influencing the final water content. Whether Otten's explanation is the correct one is at the moment an open question, but most of the more modern work seems to show that some protective colloid is necessary to obtain the best results.

Elser *et al.* (1935) did some comparative experiments in saline, broth, and inactivated serum. They found that serum was better than either saline or broth as a suspending medium for *N. meningitidis* and *N. gonorrhoeae*. They give no figures, but from their statement that these two organisms were recovered after 18 years there is no doubt that their drying technique was a successful one. These authors conclude "that when attention is paid to the menstruum used and a high vacuum is obtained to exclude practically all the oxygen . . . bacteria can be maintained in a viable state for almost an indefinite period."

Leifson (1936) compared times of survival of *Salm. typhi*, *Vib. cholerae*, and *N. meningitidis* after drying in five different media—water, 0.3% beef extract, 1.0% peptone, pork infusion, and pork infusion with blood. Suspensions made in these media were dried in his modification of Brown's apparatus both on pieces of paper and on glass beads, stored *in vacuo* over calcium chloride, and examined at intervals up to 64 days. *Salm. typhi* survived to the 64th day in all media. *Vib. cholerae* and *N. meningitidis* both died off quickly in the first four but were viable after 64 days in pork infusion with blood, *Vib. cholerae* only on the glass beads.

Up to this point, the choice seems to have been between saline, water, serum, blood, and some form of meat extract. Comparative experiments just described had shown that water or saline were inferior to broth, and that broth was inferior to serum. Although Otten obtained some survival in water, saline, or meat extract with a very sensitive organism, this was only immediately after drying, and Leifson's results suggested that, for *Vib. cholerae* to survive even for 64 days, meat extract alone was not sufficient and the addition of blood was necessary. It appeared therefore that Otten's idea of the necessity for a protective colloid must be stated more specifically, since some colloids seemed more protective than others.

Heller (1941) investigated the effect of a number of simple substances in aqueous solution. As crystalline substances he used glucose, sucrose, salicin, and tryptophan, all in 1% solution, and, as colloids, starch, gum tragacanth, gastric mucin, and peptone in 1% solution. Peptone was also used as a 10% solution, and, in addition, he used distilled water, physiological saline, and a thick washed gel of aluminium hydroxide. Two test organisms were used, *Strep. pyogenes* and *Bact. coli*, and all suspensions were dried by the "lyophile" process for 24 hours. Viable counts were done immediately after drying, and after 4, 7, 14, 28, 56, and 84 days. Survivals were calculated as percentages of the counts obtained immediately after drying, and by this method a close approximation to a logarithmic death rate was observed in all menstruums during the 84 days of the experiments.

The highest death rates were always observed with water and saline. Among the crystalline compounds, the lower death rates were observed with those which the particular organism was capable of dissimilating during normal growth; and among such dissimilable compounds, the higher the solubility, the lower was the death rate. This inverse correlation between dissimilability of a crystalline compound and the death rate of an organism dried in it is not in agreement with the finding of Fry and Greaves that *Salm. typhimurium* showed no significant difference in survival after drying in 7.5% glucose broth and 7.5% lactose broth. Heller also showed that, with colloid solutions, the death rates decreased with increase in the hydrophilic property of the colloid. The lowest death rates were obtained with a mixture of a dissimilable crystalline compound and a hydrophilic colloid.

Apart from this work of Heller's, most of the bacterial drying reported between 1920 and 1947 was done in broth or serum, and occasionally in blood. Most of those who used broth alone were working with the more resistant organisms, with the exception of Rake (1935), who preserved meningococci up to 151 days after drying in hormone broth. Then Stamp (1947) produced results of experiments designed to find a suitable suspending medium. Nutrient gelatin was first selected as being likely to provide a useful protective colloid, and ascorbic acid was used as a substance which might prevent death due to oxidation. The medium finally adopted was 10% nutrient gelatin with ascorbic acid, usually in a concentration of 0.25% or 0.5%. Decreasing the concentration of gelatin gave somewhat lower survival rates; concentrations higher than 10% gave no better results and were difficult to use because of the high viscosity. Increased concentration of ascorbic acid above 0.5% produced a drop in the survival rate, but this appeared to be due to the lowering of the pH and could be counteracted by neutralizing the acid with sodium hydroxide solution before drying.

Most of these experiments were carried out with *Chromobacterium prodigiosum*, *Salm. typhisuis*, or *Bact. coli* as test organisms, and the survival rates obtained were good. Stamp then gives two tables of results using a large number of different organisms. The first (his Table 3) shows that *F. fusiformis* and *N. meningitidis* failed to survive 2 and 1 days of drying, respectively, either with or without ascorbic acid. *H. influenzae* dried for 2 days and *H. parainfluenzae* dried for 3 days showed survival rates well under 0.1% without ascorbic acid, and under 1% with ascorbic acid. A strain of anaerobic streptococcus and *Cl. welchii* also had survival rates well under 1% and showed no significant improvement with ascorbic acid. In his Table 5, Stamp gives results after storage for a number of organisms, most of which are recognized as being fairly resistant to drying and which show very good survival rates up to 4 years. Exceptions to this are two strains of *Vib. cholerae*, showing 0.13 and 0.15% survival 2 to 3 days after drying, and no survival after 2 years. Admittedly all these organisms quoted are severe tests of a technique, but it is only by such severe tests that its value can be judged.

Naylor and Smith (1946) worked along the same lines as Stamp, and for many of their experiments they used his technique of drying from the liquid state under reduced pressure. They confirmed his finding that 0.5% ascorbic acid added to the nutrient gelatin was the optimum concentration and found that best results were obtained at pH 6 to 7. They tried a number of different samples of gelatin and could detect no difference. They also found that gelatin could be replaced by white dextrin or by pectin without affecting the survival rate. The addition of marmite to the gelatin–ascorbic acid mixture appeared to stimulate survival, which steadily increased as the marmite concentration was raised from 1 to 10%. These experiments were done by Stamp's technique. They next tried to confirm their results using the Flosdorf and Mudd "lyophile" technique and found that, although the survival in nutrient gelatin alone was very poor, the protective effect of marmite and ascorbic acid was very marked. With this technique the optimum concentration of ascorbic acid was about 2%. This, together with large amounts of marmite, proved very difficult to dry, but it was found that the marmite could be entirely replaced by ammonium chloride at a concentration of about 0.5%. The ascorbic acid could be partially, but not entirely, replaced by thiourea, and a concentration of 0.5% of each gave an optimum balance. In the final medium the 10% gelatin was replaced by 2% dextrin.

This suspending medium appears to have been logically worked out step by step, with control by viable counts at every stage, but unfortunately only one organism, *Serratia marcescens* (*Chr. prodigiosum*), has been used throughout as a test. Judging by Stamp's results, this is a fairly resistant organism which survives drying well, and Naylor and Smith give us no hint of the effect of their medium on more sensitive organisms. Without this information, no opinion can be formed as to the value of their medium.

Weiser and Hennum (1947) compared the survival after drying of *Bact. coli* suspended in 1% peptone at pH 7.0, inactivated rabbit serum, and skim milk. They found that the initial survival rate was about 5 to 15% in peptone water, and 35 to 50% in serum; the survival in skim milk, although irregular, generally lay between the other two. The appearance of milk as a suspending medium is interesting, as it had not been much used previously. Rogers (1914) used it for drying organisms found in milk and cheese; he met with some difficulties and was unable to recommend his drying process unconditionally for preservation of cultures. After this unpromising start, milk next seems to appear in the literature 26 years later, when Flosdorf and Kimball (1940) obtained satisfactory 2-year survival of *H. pertussis* suspended in skim milk and dried by the "lyophile" and Cryochem processes. Topping (1940) used milk for the suspension of rickettsial material before drying by the "lyophile" process and found it to be better than serum. He attributed the failure of serum to the rise of pH that occurs when serum is exposed to a high vacuum and loses carbon dioxide. In support of this he quotes Scherp *et al.* (1938). Hornibrook (1949), using a modification of Flosdorf and Mudd's method already described, dried *Vib. cholerae* with some success in skim milk. In a later paper (Hornibrook, 1950) he described the use of a milk dialyzate and found that, with *Vib. cholerae* as a test organism, this was as good as or better than dialyzed milk, but that both were inferior to milk. He then made up a salt-lactose mixture containing all the dialyzable constituents of milk and found that most organisms showed a better immediate survival after drying in this than in milk. With *Vib. cholerae* he found a better survival in the salt-lactose mixture than in lactose alone at 5, 10, or 15%, Naylor and Smith's solution, milk, or broth. The salts alone without lactose were inferior to the whole mixture.

Fry and Greaves (1951) carried out a series of experiments, with a limited range of bacteria, both sensitive and resistant, to determine the most suitable suspending medium and to investigate the other conditions during drying which might influence survival. Using for the most part one particular strain of paracolon bacillus, they started by drying in Hiss's serum water, which, though moderately good for *Strep. pyogenes*, was of little use for most other organisms. With nutrient broth or nutrient gelatin, they obtained fair survival rates, and similar results were obtained with serum. Other substances which might have acted as protective colloids, hemoglobin, albumin, and gum acacia, gave moderate results immediately after drying, but the viability fell very rapidly on storage for a few months. Two things were clear from these results: different colloids behaved very differently in their protective power, and a fairly good survival immediately after drying was no guarantee that the culture would last long in storage. As a result of a statement by Leshchinskaya (1944) that B.C.G. could be dried in 50% aqueous glucose, Fry and Greaves tried varying concentrations of glucose, first in aqueous solution and, later, added to nutrient broth. The addition of glucose to broth produced a remarkable rise in the survival rate, with an optimum concentration of glucose usually between 5% and 10%. Similar results could be obtained by adding lactose to broth. This beneficial effect of glucose was evident, not only immediately after drying, but after storage for long periods. Figure 4 shows the survival rates with a paracolon bacillus, "D.201H," in many different experiments in broth containing from 5 to 10% of glucose and in broth without glucose, both immediately after drying and after storage. It is seen that, without glucose, only three survival rates lie above the 10% line, whereas with glucose most lie between 10% and 30%, and many are much higher.

Still using the paracolon bacillus mentioned above, they then tried the addition of glucose to other colloids. Serum, 10% hemoglobin, 25% human albumin, 25% gamma globulin, and milk, defatted by skimming and subsequent filtration, all gave good results, as also did a mixture of 3 parts serum and 1 part broth with 7.5% glucose added, which received the laboratory nickname of "*Mist. desiccans.*" Hemoglobin or albumin in a 5% concentration, and 10% aqueous gelatin, all gave a fairly good immediate survival but showed a serious drop in survival on storage for periods from 1 to 2 years.

These results had all been obtained with a moderately resistant organism, and Fry and Greaves now applied the information gained to more sensitive organisms, *N. gonorrhoeae* and *Vib. cholerae*, which they had been unable to dry satisfactorily without the help of glucose. A preliminary experiment performed with a liquid air condenser showed that with *N. gonorrhoeae* the optimum concentration of glucose was again between 5 and 10%, and a number of different experiments were carried out, using many different protective colloids with 7.5% glucose added to each. The results are shown in Table 1, in which the last two columns show unpublished results of later survival rates from some of these experiments with *Vib. cholerae*. It is seen that fairly long-term survival has been obtained with *Vib. cholerae* in "*Mist. desiccans*," and in 25% albumin, 10% hemoglobin, and egg yolk, all with the addition of 7.5% glucose. The other colloids were not so good, and 25% gamma globulin, which gave the best immediate survival, was lethal in 2 years.

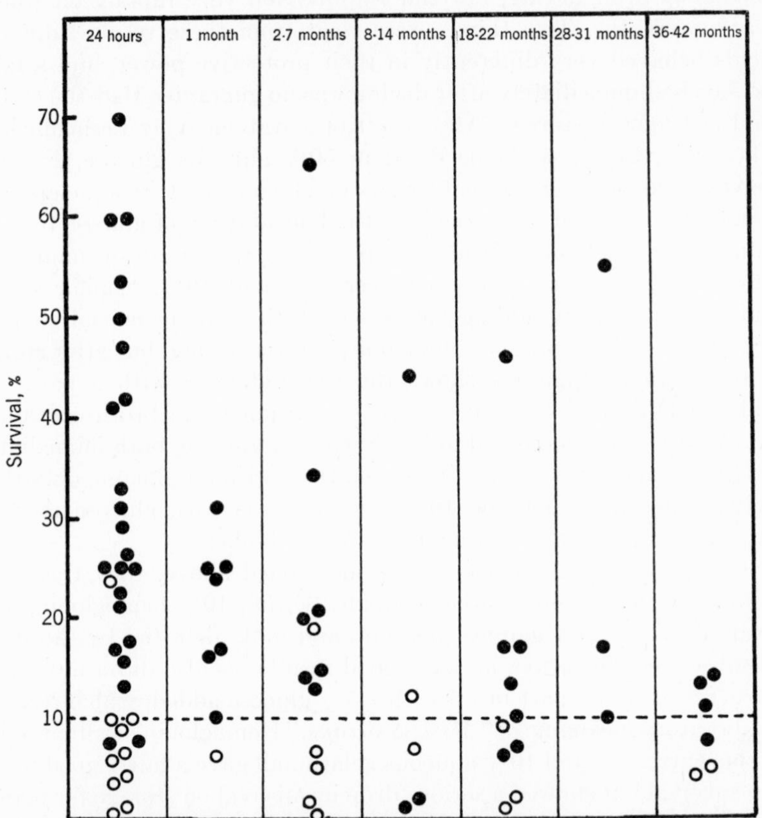


Fig. 4. The percentage survival of D.201H in broth containing from 5 to 10% glucose in many different experiments, immediately after drying and after storage for periods up to 42 months, compared with the survival in broth without added glucose. ● survival in glucose-broth; ○ survival in broth.

It appears from the foregoing account that the nature of the medium in which bacteria are dried has a very great effect on the survival rate, and it is possibly the most important single factor in the whole drying process. Water and saline, though giving some immediate survival even of *Vib. cholerae* according to Otten, do not give sufficient protection for the prolonged survival of any but the most resistant organisms, such as *Strep. pyogenes*. Most workers have accepted the idea of the necessity for a protective colloid, and broth, serum, blood, or milk have been most commonly used. Stamp's medium has been mainly used with his own technique, but Fry and Greaves reported that they found no benefit from the addition of ascorbic acid when freeze-drying, and that nutrient gelatin appeared to be no better than nutrient broth. It is clear that Stamp's method cannot be adopted as a routine method for all organisms, since he reported failures with several of the more sensitive strains which he dried. It is not possible to comment on Naylor and Smith's medium, since it has been tested by them only on one not-very-sensitive organism. The finding by Fry and Greaves that the addition of 5 to 10% glucose or

TABLE 1

PERCENTAGE SURVIVAL OF *Neisseria gonorrhoeae* AND *Vibrio cholerae* AFTER DRYING IN VARIOUS MEDIA CONTAINING GLUCOSE

| Drying medium containing 7.5% glucose | Percentage survival after | | | | | | |
|---|---|---|---|---|---|---|---|
| | 24 hours | 3–4 months | 12 months | 24 hours | 26–28 months | 42–52 months | 5 years |
| | *Neisseria gonorrhoeae* | | | *Vibrio cholerae* | | | |
| "*Mist. desiccans*" | — | 1 | — | 5 | 3 | 1.2 | 0.6 |
| Albumin 5% | 1.3 | 1 | 0.02 | 0.3 | 0.04 | 0.0004 | |
| Albumin 25% | — | — | — | 7 | 0.4 | 0.5 | 0.3 |
| $\alpha + \beta$ Globulin 20% | — | — | — | 2 | 0.03 | 0.03 | 0.025 |
| $\gamma$ Globulin 25% | — | — | — | 12 | 0 | | |
| Serum | 1.7 | — | 0.002 | 3 | 0.08 | 0.0001 | |
| Hemoglobin 10% | 9 | — | 0.25 | 5.5 | 0.5 | 0.2 | 0.26 |
| Reduced hemoglobin | — | 0.5 | 0.025 | 2 | 0.01 | | |
| Egg yolk | 1.7 | 0.3 | 0.6 | 10 | 0.9 | 0.6 | 0.4 |

lactose greatly enhances the survival rate is interesting when taken in conjunction with the results with milk mentioned above. In milk we have a protective colloid and lactose, and it is therefore similar in constitution to some of the media used with success by Fry and Greaves. It is possible that milk may prove to be a very useful drying medium, but more experimental work is necessary before a definite opinion can be formed. Table 1 shows that, with *Vib. cholerae* dried in albumin, the concentration of the protein is a matter of some importance, and the survival rate is increased tenfold when the albumin is raised from 5 to 25%. Both 25% albumin and 10% hemoglobin give a much higher survival rate than serum, which contains about 7% protein. The protein content of milk is lower still, and it seems possible therefore that long-term survival of delicate organisms in milk may not be good.

### 3. *Conditions of Growth and Age of the Culture*

Very little information is available about the conditions under which a culture should be grown to ensure the best survival after drying. Naylor and Smith (1946) state that cultures of *Serratia marcescens* grown at 30° to 34°C. for 18 to 24 hours were more resistant to drying than those grown for longer or shorter periods. They also found that cultures of the same organism aerated by vigorous shaking during growth were more resistant than non-aerated cultures. Fry and Greaves (1951) confirmed part of these findings by showing that, with their paracolon bacillus, a culture grown on agar for 20 hours had a survival rate five to six times greater than a similar culture grown for 4½ hours. This difference was apparent not only immediately after drying but after storage for 13 and 29 months. It is possible that this is not a general rule, and other organisms may behave differently, but until further evidence is available it is wise not to attempt to dry very young cultures.

### 4. *Cell Concentration of the Suspension*

The effect of the concentration of the bacterial suspension has been investigated by three workers, with three different results. Otten (1930) dried *Salm. typhi*, *Shigella shigae*, and *Vib. cholerae* in concentrated suspensions and in the same suspensions diluted tenfold and found that in each case the more concentrated suspension had the higher survival rate. Stamp (1947) says "with a diminution in cell concentration, the percentage survival rate rises." Fry and Greaves (1951) give figures to show that, with three different suspensions of the same organism, with a factor of 10,000 between the weakest and the strongest, there was no significant difference in the survival rates after storage for 3 months and for 8 months. Immediately after drying the weakest suspension gave a somewhat higher survival than the other two, which were approximately equal.

It seems possible that these conflicting views may be reconciled if we examine the methods employed. Otten was drying in a medium containing no protective colloid, and it is very probable that the high proportion of cells killed in the early stages of drying provided protection for the remainder, so that the subsequent death rate was lower than would have occurred with an initially weak suspension. He quotes experiments to show that the addition of dead cells to a living suspension increases the survival rate. Stamp was drying slowly from the liquid state, at room temperature, and, as has already been mentioned, there was opportunity for growth to occur during the early stages of drying. This would be unlikely to happen with highly concentrated suspensions, but with weaker suspensions growth might balance some of the killing, giving an apparently higher percentage survival. As these organisms were being dried in nutrient gelatin, there was already an ample supply of protective colloid, so that Otten's effect would not be operative.

It is probable, therefore, that when cultures are dried from the frozen state with an adequate protective colloid the percentage survival is independent of the initial cell concentration. This does not apply to the total numerical survival, and in order to keep this as high as possible and ensure a long survival time it is clearly advantageous to use fairly concentrated suspensions.

### 5. *Degree of Vacuum, and Drying Temperature*

These two factors may be considered together, since they are interdependent in many techniques. All workers, with the exception of Hammer (1911), who used a water pump to lower the pressure to 18 mm. Hg, and Stamp (1947), who dried at a pressure of 100 to 300 mm. Hg, have apparently used the best vacuum obtainable with the apparatus at their disposal, with the object of getting through the initial stages of drying as quickly as possible. Most of those who give any figures mention a vacuum of 0.01 mm. Hg or less, and there is reason to believe that such a vacuum is likely to give satisfactory results, provided that other conditions are suitable.

The temperature of the suspension during drying is a point on which there are a variety of opinions. Shackell in 1909 pointed out the danger of concentration of salts if drying were done from the liquid state. He stipulated that complete freezing was essential if this salt concentration were to be avoided. This method of prefreezing, first with an ice-salt mixture and later, as it became readily available, with solid carbon dioxide, has been employed by many workers with success. There is, however, a large group of workers, whose methods have been described under "Brown's Method" and "Sordelli's Method," who employed no prefreezing, and the temperature during drying must have been entirely dependent on the rate of evaporation and the volume of fluid to be evaporated. In most of these methods a single drop of suspension was dried, on filter paper, Cellophane, sand, or beads, or put directly into a glass tube. If such a drop of suspension could be completely insulated from its surroundings, its size would be immaterial and, in the case of water, assuming an initial temperature of 20°C., about one-sixth of its volume would have to be evaporated from the liquid state in order to freeze the remaining five-sixths. In contact with a glass tube, the proportion dried from the liquid state depends on the ratio between the mass of water and the mass of glass to be cooled, and the latter depends to some extent on the conductivity of the glass. If the conductivity were infinite and if 1 gram of water were placed in a glass tube weighing 5 grams, the amount of water to be evaporated before freezing occurred would be increased from 0.152 to 0.182 gram—a relatively small increase. If 0.1 gram of water were dried in such a tube, however, the amount of water to be evaporated before freezing would be 0.0455 gram, very nearly half the total. In actual practice conditions are not so bad as this, since the poor conductivity of glass ensures that only a small part of the tube has to be cooled as low as 0°C. before evaporative freezing occurs, provided that this state is reached quickly. For this reason it is essential to evaporate the fluid rapidly with good pump if small volumes are to be dried. Greaves (1944), describing his method of centrifugal vacuum freezing, said: "This method has also worked well even with very small quantities, for example, quantities so small as 1/40 ml. have been dried successfully from the frozen state; but with these very small quantities it is necessary to attain the requisite vacuum rapidly or there will be a tendency for them to dry out from the liquid state."

Rayner (1943) was aware of this difficulty and overcame it by placing single drops of suspension on small Cellophane squares, resting on a layer of filter paper in a glass Petri dish. Though the total mass of glass was considerable, the Cellophane strips were so well insulated from it that single drops could be frozen by evaporation without difficulty. Campbell-Renton (1942), who also used one drop of suspension, put this directly into a glass tube of 8 mm. internal diameter; the length was not stated, but the tube may well have contained between 2 and 5 grams of glass. Each tube was plugged so that considerable obstruction was presented to the flow of water vapor. Campbell-Renton states that freezing occurred in 4 to 5 minutes, but it is probable that by this time a large proportion of the drop had already dried from the liquid state. Rhodes (1950), on the other hand, with a rather similar technique, said that her suspensions (a loopful on the inner wall of a glass tube, 8 mm. × 60 mm.) appeared dry in 2 to 3 minutes, and it is therefore very doubtful if any freezing occurred.

It is generally assumed that freezing by itself is not harmful to bacteria; there is, however, some evidence to the contrary. Haines (1938) rapidly froze small volumes of bacterial suspensions in water, using a limited number of different bacteria. He found that, after freezing at −70°C. and subsequent thawing, a certain proportion of the cells was killed, varying from about 80% with *Ps. aeruginosa* to little or none with sporebearers. He also found that the mortality with *Ps. aeruginosa* was about the same at three different temperatures, −70°, −20°, and −5°C. These results were obtained in water, but some of the author's unpublished results suggest that a suitable colloid may protect against the effects of freezing as well as of drying. A paracolon bacillus suspended in 10% nutrient gelatin showed no fall in viable count after rapid freezing and storage for 1 hour at −20°C. and in liquid air. In another experiment, rapid freezing at −20°C. of a suspension of the same organisms in Hiss's serum water gave a survival rate of only 40%. Suspended in 25% human albumin, this organism showed 91% survival after freezing and storage for 24 hours at −20°C.; the same albumin suspension frozen and held in liquid air for 1 hour showed 88% survival. It seems probable therefore that, although freezing in aqueous suspensions may be lethal for some organisms, this action may be partly counteracted by the presence of the protective colloid usually used in freeze-drying.

All the evidence shows that drying from the frozen state is desirable for all organisms and is apparently essential for the more sensitive ones, if long survival is desired. Whether this is achieved by prefreezing or by evaporative freezing is a matter of choice, but it must be remembered that, with evaporative freezing, if the volume is very small it may not freeze unless evaporation is very rapid, and if large it will have to be degassed first, or else dried by the centrifugal process.

### 6. *Atmosphere of Storage*

The choice in practice lies between air, nitrogen or some other inert gas, and vacuum. Very little experimental evidence is available as a guide. Rogers (1914) stored dried cultures of bacteria *in vacuo*, and in air, oxygen, nitrogen, hydrogen, and carbon dioxide. He found the highest survival with vacuum storage, and the lowest survivals with air and oxygen; results with nitrogen, hydrogen, and carbon dioxide were intermediate. All these gases were carefully dried except air, which gave worse results than oxygen, possibly on account of the contained moisture. Naylor and Smith (1946) stored lyophilized cultures of *Serratia marcescens* in air, vacuum, "ordinary tank nitrogen," and nitrogen which had been treated to remove oxygen, carbon dioxide, and moisture. After 49 days the survival rates were: in air 9%, in vacuum 99%, in untreated nitrogen 28%, and in treated nitrogen 26%. It appeared that the deleterious effect of nitrogen was not due to impurities or moisture. Stark and Herrington (1931) state: "Tests showed that exposure of extremely dry bacteria to free oxygen gas causes a pronounced killing of the bacteria."

What evidence there is seems to be against free oxygen; a few workers (Swift, Morton and Pulaski, and Stillman), however, have admitted air to the tubes before sealing the cotton plugs with melted wax. In most cases air was admitted without drying, so that an unknown amount of moisture also reached the dry culture. Swift (1937) does suggest that it might be better to pass the air over calcium chloride, but he does not appear to have done this as a routine. Stillman says: "It is essential that no moisture be permitted to enter the tube"; but he apparently did not take any steps to dry the air. None of these workers has given any quantitative results, but neither Stillman nor Morton and Pulaski have been able to record certain survival of cultures of moderately resistant organisms for periods much over 3 years. Swift reports long survival of many strains of hemolytic streptococci, but these organisms are so resistant to drying that their survival is no evidence that the technique is a good one.

Ruling out air, whether dried or not, we are left to choose between an inert gas or vacuum. Rogers' experiments quoted above showed that nitrogen is inferior to a vacuum, and this is confirmed by Naylor and Smith's results. The great majority of workers have stored their cultures *in vacuo*, and this includes all those who have shown good long-term survival of the most sensitive organisms. Proom and Hemmons (1949), however, filled their tubes with dry nitrogen before sealing. They give no information about how the nitrogen was dried, but Proom (1951), describing his technique, says: "Dry nitrogen from a cylinder is run into the desiccator"; he apparently assumes that the gas as coming from the cylinder is dry. This is a dangerous assumption.

Since so many workers have used vacuum storage with success, and since it is clearly the most certain way of ensuring that no uncontrolled amount of moisture reaches the dried cultures, it is interesting to find that some of those who used air or nitrogen did so because of the difficulty encountered in opening tubes sealed *in vacuo* with safety. Swift (1937) refers to this difficulty, and Proom and Hemmons speak of the inrush of air which "is likely to contaminate the culture, or, when the tubes are sealed over a cotton-wool plug, to push the plug down to the bottom of the tube when it is opened." Flosdorf and Kimball (1940), who used vacuum sealing, give an account of their method of opening tubes, in which the container, after being scratched with a file, "is wrapped under a cloth impregnated with antiseptic to prevent the spreading of dry organisms as air rushes in." At least one account has been reported of a laboratory worker who was infected through carelessly "popping open" a dried culture sealed *in vacuo*. This difficulty is overcome very simply by using the method described by Wright (1912) for accurately breaking a wide-bore glass tube. A nick is made with a file, and a small hot bead of glass is pressed into the nick. A minute crack develops round the tube, through which air enters gently, and in a few seconds the top of the tube can be removed with no inrush of air.

### 7. *Temperature of Storage*

This is another point about which there is very little experimental evidence available. Rogers (1914) reported results which showed that, with lactic acid bacteria dried in milk, the higher the temperature of storage, the lower was the survival rate. His cultures were held for 30 and 60 days at temperatures from −6° to 37°C. He found very little survival after 60 days at 30° or 37°C. Weiser and Hennum (1947) reported that dried cultures of *Bact. coli* gave a higher survival rate when stored in the refrigerator than at room temperature. Proom and Hemmons (1949) found similar results with *Bact. coli* and *N. meningitidis* stored at 4°C., room temperature, and 37°C. From these few results it appears that a low storage temperature is desirable when possible. Most workers have stored their cultures in the dark at room temperature with success, and if large collections are to be maintained it is obviously impracticable to keep them all in a refrigerator. It is wise, however, to choose the coolest place available in the laboratory for storage.

### 8. *Residual Moisture*

Rogers (1914) divided a dried culture of lactic acid bacteria in milk into three parts. One part was exposed to sulfuric acid to reduce the water content from 1.39 to 0.90%. Another was exposed to water vapor to increase the water content to 5.77%. All were then sealed and kept at 28°C. for 157 days. The one containing the highest water content was much less viable than the other two, which were approximately equal. From this he argued that the lower the residual moisture, the better would be the survival rate, and this view has been generally accepted ever since. The literature of bacterial drying abounds with phrases such as "the cultures must be as dry as possible." Fisher (1950), however, says that, with Sordelli's method, "experience has shown that an increase in the drying time is accompanied by an increase in the killing effect of the process." Fry and Greaves (1951) confirmed this by showing that, if a number of tubes of the same suspension were dried together, some receiving a short and some a long drying, the tubes which had been dried for the longer time, and were therefore dried more completely, showed the lower survival rate, both immediately and after storage for many months. Table 2 shows these results, with four different suspending media, serum, 10% hemoglobin, 5% albumin, and 5% aqueous gelatin. In view of these results, and the greatly increased survival when 5 to 10% glucose is added to almost any medium, Fry and Greaves put forward the hypothesis that glucose acts by regulating the final moisture content of the culture and preventing it from becoming too dry. Strong solutions of glucose, 50% or more, are impossible to dry by any means, and it seems reasonable to suppose that lower concentrations may retain a certain amount of water which cannot be removed however much the drying time is prolonged. This hypothesis needs further investigation, but it is probably best, unless glucose is used in the drying medium, to dry for a few hours only and not to attempt to achieve the highest degree of desiccation.

TABLE 2
PERCENTAGE SURVIVAL OF A PARACOLON BACILLUS AFTER SHORT AND LONG DRYING IN FOUR DIFFERENT COLLOIDS WITHOUT ADDED GLUCOSE

| Drying medium | Drying time, hours | Percentage survival after | | | |
|---|---|---|---|---|---|
| | | 24 hours | 1 month | 9–13 months | 20–22 months |
| Serum | 18 | — | 8 | 10 | 10 |
| | 336 | — | 0.2 | 0.6 | 0.1 |
| Hemoglobin 10% | 2½ | 2.2 | 0.1 | $8 \times 10^{-5}$ | |
| | 24 | 1.4 | 0.01 | $8 \times 10^{-6}$ | |
| Albumin 5% | 2½ | 6.5 | 0.9 | $4 \times 10^{-5}$ | |
| | 4½ | 3 | 0.1 | $2 \times 10^{-5}$ | |
| Gelatin 5% | 2½ | 5.5 | 2.2 | 0.06 | |
| | 24 | 0.9 | 0.007 | $4 \times 10^{-5}$ | |

### 9. *Absorption of Water*

The chemical desiccants which have been employed are few in number and include sulfuric acid, phosphorus pentoxide, calcium chloride, and anhydrous calcium sulfate. These are all satisfactory, provided that they are used properly. With sulfuric acid occasional agitation is essential to prevent irregular dilution. Phosphorus pentoxide is a very convenient dry desiccant, but it is more expensive than calcium chloride or calcium sulfate. Calcium sulfate is very economical, as it can be regenerated by heat and used repeatedly. Larger amounts of calcium chloride and calcium sulfate are required than of phosphorus pentoxide, so that space has to be provided in the drying chamber for larger desiccant trays.

When drying with evaporative freezing, it is essential that an excess of desiccant be available. Unless this is done, the upper surface of the desiccant becomes "flooded" and forms a hard layer which prevents further rapid absorption of water. Although all the water will ultimately be absorbed, it may be impossible to get a satisfactorily-rapid snap-freeze. The total amount of desiccant needed may be reduced somewhat if it is spread out in a thin layer in several trays to increase the surface area.

The alternative to chemical desiccants is the use of a refrigerated condenser. This may take the form of coils in the drying chamber, mechanically refrigerated, or of one or more external condensers in the vacuum line, usually cooled with solid carbon dioxide in alcohol or some other suitable liquid. Technical details have been discussed by Greaves in an earlier chapter of this book.

## V. THE DEATH OF DRIED BACTERIA

One clear fact emerges from all the results quoted above. Whatever the technique, and whatever the organism, some will die during the process or at some later date. It is of interest to see when and why this occurs, even though some of the conclusions may be of a negative kind.

### 1. *The Time of Maximum Killing*

Fry and Greaves (1951) performed five experiments to determine this point for the paracolon bacillus with which they chiefly worked, using four different suspending media. In each experiment a number of tubes, each containing 0.25 ml. of the suspension, were dried together by the centrifugal vacuum freezing method, and at intervals one tube was taken out and counted. The vacuum had to be broken each time this was done, but, with the particular apparatus in use, this occupied only about 2 minutes and the remaining tubes had only a short exposure to air. The results of these experiments are given in Table 3. It is seen that

TABLE 3
Rate of Death of a Paracolon Bacillus in the Early Stages of Drying in Four Different Media

| Time after start of drying | Glucose broth, 7.5% | Glucose broth, 7.5% | Albumin, 5% | Aqueous gelatin, 5% | Hemoglobin 10% |
|---|---|---|---|---|---|
| 30 min. | 85 | — | 69 | 87 | 61 |
| 1 hr. | 61 | 78 | 56 | 85 | 25 |
| 2 hr. | 50 | 72 | 19 | — | 8.5 |
| 3 hr. | — | — | 16 | 35 | — |
| 4 hr. | 53 | 65 | 9 | 9 | 3.5 |
| 6 hr. | 68 | 72 | — | — | 3 |
| 8 hr. | — | — | 3 | — | — |
| 10 hr. | — | 60 | — | — | — |
| 12 hr. | — | 60 | — | — | — |
| 24 hr. | 50 | — | 0.4 | 0.9 | 1.4 |

in 7.5% glucose broth most of the killing has occurred in the first 2 hours. In the three colloids with no added glucose, two, albumin and hemoglobin, show a steep drop in the first 2 hours, followed by a slower steady fall up to 24 hours. Gelatin, however, shows a reversed effect with little killing in the first hour and a more rapid fall during the next 23 hours. This may be due to the early formation of a thin scale on the surface of the gelatin which hinders loss of water from the deeper layers.

Whether similar results would be found with other organisms is a matter for conjecture, but these figures suggest that the most lethal time is during the first few hours, when the most rapid removal of water is occurring.

### 2. *The Factors Determining Death or Survival*

With drying, as with most other adverse conditions to which bacteria may be subjected, it is remarkable that a certain proportion will die, and others survive. There seem to be only two possibilities as to what determines whether a particular organism shall survive or die. Either it is purely a matter of chance, or else the survivors are more resistant to drying than are those that die. In an attempt to settle this question, Fry and Greaves put up 18 tubes containing equal volumes of a suspension of their paracolon bacillus, in 10% hemoglobin with 7.5% glucose. Two tubes were counted immediately, and the remaining 16 were dried together *in vacuo* over phosphorous pentoxide. After 24 hours' drying, all the tubes were reconstituted with their original volume of water, 3 taken at random were counted, and the remaining 13 redried, with no interval for further growth to occur. This was repeated on the two succeeding days, 2 tubes being counted each day. The results are shown in Table 4. It is apparent that,

TABLE 4

EFFECT OF SUCCESSIVE DRYINGS WITHOUT INTERMEDIATE GROWTH

(24-hr. culture of a paracolon bacillus dried in 10% hemoglobin with 7.5% glucose)

| No. of times dried | Viable count, millions per ml. | Percentage of original count | Percentage of previous day |
|---|---|---|---|
| 0 | 193 | — | — |
| 1 | 42 | 22 | 22 |
| 2 | 12 | 6 | 29 |
| 3 | 3.5 | 1.8 | 29 |
| 4 | 1.3 | 0.7 | 37 |

apart from a slight rise in the survival rate after the fourth drying, there is no evidence that the survivors at any stage showed increased resistance to drying.

### 3. *The Vitality of Surviving Organisms*

Some workers have found difficulty in recovering cultures from the dried state. Proom and Hemmons (1949) say that dried cultures have an unusually long lag phase when subcultivated. This has not been the experience of the author, who routinely subcultures one 0.02-ml. drop of the reconstituted culture, often after diluting 100- or 1000-fold, on the surface of a solid medium. Such a method gives growth which cannot be distinguished, in speed or colony size, from that given by a fresh undried culture. If a dried culture is so nearly dead that no colonies are obtained from one drop in this way, the drying technique should be very carefully examined and changed if necessary.

If subculturing is done only in a fluid medium, which is a method to be heartily condemned as giving no information as to the approximate survival rate, there may well be an increase in the lag phase if the number of surviving organisms is very small. Fry and Greaves give the results of an experiment which illustrates this, but they also show that when the proportion of surviving bacteria to medium is corrected the lag phase and rate of growth are almost identical with those shown by the same culture before drying.

## VI. FURTHER WORK

As a result of the enormous amount of work that has been done in the past forty years on drying of bacteria, a few points emerge as probably essential to success if sensitive organisms are to be preserved. A good vacuum ensures rapid removal of water, and a satisfactory desiccant or refrigerated condenser must be provided to deal with this water. Unless cultures are dried from the frozen state, harm will be done by salt concentration during drying; the frozen state may be achieved either by prefreezing or by evaporative freezing. With the latter method, the necessary vacuum must be attained quickly, and some means, either degassing or centrifugation, must be employed to overcome frothing unless the quantities of suspension are very small. If these are too small, evaporative freezing may not occur. The suspending medium is a matter of great importance, and most of the evidence is in favor of a fairly concentrated solution of some colloid. Unless glucose is added to the colloid, a fairly short drying time of a few hours is advisable, but this must depend on the volume of fluid to be dried and the efficiency of the apparatus. Storage *in vacuo* is the simplest and most certain method of ensuring that the cultures remain dry; oxygen appears to be harmful, and if an inert gas is used it must be thoroughly dried before exposing the dried cultures to it.

These few positive facts leave considerable scope for further investigation. The mechanical side of the problem is now fairly simple, and it is easy to buy, or even make, an efficient drying apparatus. How to use it is another matter. Probably the most vital question is still that of the suspending medium. We know nothing of the mode of action of the colloid, except that some are more protective than others. If we can find out why this is so, we may have a clue as to how colloids exert their protective power. The action of crystalline substances is likewise obscure; certain carbohydrates appear to protect, but the explanation of this is still hypothetical. Is it bound up with the question of the residual water content? If not, what is the optimum water content, and is it the same for all organisms? If these questions can eventually be answered for a number of different organisms, it may be possible to understand why some are so resistant and some so sensitive to drying. Finally, we must remember that there are two separate problems involved, death by drying and death in the dried state. Usually these appear to be fairly well correlated, but this is not always so, and it is necessary to bear in mind that an organism which may survive drying fairly well may not survive long storage in the dried state.

## REFERENCES

Brown, J. H. 1925. The Preservation of Bacteria *in Vacuo*. I. *Abstr. Bacteriol.* **9,** 8.

Brown, J. H. 1932. The Preservation of Bacteria *in Vacuo*. II. *J. Bacteriol.* **23,** 44.

Campbell-Renton, M. L. 1942. The Recovery of Cholera Vibrios after Drying. *J. Pathol. Bacteriol.* **54,** 121–125.

Elser, W. J., Thomas, R. A., and Steffen, G. I. 1935. The Desiccation of Sera and Other Biological Products (Including Microorganisms) in the Frozen State with Preservation of the Original Qualities of Products So Treated. *J. Immunol.* **28,** 433–473.

Fisher, P. J. 1950. Viability of Dried Cultures. A Note on the Immediate Death Rate. *J. Gen. Microbiol.* **4,** 455–456.

Flosdorf, E. W., and Kimball, A. C. 1940. Studies with *H. pertussis*. II. Maintenance of Cultures in Phase I. *J. Bacteriol.* **39,** 255–261.

Flosdorf, E. W., and Mudd, S. 1935. Procedure and Apparatus for Preservation in "Lyophile" Form of Serum and Other Biological Substances. *J. Immunol.* **29,** 389–425.

Flosdorf, E. W., and Mudd, S. 1938. An Improved Procedure and Apparatus for Preservation of Sera, Microorganisms and Other Substances—the "Cryochem" Process. *J. Immunol.* **34,** 469–490.

Frobisher, M., Parsons, E. I., Pai, S. E., and Hakim, S. 1947. A Simplified Method for the Preservation of Bacteria by Desiccation *in Vacuo*. *J. Lab. Clin. Med.* **32,** 1008–1015.

Fry, R. M., and Greaves, R. I. N. 1951. The Survival of Bacteria during and after Drying. *J. Hyg.* **49,** 220–246.

Glover, R. E. 1946. The Effects of (a) Freeze-Drying and (b) Low Temperature on the Viability of *Mycobacterium tuberculosis*. *J. Pathol. Bacteriol.* **58,** 111–114.

Greaves, R. I. N. 1944. Centrifugal Vacuum Freezing. Its Application to the Drying of Biological Materials from the Frozen State. *Nature* **153,** 485–487.

Haines, R. B. 1938. The Effect of Freezing on Bacteria. *Proc. Roy. Soc.* (*London*) **124B,** 451–463.

Hammer, B. W. 1911. A Note on the Vacuum Desiccation of Bacteria. *J. Med. Research* **24,** 527–530.

Harris, M. M., and Lange, L. B. 1933. A Note on the Preservation of Acid-Fast Bacteria *in Vacuo*. *J. Lab. Clin. Med.* **18,** 1066–1067.

Harris, D. L., and Shackell, L. F. 1911. The Effect of Vacuum Desiccation upon the Virus of Rabies with Remarks upon a New Method. *J. Am. Public Health Assoc.* **1,** 52.

Heller, G. 1941. A Quantitative Study of Environmental Factors Involved in the Survival and Death of Bacteria in the Desiccated State. *J. Bacteriol.* **41,** 109–126.

Hornibrook, J. W. 1949. A Simple, Inexpensive Apparatus for the Desiccation of Bacteria and Other Substances. *J. Lab. Clin. Med.* **34**, 1315–1320.

Hornibrook, J. W. 1950. A Useful Menstruum for Drying Organisms and Viruses. *J. Lab. Clin. Med.* **35**, 788–792.

Knox, R. 1939. Desiccation of Filterable Tumors and Other Biological Materials. *J. Pathol. Bacteriol.* **49**, 467–481.

Leifson, E. 1936. The Preservation of Bacteria by Drying *in Vacuo*. *Am. J. Hyg.* **23**, 231–236.

Leshchinskaya, E. N. 1944. The Immunizing Value of the B.C.G. Dry Glucose Vaccine. *Problemy tuberk.* No. **6**, pp. 55–59; translated in *Am. Rev. Soviet Med.* Feb. 1946, pp. 210–215; reviewed in *Public Health Repts.* (*U.S.*) 1947, **62**, 211.

Morton, H. E., and Pulaski, E. J. 1938. The Preservation of Bacterial Cultures. I. *J. Bacteriol.* **35**, 163–183.

Naylor, H. B., and Smith, P. A. 1946. Factors Affecting the Viability of *Serratia marcescens* during Dehydration and Storage. *J. Bacteriol.* **52**, 565–573.

Otten, L. 1930. Die Trockenkonservierung von pathogenen Bakterien. *Zentr. Bakteriol. Parasitenk. I. Orig.* **116**, 199.

Otten, L. 1932. The Preservation of Viability and Virulence in Dried Pathogenic Bacteria. *Trans. 8th Congr. Far East. Assoc. Trop. Med.* 1930, p. 89.

Potter, T. S. 1935. The Survival of Tubercle Bacilli Subjected to a Vacuum of a High Order. *J. Infectious Diseases* **57**, 149–159.

Potter, T. S. 1937. Survival of Oxygen and Water Deprival by Tubercle Bacilli. *J. Infectious Diseases* **60**, 88–93.

Potter, T. S. 1939. Survival and Death of Tubercle Bacilli Subjected to Oxygen Restriction. *J. Infectious Diseases* **64**, 261–268.

Proom, H. 1951. Some of the Factors Affecting the Viability of Bacterial Cultures Subjected to the Freeze-Drying Process, in *Freezing and Drying.* Edited by R. J. C. Harris. The Institute of Biology, London. Pp. 117–126.

Proom, H., and Hemmons, L. M. 1949. The Drying and Preservation of Bacterial Cultures. *J. Gen. Microbiol.* **3**, 7–18.

Rake, G. 1935. Viability and Virulence of Frozen and Dried Cultures of Meningococcus. *Proc. Soc. Exptl. Biol. Med.* **32**, 975–977.

Rayner, A. G. 1943. A Simple Method for the Preservation of Cultures and Sera by Drying. *J. Pathol. Bacteriol.* **55**, 373–375.

Rhodes, M. 1950. Viability of Dried Cultures. *J. Gen. Microbiol.* **4**, 450–455.

Roe, A. F. 1936. Preserving Anaerobes by Desiccation. *J. Bacteriol.* **31**, 28–29.

Rogers, L. A. 1914. The Preparation of Dried Cultures. *J. Infectious Diseases* **14**, 100–123.

St. John-Brookes, R., and Rhodes, M. 1936. Some Useful Media for the Preservation of Stock Cultures. Notes on High Vacuum Desiccation. *Rept. Proc. 2nd. Intern. Congr. Microbiol.* P. 43.

Shackell, L. F. 1909. An Improved Method of Desiccation with Some Applications to Biological Problems. *Am. J. Physiol.* **24**, 325–340.

Scherp, H. W., Flosdorf, E. W., and Shaw, D. R. 1938. Survival of the Influenzal Virus under Various Conditions. *J. Immunol.* **34**, 447–454.

Siler, J. F. 1936. Typhoid Vaccine Studies. Investigation of Virulence and Antigenic Properties of Selected Strains of the Typhoid Organism. *Am. J. Public Health* **26**, 219–228.

Stamp, Lord 1947. The Preservation of Bacteria by Drying. *J. Gen. Microbiol.* **1**, 251–265.

Stark, C. N., and Herrington, B. L. 1931. The Drying of Bacteria and the Viability of Dry Bacterial Cells. *J. Bacteriol.* **21,** 13.

Stillman, E. G. 1941. The Preservation of Pneumococcus by Freezing and Drying. *J. Bacteriol.* **42,** 689–693.

Swift, H. F. 1921. The Preservation of Stock Cultures of Bacteria by Freezing and Drying. *J. Exptl. Med.* **33,** 69–75.

Swift, H. F. 1937. A Simple Method for Preserving Bacterial Cultures by Freezing and Drying. *J. Bacteriol.* **33,** 411–421.

Topping, N. H. 1940. The Preservation of the Infectious Agents of Some of the Rickettsioses. *Public Health Repts.* (*U.S.*) **55,** 545–547.

Weiser, R. S., and Hennum, L. A. 1947. Studies on the Death of Bacteria by Drying. I. The Influence of *in Vacuo* Drying from the Frozen State and from the Liquid State on the Initial Mortality and Storage Behaviour of *Escherichia coli*. *J. Bacteriol.* **54,** 17–18.

Wright, A. E. 1912. *Handbook of the Technique of the Teat and Capillary Glass Tube.* Constable & Co., London.

CHAPTER 11

# The Preservation of Tissues

R. E. BILLINGHAM

*Department of Zoology, University College, London, England*



## I. INTRODUCTION

In recent years the transplantation of tissues has been much used for the study of a wide variety of biological problems. Moreover, it is now a commonplace of surgical practice that certain types of tissue defect can be repaired by means of grafts. Although for the permanent repair of some tissues, such as skin, only grafts removed from the intended recipient's own body are of any value, in the case of other tissues, including bone, cartilage, cornea, and blood vessels, a satisfactory functional repair may be effected by means of grafts obtained from another individual; *postmortem* material and that obtained from the operating theater constitute useful sources of grafts. Thus the problem of preserving tissues for their future use as grafts has arisen and is now of considerable importance both clinically and experimentally.

In the case of bone and cartilage, in both of which a hard, relatively inert matrix predominates, it is known that the actual cells, even in freshly removed and transplanted grafts, die very soon after transplantation presumably as a consequence of the delay before host vessels penetrate the grafts and so play practically no part in the healing process. It is scarcely surprising, therefore, that grafts of dead bone or cartilage—including even those which have been sterilized by boiling or autoclaving—are nearly, if not quite, as effective as live grafts. Provided that grafts of those tissues are aseptic, they are accepted by the body and serve as a sort of scaffolding on which new living bone or cartilage is built up although eventually their original matrices undergo absorption. The actual preservation of these tissues therefore presents little problem because of the inert nature of their matrices; they may simply be stored in a solution of a suitable antiseptic and preservative agent such as Merthiolate (sodium ethylmercurithiosalicylate) which has a relatively low cytotoxic action (*v.* Reynolds *et al.*, 1951). In practice, although cartilage grafts are normally "banked" in this manner, bone grafts are usually stored in a deep-freeze at temperatures ranging from $-20°$ to $-30°C$. (*v.* Le Cocq *et al.*, 1950).

With the remaining soft tissues of the body the problem of storage is more complicated. Even in the case of tissues where it is not obligatory for grafts to be living at the time of transplantation, preservation by means of chemical reagents such as weak antiseptics, alcohol, and formaldehyde is contraindicated since these cause, among other changes, denaturation of the native proteins. Not only does this result in alterations in the physical consistency of the tissues, but frequently their antigenic constitution becomes so modified that they are liable to be treated as foreign bodies when transplanted. There are, theoretically, two ways in which it should be possible to preserve tissues without necessitating changes even in their more labile biochemical constituents (*v.* Greaves, 1946): (a) by freezing and storage at temperatures well below the eutectic point of the tissue fluids, so that the entire tissue becomes solid and there is no liquid phase; and (b) by freezing to a low temperature and then drying directly from the frozen state *in vacuo* until the level of residual water has been reduced to a low value. If the desiccated material is then sealed off under vacuum, storage at room temperature should be possible—a consideration of some importance. In practice a third, rather short-term, method of storage, comprising refrigeration of tissues at a few degrees above freezing point, has been most widely used in the past. Its main disadvantage is that tissues so preserved are only suitable for grafting after periods of storage not exceeding a few weeks at best, while their cells are still viable and the degree of autolysis is insignificant.

It is known that prolonged storage of several tissues at low temperatures is compatible with at least some degree of cellular viability on subsequent thawing, and increasing use is being made of this method for the maintenance of tissue "banks." The almost universal availability and comparative cheapness of solid carbon dioxide makes the maintenance of such "banks" relatively simple.

Numerous histological and histochemical investigations on tissues preserved by the Altmann-Gersh freeze-drying technique (Gersh, 1932; Hoerr, 1936) have established that, if the fresh tissue is frozen as rapidly as possible and the dehydration is effected at a sufficiently low temperature, both the microstructure and the major biochemical constitution, including enzyme systems (*v.* Boell, 1945, and Gersh and Stephenson, this volume), are preserved without essential change. These facts have formed the basis of the various experimental studies that have been carried out on the possible applications of frozen-dried tissues as grafts. A general survey of this work will be presented in this chapter.

## II. STUDIES ON PRESERVED NERVE GRAFTS

When a peripheral nerve is cut, the component nerve fibers in the portion distal to the lesion are isolated from their cell bodies and rapidly degenerate. Ultimately they are absorbed altogether, mainly by the activity of macrophage cells which are derived either from the surrounding tissue or by a transformation of some of the Schwann cells (Weiss and Wang, 1945). The Schwann cells, whose protoplasm normally invests the medullary sheaths of the nerve fibers, proliferate, forming masses of protoplasmic strands which extend in parallel formation along the course of the degenerated portion of the nerve, occupying the now empty endoneurial tubes—the matrices or channels of connective tissue in which the individual nerve fibers are normally embedded and which provide for them a supporting framework. In the proximal stump of the cut nerve a similar degenerative process may extend up for a short distance. In the regeneration of a cut nerve, provided that the stumps are brought together and held in fairly close approximation—either by fine sutures uniting the relatively tough epineurial sheaths, or by means of a plasma clot (Young and Medawar, 1940)—the fibers in the proximal stump send out processes, some of which may go astray in the surrounding tissues where they are absorbed, while others penetrate the scar tissue which forms at the site of the injury. These may eventually find their way into the degenerated peripheral stump of the cut nerve. The successful fibers grow down along the channels provided by the original endoneurial tubes at a rate of several millimeters a day, and many of them eventually complete the formation of motor and sensory endings with a corresponding functional recovery. It is believed that the proliferated Schwann cells help to preserve the patency of these endoneurial tubes and also that their protoplasm provides suitable surfaces along which the regenerating nerve axons adhere and glide as they grow peripherally. Moreover, these Schwann cells actually migrate out from the stumps of a cut nerve and may form a sort of protoplasmic connecting bridge which serves to conduct the outgrowing axons from the central stump across the gap to the peripheral stump.

If as a result of injury a considerable length of peripheral nerve is destroyed, the surgeon may be unable to approximate the stumps, even by mobilizing and rerouting the nerve. In such cases if any functional recovery is to take place the loss has somehow to be made good. Experimental studies (Sanders and Young, 1942) on animals established the fact that a gap in a peripheral nerve could be successfully repaired by the use of a nerve autograft—i.e., a suitable length of nerve cut from another intact peripheral nerve elsewhere in the recipient's own body. The ends of the graft are simply approximated to the proximal and peripheral stumps of the cut nerve, and, eventually, regenerating fibers from the proximal stump grow down through the endoneurial channels provided by the graft, which acts as a sort of bridge, and so enter and reinnervate the peripheral portion of the nerve. There is now ample clinical evidence as to the success of nerve autografts in man (Seddon, 1947). The surgeon, of course, has to face the problem of obtaining a suitable nerve autograft, and normally only minor and relatively unimportant cutaneous nerves can be sacrificed. Since the graft has to be of approximately the same diameter as the nerve to be repaired, it may be necessary to place two or more strips of cutaneous nerve side-by-side—forming a so-called cable graft—to conduct all the fibers growing out from the proximal stump across the gap.

The desirability of being able to make use of nerve homografts—i.e., grafts cut from other individuals—is obvious since such grafts could easily be removed from freshly amputated limbs, etc., and possibly stored under appropriate conditions until required. The problem of procuring grafts of the requisite size would thus be greatly simplified. Extensive experimental trials in which nerve homografts were used to bridge experimentally created gaps in limb nerves in animals, particularly in the rabbit, have given very promising results, since the degree of functional recovery obtained was comparable to that achieved when autografts were used (Sanders and Young, 1942; Gutmann and Sanders, 1942). The cellular reactions that took place in transplanted nerve homografts differed considerably from those in autografts in that there was a marked lymphocytic infiltration in the former. However, with homografts which had been stored in Ringer's solution for 7 to 21 days at 2°C., the cellular reaction was very much less and the functional recovery almost as good as when fresh homografts were used (Gutmann and Sanders, 1942).

Unfortunately, the optimistic hopes aroused by the results obtained with nerve homografts in animal experiments have, so far as clinical trials are concerned, not been sustained. Careful trials in which either fresh or stored (in Ringer's solution in an icebox) nerve homografts have been used to repair gaps in peripheral nerves in man have all proved failures (Seddon and Holmes, 1944; Barnes *et al.*, 1946). Although the regenerating fibers of the host did penetrate the proximal end of the graft for a short distance, they eventually stopped as the homografted nerve progressively lost its characteristic properties and became hard and fibrosed. It is now believed that these homologous nerve grafts, like those of blood vessels and most other tissues, sooner or later elicit a transplantation immunity reaction on the part of the host as a consequence of which an inflammatory reaction occurs in the grafted tissue and its cell population is destroyed. New connective tissue fibers are laid down within a nerve homograft by the invading fibroblasts of the host, and eventually the very channels along which it was hoped that the regenerating nerve fibers would be able to grow become obliterated and are no longer patent. It has been suggested that the difference between the experimental and the clinical results obtained with nerve homografts may be attributable to the relatively short grafts used experimentally (Seddon and Holmes, 1944). In such cases either the immune reaction on the part of the host may not have become effective before the regenerating fibers have actually grown through the grafted segment, or, more probably, sufficient fibrous tissue may not have been laid down to prevent the passage of the regenerating nerve fibers. In human neurosurgery, in which relatively long homografts are normally required, the immune reaction is probably evoked and fibrosis takes place long before the regenerating fibers have progressed very far across the nerve bridge.

Attempts have been made by various workers to use preserved or fixed nerves in experimental investigations, but these have all been more or less unsuccessful. Weiss and Taylor (1943a), attributing these failures to denaturation, have investigated the Altmann-Gersh freeze-drying method (Gersh, 1932) as a preservative; a non-denaturing treatment known to preserve microstructure and biochemical constitution without essential alteration. They dissected out peripheral nerves aseptically and then froze them instantaneously by dropping them into *iso*pentane chilled to about −150°C. with liquid nitrogen. These grafts were then desiccated by maintaining them under a high vacuum over phosphoric oxide for 1 week at a temperature of −40°C., after which they were sealed off in sterile containers and stored for 2 to 4 months. Before grafting, the stored frozen-dried nerves were rehydrated in Ringer's solution *in vacuo* at room temperature when they resumed their normal outward appearance and characteristic histological structure. The authors claimed that when segments of homologous devitalized nerves, about 1 to 2 cm. in length, were grafted into gaps in hind limb nerves of rats, cats, and monkeys the grafts healed and promoted regeneration much as live nerves do and good functional recovery was eventually attained (Weiss, 1943a). It was reported that most heteroplastic grafts devitalized in this manner behaved like foreign bodies. Taylor and Weiss concluded that, as their experimental results indicated that freeze-drying preserved the essential biophysical and biochemical requirements for regenerative nerve growth inherent in peripheral nerve, the supply problem in nerve grafting had been brought nearer to its solution. Assorted nerves of various sizes could be stored in the dry condition. So far no reports have appeared of any clinical trials of frozen-dried nerve homografts. Since only living homologous cells are known to be capable of eliciting a homograft reaction, devitalized but undenatured nerve homografts may well fail to provoke an inflammatory reaction after transplantation. Nevertheless it seems quite certain that these grafts would become recolonized by host fibroblast cells and, presumably, new collagen fibers would eventually be laid down exactly as in the case of fresh homografts. The successes reported by Weiss and Taylor may reasonably be ascribed to the relatively short grafts used. There appears to be much justification for Seddon and Holmes's (1944), remark that "the results of animal experiment have not been uninformative so much as actually misleading, and the proper study of homografts, so far as clinical surgery is concerned, must be in man," at least so far as nerve homografts are concerned.

## III. A METHOD OF EFFECTING NERVE REUNION WITH FROZEN-DRIED ARTERY SEGMENTS

As an alternative to the more conventional technique of approximating the stumps of a severed nerve, or of inserting a nerve graft, by suturing, Weiss (1943b) and Weiss and Taylor (1943b) have devised a technique in experiments conducted on rats, rabbits, cats, and monkeys whereby the stumps can be satisfactorily spliced together by inserting them into a close-fitting sleeve of live artery. This becomes securely fixed to the surfaces of the inserted nerve ends through the clotting of blood plasma and tissue fluids and thus holds them together in fairly close proximity. Initially a blood clot cements the nerve ends together, but this undergoes various changes so that eventually the gap is bridged by longitudinally oriented fibrin strands which, it is claimed, greatly facilitate the passage of the regenerating nerve fibers and their accompanying sheath cells. The particular advantages claimed for this technique of "tubular splicing" are that no foreign bodies in the form of sutures have to be inserted, and the uninterrupted canalization between the stumps prevents escape of regenerating nerve fibers into the surrounding tissues and also the ingrowth of scarifying tissue into the gap between the stumps which would prevent the passage of the regenerating fibers.

Subsequently, Weiss (1943c) reported that homoplastic frozen-dried artery sleeves, after rehydration, gave satisfactory results since their most desirable properties were conserved. It was stated that these frozen-dried sleeve grafts persisted as such for many months, at least, and became partially repopulated by host cells. No marked inflammatory reactions were provoked, although the adhesions between such sleeves and their surroundings were more extensive than those that occurred with live arteries, and local lesions between the inner wall of the sleeve and the union tissue between the nerve ends were not uncommon. Arteries preserved by more drastic methods, such as boiling, alcohol, or formaldehyde, were contraindicated, since these methods transformed the artery into a foreign body and at the same time deprived it of many properties essential for nerve splicing. The great advantage claimed for the frozen-dried artery sleeve was that it could easily be stored for many months. So far no clinical reports have appeared as to the efficacy of this mode of nerve splicing in human surgery.

Taylor (1944) has described a relatively simple apparatus for freeze-drying tissue for storage. The drying chamber is kept cold, at about −40°C., by the circulation of cold carbon dioxide. A reservoir containing solid carbon dioxide is arranged so that a stream of the cold gas flows down through the drying chamber whence it is returned to the reservoir. Fairly accurate temperature control is achieved by means of a thermostatic device which regulates the rate at which the gas circulates.

## IV. THE PRESERVATION OF CORNEAL TISSUE

It is now generally agreed that a permanent and clinically successful repair of certain types of corneal lesion can be effected by a graft of normal, healthy corneal tissue from someone other than its intended recipient. Whether the cellular population of such grafts, including both the stromal and the epithelial cells, survives or not is still controversial. Some authorities maintain that, as a consequence of a tissue transplantation immunity reaction, the cellular population of a corneal homograft is eventually destroyed and becomes replaced by the inward migration of host corneal cells from the margins of the graft. According to this view the graft itself thus functions as a sort of framework or bridge, which at least temporarily guides and supports the ingrowing native cells. Billingham and Boswell (1953) have demonstrated experimentally that tissue transplanation immunity is ineffective within the cornea as long as it remains avascular, and they suggest that this offers a sufficient biological explanation for the indefinite survival of the entire cellular population of a successful corneal homograft.

The clinical success of corneal homografts has created the need for the maintenance of "eye-banks" in which healthy corneas, which may be obtained from donors up to a few hours after death, are stored against future requirement. Of the numerous possible methods of preservation investigated at the Corneal Research Laboratory of the New York Eye-Bank for Sight Restoration, the most effective was a moist chamber maintained at 3° to 5°C. in which the donor eye was suspended over a physiological saline solution in such a manner that the cornea did not become immersed (Katzin, 1947a). However, even when preserved in this way, it is stated that the cornea of the donor eye remains satisfactory for grafting only for about 3 days, a thoroughly unsatisfactory state of affairs. Another method of preserving eyes for corneal grafting entails their immersion in liquid paraffin and maintenance at a few degrees above 0°C. (Paufique *et al.*, 1948; Rycroft, 1952). Stored in this manner, the grafts may be used successfully up to 10 days. It may be added that skin, by contrast, stored in an essentially similar manner, is satisfactory for grafting purposes after as long as 8 weeks of storage (Matthews, 1945).

The results reported by Weiss and Taylor (1944), who investigated the possibility of using stored frozen-dried corneal grafts in rats, appeared to be very promising. These authors rapidly froze the corneas in *iso*pentane chilled to −150°C. and desiccated them under a high vacuum at −40°C. for several days. The grafts were then sealed in ampoules and stored. Before use they were rehydrated in Ringer's solution *in vacuo* when their normal consistency and appearance was regained. The grafts were transplanted to host eyes from which the corneas had been removed save for a narrow rim. It was reported that the grafts became incorporated with the remaining host corneal tissue at their margins and retained their laminated structure. They became repopulated by host cells in supranormal numbers and remained transparent up to 6 weeks when the experiments were terminated. It was also claimed that the grafts became reinnervated during this period.

Subsequently Katzin (1947b), who carried out essentially similar experiments with frozen-dried corneal grafts in rabbits, reported failure to obtain transparent grafts. He removed discs of corneal tissue from freshly enucleated eyes, dropped them into *iso*pentane chilled to −150°C. to achieve rapid freezing, and then transferred them to glass vials which were coupled up to a freeze-drying apparatus similar in design to that described by Taylor (1944). After being desiccated *in vacuo* at a temperature of −40°C. for periods varying from 4 to 11 days, the glass vials were sealed *in vacuo* and stored in an ice chest for not longer than 48 hours. About an hour before transplantation the grafts were rehydrated by dropping them into normal saline. About half of the grafts became transparent on rehydration, and the remainder became clear in the center but translucent at the edges. It was found that the epithelium came off in flakes. In different experiments modifications of the technique were employed: instead of being dropped into chilled *iso*pentane some of the grafts were dropped directly into liquid nitrogen; the dehydration period was varied between 4 and 11 days; some of the grafts were frozen directly after cutting, and others were first washed with diluted rabbit's serum. Although it was claimed that the grafts took and healed in place satisfactorily, they all became opaque within 1 or 2 weeks. The various modifications in technique were without any significant effect on the result.

Leopold and Adler (1947), also working with frozen-dried corneal grafts in rabbits, have reported similar findings. They adopted Weiss and Taylor's technique for freezing, drying, and preservation and transplanted grafts after periods of storage ranging from 10 days to 3 months. Rehydration was effected *in vacuo* using Ringer's solution, 0.9, 1.2, or 1.5% sodium chloride solution, serum, or aqueous humor. Irrespective of the rehydrating agent used their reconstituted grafts were never clear. These authors stated that, although the majority of reconstituted grafts healed in and did not provoke unusual host reactions, none of their grafts was transparent at any time during the 6-month period of observation.

So far, attempts to preserve corneal grafts by storage at temperatures below 0°C. have not been successful. Smelser and Ozanics (1946) froze freshly excised donor rabbit's eyes by immersion in liquid nitrogen where they were left for 1 or 2 hours, or for 3 or 4 days in some cases. After the stored eyes were removed from the liquid nitrogen, they were allowed to thaw at room temperature. When the degree of thawing was sufficient, full thickness corneal grafts were cut. Although these were absolutely clear and of normal thickness initially, they rapidly became thick and edematous when their cut edges came into contact with physiological saline solution. On transplantation of these grafts to defects cut in host eyes it was noted that the epithelium loosened readily and was soon lost. Although the grafts healed well and remained clear like living grafts up to the fourth day, they subsequently became edematous and progressively hazy and opaque. From about the second week the grafts became vascularized, but although this vascularization subsided they remained translucent or opaque. The authors, who believed that their grafts, although structurally unchanged, were no longer alive after freezing and thawing, concluded that the results indicated that for the production of clear corneal transplants the use of viable tissue is obligatory. It is unfortunate that they allowed their frozen material to thaw out slowly (at room temperature), since it is generally agreed that rapid thawing is less harmful to tissues.

A possible hint towards an explanation of the apparently conflicting experimental results obtained with preserved corneal grafts in the rat and the rabbit respectively lies in the great disparity in size between the corneas of these two species. A non-living but structurally intact corneal graft in the rat may well be rapidly recolonized by ingrowth of host corneal cells before degenerative changes in the preserved graft matrix can occur. In rabbits, repopulation of the relatively larger preserved grafts will take correspondingly longer so that secondary changes may occur, especially at the center, which might preclude the re-establishment of the transparent state. If this explanation is correct, then the rat is unsuitable for experiments of this type, when it is anticipated that the results may be applicable clinically.

It is to be hoped that, before any further work is done on the preservation of corneal tissues by freeze-drying, attempts will be made to determine the conditions under which this tissue may be frozen so that it will remain transparent after grafting. Improvement in the availability of donor eyes now makes a solution to the problem of the long-term storage of this valuable material an urgent necessity.

## V. THE PRESERVATION OF BLOOD VESSEL GRAFTS

It has long been established experimentally that arterial defects can be restored by the use of homologous blood vessel grafts. Such grafts are now being used clinically on an increasing scale, not only in the surgical repair of congenital vessel defects and traumatic injuries to essential vessels but also in the course of extensive resections for malignant diseases. Indeed their use makes these bold resections possible.

Some of the methods at present in use for the storage or "banking" of blood vessel segments involve refrigeration in various types of nutrient media at temperatures a few degrees above freezing point. This restricts the use of such stored grafts to a few weeks, especially since some authorities have claimed that viability of the stored graft, as evidenced by proliferation of cells from fragments cultured *in vitro,* is associated with better results after transplantation (Peirce, Gross *et al.*, 1949). That viability of these grafts, even at transplantation, is not obligatory is indicated by the fact that a graft of dead blood vessel even after fixation and storage in 4% neutral formalin may produce a functional vascular channel (Peirce, Rheinlander *et al.*, 1949), although it is generally agreed that more reliable results are obtained when living tissue is employed. However, even with fresh, living blood vessel homografts there is convincing evidence that the homologous or "foreign" cellular elements eventually die, presumably as a consequence of a tissue transplantation immunity response on the part of the host, leaving behind an inert, but nevertheless functional, fibrous tube. This acts as a sort of scaffolding which becomes repopulated and histologically reconstructed by invading cells of native origin (Gross, 1951; Hufnagel and Eastcott, 1952).

There is now ample experimental evidence to indicate that the best method at present available for the long-term preservation of blood vessel segments for grafting purposes comprises freezing the grafts and storing them at the lowest temperature practicable, usually in a solid carbon dioxide bank at −79°C. (Blakemore and Lord, 1945; Deterling *et al.*, 1950). The experimental and clinical studies of Hufnagel and Eastcott (1952) have established that arterial grafts, after freezing and storage at the temperature of solid carbon dioxide for as long as 180 days, when rapidly thawed by immersion in isotonic saline at body temperature, function quite as well as fresh ones. On the basis of their experimental results obtained with frozen aortic and carotid grafts in dogs, these workers emphasize the necessity for freezing by the steepest available gradient, on the ground that the functional and histological results obtained by *slow* freezing were inferior. However, attention must be drawn to the fact that, since both the temperatures of storage and the rates of thawing adopted by these authors differed considerably according to whether the grafts had been rapidly or slowly frozen, there is no justification whatsoever for attributing differences in the results they obtained to the two different rates of freezing. Their quick-frozen grafts were frozen by direct immersion in liquid nitrogen for 15 seconds and then transferred to sterile storage tubes already at −70°C. in a box containing solid carbon dioxide. After storage at this temperature these grafts were rapidly thawed by immersion in saline at body temperature. On the other hand, their slow-frozen grafts were placed in sterile tubes in a deep-freeze at −15° to −18°C. or in the freezing chamber of a household refrigerator at −10°C. and stored thus. Before transplantation, these grafts were simply allowed to come gradually to room temperature in their storage tubes. It is generally agreed that rapid thawing is less harmful than slow thawing.

The possibility of preserving arterial segments by the freeze-drying method was first investigated experimentally in dogs by Marragoni and Cecchini (1951) with promising results. They removed arterial segments aseptically and placed them in sterile jars in a deep-freeze for 24 hours, after which they were transferred to a lyophilizer and dried at a temperature of −15° to −20°C. under a vacuum of 0.001 mm. Hg for 3 or 4 days. The dried grafts were then stored for as long as 69 days in sealed jars under a vacuum at room temperature pending requirement. Reconstitution was carried out in warm physiological saline solution when the grafts regained the elasticity and appearance of fresh vessels, save for their pale color. On implantation of these grafts with end-to-end anastomosis into either the abdominal aorta or the femoral artery, vascular channels of satisfactory size resulted in most cases, as was shown by arteriograms. The grafts were reported as remaining functional up to 180 days after transplantation, the longest trial period attempted. Negative results were obtained in tissue culture attempts to demonstrate viability of reconstituted grafts after storage. Further very encouraging results with frozen-dried arterial homografts in experimental animals have also been obtained by Hyatt *et al.* (1952).

Satisfactory results have recently been reported by Hufnagel (1953), who has emphasized that the results obtained with fresh, frozen, or frozen-dried grafts are practically indistinguishable. He has also claimed successful experimental and clinical results following the use of frozen-dried *heterografts*.

In the establishment of a blood vessel bank, or any other type of tissue bank, there is considerable difficulty in obtaining adequate amounts of sterile material since tissues may often be contaminated before, during, or after removal from the body, whether this is done at operation or at autopsy. There is thus a great need for a method of sterilizing contaminated tissues which does not denature them. In 1948 the Massachusetts Institute of Technology reported that high-voltage cathode rays were effective in sterilizing food. Subsequently, Meeker and Gross (1951) successfully applied this technique to contaminated blood vessels. Unsterile aortic segments frozen to −80°C. and irradiated with 1.5 to 3 million r.e.p. (roentgen equivalent physical units) functioned perfectly satisfactorily when transplanted in dogs. It was found necessary to maintain the vessels at a low temperature during the irradiation to avoid the chemical effects of ionization. Vessel grafts sterilized in this manner have now been used clinically with success (Gross, 1951). Hufnagel (1953), who has abandoned cathode ray sterilization on the grounds that the sterilization dose leads to structural damage, has strongly advocated the use of ethylene oxide gas as a sterilizing agent for frozen-dried blood vessel grafts.

## VI. STUDIES ON FROZEN AND ON FROZEN-DRIED TUMOR TISSUES

It is well established that a wide variety of tumor tissues can be stored for long periods at low temperatures without losing their capacity to elicit further tumors on subsequent thawing out and inoculation into suitable animals. The continued activity of such stored tumor material has generally been ascribed to the survival of at least some of its cells;

a view which receives support from the fact that the cells of mammalian skin and certain other normal tissues have been shown to withstand freezing to low temperatures and storage in the frozen state. However, the rather remote possibility has always remained that in the case of tumor material the actual cells themselves do not survive the freezing, its continued activity depending on the presence of some infective agent within the cells, capable of surviving under certain conditions or treatments which result in their death. Any tumor which could be shown to be transmissible in the absence of *living* cells would of course qualify for admission to the relatively minute group of tumors of known virus etiology.

Gye *et al.* (1949), working on three mouse sarcomas—a methylcholanthrene-induced sarcoma (C48 in inbred C57 mice) and two which had arisen as stromal transformations from sporadic mammary cancers (the R3β R.T. and the C3H R.T.)—which had hitherto resisted all previous attempts at cell-free transmission, reported that these tumors retained their activity after a variety of treatments in addition to freezing and thawing, such as fine mincing and dispersion, dilution with solutions of glucose and cysteine, buffering to pH 6, storage in glycerol, and treatment with distilled water. Mann (1949a) had shown that all these treatments were lethal to embryonic cells of the mouse. Moreover, it was stated that neither the histological examination of frozen tissue implants nor examination of the material itself yielded evidence for the survival of cells, although the authors were aware that conclusive proof of their total destruction could not be expected since a few surviving cells might have escaped detection.

In an attempt to settle the matter decisively, they proceeded to "dry the refrigerated tissue completely to dust *in vacuo* at a temperature of −25°C.," a procedure which they claimed to be "universally allowed to be lethal to both normal and tumour cells." For this purpose they used either a freshly prepared tumor mince suspended in an equal volume of 5.3% dextrose solution (the dextrose was said to favor the survival of tumor activity on freezing and thawing) or, in some experiments, minced tumor tissue which had been subjected to a preliminary period of storage in the frozen state at −79°C. The tumor material was frozen in the form of a thin layer over the bottom of a drying flask which was then coupled up to a freeze-drying apparatus designed by Craigie (1949), and the dehydration carried out at a constant temperature of −25°C. To follow the progress of the desiccation a specially designed vapor flow indicator was used in preference to the more conventional pressure gauge. This comprised a light vane, freely suspended from a pivot, which was fitted in the vertical tube leading from the drying flask to the condenser so that the flow of vapor from the drying flask displaced it from its vertical position. To be absolutely certain of removing the last traces of water, pumping was continued for half an hour after the displacement of the vane was zero. The average drying time was about 2½ hours. After the vacuum was slowly released, the drying flask was removed and its contents rehydrated by the addition of a 1 in 500 neutral solution of cysteine. When this material was injected into mice, tumors subsequently appeared. In the case of the C48 sarcoma, the least malignant of the tumors studied, the authors did not succeed in obtaining active desiccates from the freshly prepared mince; to obtain active desiccates they claimed that preliminary storage at −79°C. for 5 to 8 weeks was required.

On the basis of this experimental evidence Gye and his associates concluded that the continuing cause of the three tumors investigated (and, by inference, of all tumors) was a virus (*v.a.* Gye, 1949).

Mann (1949b, c) and Mann and Dunn (1949) have also carried out freezing and freeze-drying studies on various mouse mammary carcinoma tissues, which are known to have a virus-like agent, the Bittner milk factor, playing an essential role in their etiology. It was claimed that maintenance of the mammary carcinoma tissue at −79°C. for long periods killed the tumor cells and liberated the Bittner virus in an "active" form when it was capable of eliciting tumors in mice of either sex, provided that it was injected into mammary tissue. The fact that the refrigerated tissue could be shown to possess a selective infectivity for mammary tissue was cited as differentiating it qualitatively from living tumor cells which could be grafted into any situation. Stressing that sporadic mammary cancer never arises in the peritoneum, although tumors may be produced there with grafts, Mann reported failure to obtain tumors in 90% of animals which received intraperitoneal inoculations of refrigerated mammary tissue, whereas a tumor incidence of 75% was obtained when the animals were inoculated subcutaneously where mammary tissue must have been present. It was suggested that the few tumors that did appear in the peritoneum might well have arisen from mammary gland cells accidentally carried there from the subcutaneous tissue during the insertion of the syringe needle used for the intraperitoneal inoculations. This evidence was interpreted as strongly supporting the hypothesis of selective infection by the virus, as opposed to the alternative of tumor cell survival. It was also shown that frozen-dried mouse mammary cancer tissue produced tumors on inoculation into both male and female mice. On the basis of this evidence it was stated that the "active" form of the Bittner virus can be successfully dried *in vitro*. It may be added that no attempt was made to store the dried material. Mann and Dunn stated that, on the basis of repeated freezing-thawing experiments, the Bittner virus showed itself less thermostable than the sarcoma virus, since many mammary tumors would not withstand a second freezing and thawing.

Passey and his colleagues (Passey and Dmochowski, 1950; Passey *et al.*, 1950; Dmochowski and Millard, 1950) have repeated these experiments and attempted to apply more critical tests to the virus hypothesis. Using an essentially similar technique, they reported (Passey and Dmochowski, 1950) no difficulty in repeating the results obtained by Gye *et al.*, both with frozen and with frozen-dried sarcoma material, which included the 37, the C48, the C3H and the RIII (No. 4) sarcomata. In a small series of experiments on mouse mammary carcinoma tissue, they reported that the results obtained, both after freezing, and after freezing followed by desiccation, were very much inferior to those obtained with the sarcomata. They attempted to separate an active agent or virus from the sarcoma cells by centrifuging, at 3000 to 7000 times gravity, suspensions of minced tumor tissue that had either been frozen or frozen, dried, and reconstituted. This treatment was stated to be insufficient to spin down virus from fluid suspensions. On inoculation of both the resultant supernatant fluid and the sediment into mice, tumors appeared only on those sites which had been inoculated with the sediment, the supernatants being ineffective. These authors also found difficulty in detecting histologically any differences in the appearances of many of the sarcoma cells before and after freezing. Although they agreed with Gye *et al.* that in no case could intact cells be found in material fixed for histological study after freeze-drying but before reconstitution, they found that many of the tumor cells in preparations which were fixed for histological examination after reconstitution following freeze-drying were to all appearances intact. This, they emphasized, strongly suggested that some of the tumor cells survived both the freezing and the freezing and drying and so could have been responsible for the tumors induced with such material. In every case in which tumors were obtained by inoculation with treated material, microscopical examination of the material inoculated had suggested that at least some cells might be alive.

To decide more conclusively whether freezing and desiccation do not necessarily kill tumor cells, Passey *et al.* (1950) dried minced C3H sarcoma tissue suspended in glucose solutions of various concentrations (from 5.3% to 40%) from the frozen state after a preliminary period of storage at −79°C. ranging from 12 hours to 25 days. The drying periods varied between 30 minutes and 3½ hours. After reconstitution of the tumor desiccates in glucose solution, some of the material was subjected to the test of *in vitro* culture using the hanging drop technique, and some was injected into mice. Out of thirteen separate experiments, in which attempts were made to culture the frozen-dried material, only in three was cellular growth *in vitro* obtained from explants of the desiccates. The drying times for these were 30 minutes, 60 minutes, and 75 minutes, respectively. Nevertheless material from eleven of these experiments, which had been dried for as long as 2 hours, or in one case 3½ hours, produced tumors on inoculation. The authors suggested that the failure of tumor tissue which had been desiccated for periods longer than 75 minutes to grow *in vitro,* whereas it induced tumors on inoculation into mice, could be ascribed to the more favorable conditions *in vivo* for the recovery of the treated tumor cells. This is perfectly reasonable, since it is generally agreed that cultivation *in vitro* is a far less sensitive test for cellular survival than the biological one of inoculation or transplantation. However, it seems very doubtful whether the results of the comparatively few successful *in vitro* experiments reported by Passey *et al.* are sufficient to strengthen their conclusion that surviving cells and not a virus are responsible for the tumor-producing activity of frozen dried tumor material.

As an alternative and probably more sensitive method of testing the viability of C3H and C48 sarcoma cells after freeze-drying, Dmochowski and Millard (1950) prepared small plasma clots in which the reconstituted frozen-dried tumor material was embedded, and implanted fragments of these clots subcutaneously into mice, thus making use of a technique of "*in vitro* culture under *in vivo* conditions." The animals were sacrificed at various intervals and the implants examined histologically. In eight out of thirteen experiments the presence of viable tumor cells, which increased in number with the age of the "grafts," was established. The authors stated that no cells outside the grafts were actively proliferating, as would have been expected if a virus were present which was capable of diffusing out and infecting the tissues of the host. In all except one of the experiments in which surviving tumor cells were detected in the clots the drying time was 1 hour or less.

Warner and Gostling (1950) also studied the effect of freezing and freeze-drying on mouse sarcoma 37 and reported that the latter treatment completely destroyed its tumor-producing activity. They made use of a quantitative method comprising the determination of the dose of tumor mince which would produce sarcomata in 50% of the mice inoculated. They found that freezing this material quickly to below −75°C. depressed its tumor-producing activity to a greater extent than did slow freezing to the same temperature, a finding in conformity with the results of other investigators on the effect of the rate of freezing on tumor-producing activity. Repeated freezing and thawing (six times) completely inactivated the tumor material.

In their freeze-drying experiments they made use of Craigie's (1949) procedure with slight modifications. In one series of experiments the undiluted tumor mince was shell-frozen and kept at −75°C. in glass ampoules which were then coupled up to the freeze-drying apparatus; no provision was made to maintain them at a constant low temperature. Drying was carried out for 3 hours, after which the ampoules were removed, sealed, and stored overnight at room temperature. Reconstitution was effected with distilled water. In a second series of experiments the tumor mince, again without a diluent, was placed in standard 6 × 1-in. tubes and shell-frozen—sometimes with slow-freezing, sometimes with rapid freezing—after which the tubes were coupled up to the drying apparatus and dried for 3 hours as before. This time, however, provision was made to maintain the drying tube at or below −30°C. On completion of drying, the tube bearing the desiccated tumor material was removed and secondary drying over phosphorus pentoxide was carried out overnight before reconstitution with distilled water. In none of their experiments, in which a total of 113 inoculations of frozen-dried material were made, did a progressively growing tumor arise. These authors have suggested that the fact that they did not use a glucose solution as a diluent may account for their findings being at variance with those of other workers. It seems very probable that their desiccation techniques, especially that used in their second series of experiments, resulted in a drier product than that found to be active by the other workers. Moreover, the present authors stored their desiccates overnight before inoculating them into the mice.

It must be admitted that the evidence at present available does not permit a final decision as to whether or not the survival of cells was in all cases responsible for the tumors induced with frozen-dried material. Resolution of the problem will be possible only when, among other things, factual estimates are provided of the minimal residual water content of a tumor desiccate that is compatible with tumor-inducing activity. Certainly the evidence presented by Passey and his colleagues has established that at least some mammalian cells can withstand a high degree of desiccation.

### 1. *The Influence of Injections of Frozen-Dried Tissues on the Fate of Homologous Tumor Transplants*

Snell and his colleagues (1946), studying the effect of intraperitoneal injections of lyophilized tumor material on the fate of subsequent transplants of the same living tumor into foreign and therefore resistant inbred strains of mice, reported that this treatment resulted in a striking enhancement of tumor growth. The freshly excised material was cut into small pieces with scissors and then frozen in a solid carbon dioxide chest.

Freeze-drying was carried out by the Cryochem process (Flosdorf and Mudd, 1938). The dried tissues were powdered in mortars, sealed under vacuum in ampoules, and stored in the refrigerator. For injection the dried tissue was suspended in normal saline or in distilled water. Kaliss and Snell (1951) reported that, in some host-tumor combinations in which nearly 100% of the host mice were normally resistant to the growth of the implanted tumor, about 80% or more of the animals which had been pretreated with the "lyophilized" tumor material succumbed as a consequence of the proliferative growth of the tumor. It was also demonstrated that this enhancement of homologous tumor growth also followed pretreatment with certain "lyophilized" normal tissues from mice of the strain in which the tumor was indigenous. The usual dosage of "lyophilized" material required to produce this enhancing effect was 30 to 50 mg. dry weight, given in one or more injections. It was also reported that pretreatment with lower doses of the "lyophilized" tissue, 0.05 mg., produced an inhibitory effect on tumor growth (Kaliss and Newton, 1949).

It is to be hoped that further studies will elucidate the biological basis of these interesting results and also indicate whether pretreatment with "lyophilized" tissue will enhance the survival of homografts of normal tissues.

## VII. STUDIES ON THE FREEZING, FREEZE-DRYING, AND STORAGE OF MAMMALIAN SKIN

For studies on the effects of physical changes or of chemical substances on living cells, mammalian skin is particularly suitable because of the ease with which it may be removed from an animal, subjected to various treatments *in vitro*, and then grafted back orthotopically (i.e., to a position formerly occupied by skin) to the animal from which it was originally taken to test its continued viability. The fate of such grafts can be followed by visual inspection and by histological examination of biopsy specimens which can be removed without necessitating the sacrifice of the animal. Whereas the resistance of tumor tissue to freezing and other treatment can only be very crudely assessed on the basis of its rate of growth, if any, after transplantation, that of a skin graft can be scored for the survival of its epithelium, its growth rate, its degree of pigmentation, the normality of its hair crop, etc.

It is now well established that skin will withstand freezing to temperatures below the eutectic point of isotonic saline solutions (Mider and Morton, 1939; Webster, 1944; Briggs and Jund, 1944). The author and his colleague, Professor Medawar, have recently made a particular study of the conditions of freezing and thawing that result in the least possible damage to the various cellular and fibrous components of rabbit's skin and have utilized the results obtained to determine the degree to which the epithelium of this tissue will withstand desiccation from the frozen state (Billingham and Medwar, 1952).

In this study, very thin shavings of skin, about 0.25 to 0.5 mm. in thickness, were removed from the dorsal surface of rabbits' ears, subjected to treatment *in vitro*, and then transplanted to large raw areas prepared in the skin of the side of the animals' chests. In addition to determining the survival or otherwise of the epithelium of the grafts, made clear by its migratory outgrowth from their margins over the prepared bed, particular attention was paid to the survival of epidermal melanocytes (pigmentary dendritic cells) according to the growth of pigmented hairs and the appearance of superficial pigmentation in the grafts (Billingham and Medawar, 1953). It may be added that melanocytes are believed to be more susceptible to physical stresses than Malpighian cells. The general anatomical preservation of the grafts was also taken into consideration.

Before the grafts were subjected to the various freezing procedures to be described they were soaked for 1 hour at room temperature either in Ringer's solution or in a 15% w/w solution of glycerol in Ringer's solution. The latter had previously been shown by Polge *et al.* (1949) to protect fowl spermatozoa from the otherwise fatal effects of vitrification or snap-freezing.

Two extreme rates of freezing and two extreme rates of thawing were used. Quick freezing was achieved by plunging the grafts, mounted on a thin copper carrier, directly into *iso*pentane chilled with liquid air to a temperature below −150°C. Slow freezing was brought about by placing the copper strip carrying the grafts inside the inner tube of a coaxial thick-walled test tube assembly, in which a 3 mm. air gap separated the inner from the outer tube. After a preliminary immersion of the assembly in a solid carbon dioxide–alcohol bath for about 15 minutes, it was transferred to liquid air and finally the grafts were immersed directly in *iso*pentane chilled to below −150°C.

For quick thawing the frozen grafts were plunged directly into excess Ringer's solution at 37°C.; for slow thawing the grafts were placed in an air chamber maintained at 0°C.

Although the skin withstood either slow or rapid freezing down to the temperature of liquid air, when all the criteria by which the well-being of a graft can be assessed were taken into consideration, slow freezing was invariably found to be preferable to quick freezing, thus confirming the results of previous workers. It was found that previous treatment of the grafts with glycerol solution protected them against some of the harmful effects of rapid freezing—e.g., the melanocytes survived rapid freezing in glycerol-treated grafts but not in Ringer-treated grafts.

Rapid thawing gave very much better preservation than slow thawing. Indeed, even the Malpighian cells succumbed to slow thawing in grafts impregnated with Ringer's solution. Pretreatment with glycerol solution nevertheless did protect these cells from the deleterious effects of slow thawing.

The protective action of glycerol was clearly brought out in experiments in which suspensions of epidermal cells, including both Malpighian cells and melanocytes, were used. Cells suspended in Ringer's solution did not withstand even slow freezing and quick thawing, the combination found best for intact skin, although the Malpighian cells and the melanocytes survived both quick and slow freezing after suspension in a 15% solution of glycerol in Ringer.

### 1. *The Storage of Skin*

It was also found that skin grafts pretreated with glycerol solution, slowly frozen to −79°C. and stored at that temperature for more than a year (Billingham, 1953), on subsequently being thawed out rapidly and transplanted, proved indistinguishable from freshly removed grafts transplanted at the same time. There was no evidence whatever that the storage of skin under these conditions resulted in progressive deterioration during the period of storage. Indeed, there seems to be no reason to doubt that skin will survive storage in this manner for periods greatly exceeding even the most optimistic expectation of life of the individual from which it was removed.

One of the most common methods of storing skin for surgical use involves folding the grafts so that their raw surfaces are approximated, wrapping them in gauze slightly moistened with physiological saline solution, and storing them in a sealed container at 3° to 6°C. Stored in this manner they are suitable for use for about 8 weeks at the most (Webster, 1944; Matthews, 1945). Recently Allgöwer and Blocker (1952), using a tissue culture test of survival, have shown that storage of human skin in 10% serum in balanced physiological saline at 5°C. in the presence of air gives marked superiority in viability over that obtained from grafts stored by other methods at this temperature. Epithelial outgrowth *in vitro* was obtained from skin which had been stored in dilute serum for as long as 28 days. The superiority of this medium is said to depend on its provision of a nutrient and on its capacity to dilute or buffer the acids that result from metabolism (Hanks and Wallace, 1949). Hyatt *et al.* (1952) have reported successful clinical results with skin so stored.

The fact that skin can be stored for long periods at low temperatures under conditions that render it no less capable of growth and differentiation than the freshly removed tissue has both a clinical and an experimental bearing. Clinically it makes possible the establishment of efficient "skin banks" for graft purposes. Unfortunately, skin, like most other tissues, does not long survive transplantation from one individual to another; it elicits a transplantation immunity reaction on the part of the host—the so-called homograft reaction—as a consequence of which it is soon destroyed (Gibson and Medawar, 1943; Medawar, 1944, 1945). Consequently at present such grafts are useful only in so far as they provide temporary skin coverage, their limited survival tiding badly burned patients over a critical period until the surgeon can effect the permanent repair of their lesions by means of skin autografts. If the administration of cortisone to human beings could be shown to prolong the life of skin homografts, as it is known to do in rabbits (Billingham *et al.*, 1951a, b), then the case for instituting "skin banks" would be greatly strengthened. At present the main interest in stored skin depends upon its usefulness for experimental purposes.

### 2. *The Viability of Skin Epithelium after Dehydration from the Frozen State*

A number of attempts were made to dehydrate skin in a manner essentially similar to that described by Gye *et al.* (1949). In none of these tests did transplantation reveal any degree of survival, even when the grafts had been impregnated before freezing and drying with plasma or serum, or isotonic solutions of dextrose, maltose, or dextran (a bacterial polysaccharide), and it was concluded that the failure was attributable to the achievement of too high a degree of desiccation. Therefore, an attempt was made to determine, on a quantitative basis, the degree to which the cells of mammalian skin can survive dehydration from the frozen state.

Since the determination of the residual moisture content of a frozen-dried graft necessarily entails its complete desiccation (*cf.* Beckett, this volume), it was obviously not possible to carry out both a moisture determination and a viability test on one and the same piece of frozen-dried skin. In practice two similar sets of skin grafts—composed of very thin shavings—were therefore removed from adjacent sites on the same ear of a rabbit and simultaneously frozen and dried in separate but similar vessels on the same apparatus, as illustrated in Fig. 1, under exactly similar conditions. The grafts in one flask were used for initial, intermediate, and final moisture determinations, and those in the other flask were used for viability tests. Two separate series of experiments were carried out: (a) those in which the freshly removed grafts were frozen and dried directly without any special treatment, and (b) those in which the freshly removed grafts were first treated for 1 hour with one or other of various, accurately known concentrations of glycerol in Ringer's solution before drying. In each experiment the two flasks bearing the grafts, after being slowly cooled to a temperature below that at which drying was to take place, were coupled up to the freeze-drying apparatus. Dehydration was

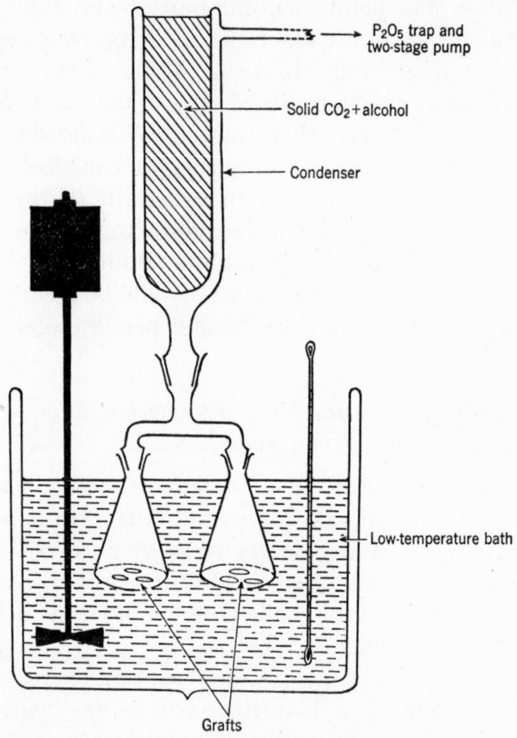


FIG. 1. The apparatus used for drying skin from the frozen state. The two sets of skin grafts are laid flat on the bottom of two 50-ml. Ehrlenmeyer flasks with their dermal (anatomically inner) surfaces upward. The temperature of the flasks is maintained constant by means of the stirred alcohol bath to which chips of carbon dioxide ice are added as required.

carried out for varying known periods of time at a pressure between 0.005 and 0.001 mm. Hg. The temperature of the drying flasks was maintained constant between $-22°$ and $-25°C$. for the glycerol-treated grafts, and between $-30°$ and $-32°C$. for the untreated grafts, this lower temperature being adopted to slow down the otherwise high rate of dehydration in the absence of glycerol. On the expiry of the particular dehydration time selected, dry air was admitted into the apparatus and the drying flask containing the grafts for the viability test was rapidly uncoupled and rehydration and thawing achieved at the maximum possible rate by pouring in excess Ringer-phosphate solution at body temperature. The grafting operation to test the viability of the rehydrated skin was carried out about an hour later.

The weight determinations made on the weighed set of grafts ended in their complete dehydration (final moisture determinations being carried out by drying the skin to constant weight over phosphorus pentoxide under reduced pressure at 60°C.; glycerol is not lost under these conditions). With the original weight of the grafts and their final dry weight known (after due allowance had been made for the weight of glycerol and Ringer salts added during the pretreatment in the second series of experiments), the water content of the original grafts was computed. As a check upon this indirect estimate a direct moisture determination was carried out on a third set of grafts removed from a neighboring area on the rabbit's ear.

*Results: Dehydration of freshly removed grafts.* It was found that the epithelium of very thin, rabbit's ear skin grafts, which immediately after removal contained about 70% water, survived the degree of dehydration represented by a final overall moisture content of 25%, although higher degrees of dehydration were fatal (see Table 1). It may be added that

TABLE 1

THE SURVIVAL (+) OR NON-SURVIVAL (0) OF SKIN GRAFTS WHICH HAVE HAD NO SPECIAL PRELIMINARY TREATMENT, AFTER DEHYDRATION FROM THE FROZEN STATE TO THE DEGREE SHOWN IN THE SECOND COLUMN

| Initial graft $H_2O$% | Final $H_2O$% after dehydration | Survival |
|---|---|---|
| 70 | 46 | + |
| 72 | 43 | + |
| 72 | 42 | + |
| 67 | 34 | + |
| 71 | 29 | + |
| 69 | 25 | + |
| 71 | 23 | 0 |
| 71 | 17 | 0 |
| 67 | 11 | 0 |

grafts containing as much as 25% residual water looked and felt "bone dry," their outward appearance being clearly misleading. Obviously there was no means of determining how the residual water was distributed in these thin, frozen-dried grafts.

*Results: Dehydration of glycerol-treated grafts.* In these experiments it was felt that, besides any other beneficial action it might have, the incorporation of glycerol into the drying system would secure a more homogeneous final distribution of water on account of its hygroscopic properties. Moreover, unless the cell surfaces are freely permeable to glycerol, water cannot fail to have been osmotically withdrawn from the cells during the later stages of drying, since glycerol-water systems are fluid at −22°C. at glycerol concentrations ranging from about 50 to 80%. The results, summarized in Table 2, show that treatment of skin grafts

TABLE 2

THE SURVIVAL (+) OR NON-SURVIVAL (0) OF SKIN GRAFTS SOAKED IN A GLYCEROL-RINGER SOLUTION OF THE CONCENTRATION SHOWN IN COLUMN 2 AND THEN DRIED FROM THE FROZEN STATE TO THE DEGREE SHOWN IN COLUMN 4

(The figures in parentheses following the entries in column 1 are the moisture contents of grafts cut from nearby donor areas, estimated by direct dehydration. The penultimate column expresses the final concentration of glycerol as an aqueous solution in the residual water.)

| Initial graft $H_2O$ % | Glycerol %, (pretreatment) | % Water in system | | Final %, glycerol | Survival |
|---|---|---|---|---|---|
| | | Initial | Final | | |
| 69 (68) | 3.77 | 85 | 33 | 24 | + |
| 71 (71) | 12.79 | 79 | 30 | 41 | + |
| 71 (69) | 12.79 | 79 | 24 | 52 | + |
| 71 (71) | 14.77 | 80 | 20 | 67 | 0 |
| 74 (70) | 14.77 | 82 | 18 | 73 | 0 |
| 69 (68) | 14.77 | 79 | 18 | 68 | 0 |
| 68 (65) | 7.48 | 84 | 17 | 59 | 0 |
| 70 (70) | 14.77 | 80 | 16 | 71 | 0 |
| 65 (65) | 14.77 | 78 | 15 | 71 | 0 |
| 72 (73) | 12.79 | 79 | 13 | 65 | 0 |
| 65 (63) | 3.77 | 83 | 13 | 45 | 0 |
| 75 (75) | 12.79 | 82 | 13 | 76 | 0 |
| 70 (68) | 14.77 | 79 | 12 | 79 | 0 |

with glycerol, which is known to protect them against some of the harmful consequences of rapid freezing and slow thawing (*cf.* Smith, this volume), does not increase the resistance of skin to dehydration from the frozen state. As a means of investigating the possibility that, during the dehydration of a glycerol-treated graft the concentration of glycerol may in some cases have increased so that it attained a toxic level, the concentration of the glycerol in the solution used for pretreatment was varied. It will be seen that, although one graft survived desiccation to 24% residual water with a final glycerol concentration of 52%, another graft failed to survive dehydration to 13% residual water although the final glycerol concentration was only 45%. The non-toxicity of glycerol was even more clearly demonstrated by the fact that freshly removed grafts survived exposure to "absolute" glycerol (98.1%) for as long as 8 hours at 0°C. and to 80% glycerol for 2 hours at room temperature. It remains to be seen whether a living tissue will withstand a higher degree of dehydration effected by soaking it in a series of glycerol solutions of ascending concentration than by desiccating it from the frozen state.

This investigation of the degree to which the epithelium of mammalian skin will withstand drying from the frozen state has been described in some detail, since it clearly indicates that this tissue, which, being exposed, is normally subjected to a wider variety of physical stresses than any other in the body and is therefore likely to be at least as resistant as any other tissue, will only withstand the limited degree of dehydration represented by a final, overall water content of about 25%. The physical appearance of partially dried tissues creates the impression that they are drier than they really are. Claims that mammalian cells will withstand something little short of complete desiccation must be accompanied by factual estimates of their residual water content, as should any claims that the possibility of cellular survival has been excluded by subjecting living tissues to freeze-drying.

There is at least one case on record in which a "lyophilized" skin autograft was used clinically (Webster, 1944). The graft was quickly frozen to −72°C. and then "lyophilized." This is reported as having "caused it to become shrunken, hard, and apparently dry." The graft was divided before transplantation, and it was stated that the portions averaged 80% takes and were definitely better than portions of other grafts stored by refrigeration. Unfortunately no details are given as to the method used for this "lyophilization," so that this case is only of limited scientific interest. It may be emphasized that "devitalized" skin grafts can be expected to serve no permanently useful clinical purpose whatsoever, since, although their fibrous dermal component could conceivably be recolonized and to some extent reorganized by native fibroblasts, the all-essential epidermal cells would still be lacking. There is no substitute for living skin.

Stored frozen-dried skin homografts have been used clinically as temporary "dressings" on areas of full-thickness skin loss in the full knowledge that such grafts are non-viable (Pate, 1953). It is claimed that these grafts are satisfactory in so far as they reduce the fluid and electrolyte losses that would otherwise take place. However, it seems very doubtful whether frozen-dried skin is as efficacious a temporary dressing as a living skin homograft.

## VIII. THE POSSIBLE APPLICATION OF FROZEN-DRIED TISSUES IN THE INVESTIGATION OF PROBLEMS OF MORPHOGENESIS

It is generally accepted that quick-freezing and drying *in vacuo* offers the best solution at present available for the problem of "devitalizing" tissues with the minimal damage to their structural and chemical properties. Weiss (1944) has suggested that this may offer a new experimental approach to some basic problems of morphogenesis. For example, the interrelationship between cells and their matrix can be investigated by combining the devitalized matrix of one tissue with living cells of another.

In a preliminary study, Weiss froze various tissues of frog tadpoles to about −150°C. and then dehydrated them at −40°C. After dehydration the tissues were transplanted to similar larvae, mostly into the dorsal fin. He reported that the grafts became incorporated, resisted absorption and substitution, and preserved their original basic structure. They eventually became invaded by cells of the host. It was significant that the cell population varied with the invaded tissue: in liver the cells were small with irregular nuclei, whereas in cartilage they were large with large vesicular nuclei. In muscle and bone the situation was essentially similar, the invading host cells imitating the histological characteristics of the original native population.

Weiss also made the observation that, when a piece of frozen-dried cartilage is grafted into the limbs of an *Amblystoma* larva, it may induce the host mesenchyme cells to elaborate new cartilage along its surface (*v.a.* Weiss, 1950).

Holtfreter (1948) suggested that the "innocuous" form of devitalization afforded by freeze-drying, when applied to early embryos, might be expected to prevent denaturation and dissociation of vital protoplasmic compounds and also preserve the specific induction qualities of the various germ layers. He studied the fate of small pieces of frozen-dried amphibian embryos of various stages which were grafted into early gastrulae of *Amblystoma punctatum.* However, the reactions of the host were not quite in accordance with his expectations. Although the grafts had no apparent toxic effect, they were broken up and later phagocytosed by the host tissues. Their inductive specificity was lost, just as through any other method of killing. None of the various tissues employed induced mesodermal structures, but all of them, including the ectoderm and endoderm from frozen gastrulae, were found to be capable of inducing neural organs. Thus it was decided that this killing procedure, in common with a variety of others of a more drastic nature, apparently liberates the neuralizing agent in normally non-inducing cells.

## IX. CONCLUSIONS

Experimental studies on mammalian skin and ovarian tissue (Parkes and Smith, 1953) have shown that these tissues may be stored in a viable condition for very long periods at low temperatures without undergoing progressive deterioration, provided that they are frozen *slowly* in media containing glycerol. It must be emphasized that it is an empirical fact based on the study of a variety of tissues, both normal and malignant, that, if continued growth and cell division are used as criteria of survival, then slow freezing is invariably preferable to rapid freezing. That this fact conflicts with the predictions of biophysicists, based on purely theoretical principles, suggests either that these principles are fallacious or that they have been mistakenly applied. It can scarcely be doubted that means can be devised, if need be, whereby many other tissues can be stored at very low temperatures for comparatively long periods, if not indefinitely, without their undergoing progressive deterioration in viability.

For replacement surgery viability is not an essential quality for all tissues, even at the time of grafting, in order that they may serve to effect the permanent repair of a defect. For example, the essential role of grafts of blood vessel segments, bone, and cartilage is the provision of a connective tissue matrix—a frame-work which acts as a guide and sometimes a stimulus to natural regeneration, irrespective of whether the grafts remain alive or not. Although storage in the frozen state at low temperatures affords a perfectly satisfactory means of preserving these tissues for long periods, it is likely that freeze-drying will be employed on a far larger scale in the future as a means of preservation. There is now ample evidence, both experimental and clinical, to justify this prediction. Even bone, which is far less exacting than most other tissues with respect to the manner in which it is preserved, has been studied with a view to its preservation by freeze-drying (Kreutz *et al.*, 1951). The superiority of freeze-drying over deep-freezing as a method of preserving certain tissues for replacement surgery lies in the fact that once the moisture content of the tissues has been reduced to below about 1% they may be sealed off in suitable containers and stored perfectly satisfactorily, even at normal temperatures, and transportation raises no difficulties.

The results of experimental studies on the preservation of corneal tissue emphasize one important point: attempts to make use of frozen-dried grafts of a tissue are not justified until some considerable measure of success has been obtained with frozen grafts. If freezing alone prejudices the usefulness of a graft, then freezing followed by desiccation is scarcely likely to improve the outcome.

From the point of view of the experimental biologist freeze-drying is a valuable technique for "devitalizing" cells with minimal biochemical and structural change. Although a variety of micro-organisms are known to withstand freeze-drying, there are not the slightest grounds for belief that any mammalian cells will withstand, for example, even that degree of dehydration represented by a final moisture content of 10%.

## REFERENCES


Allgöwer, M., and Blocker, T. G. 1952. Viability of Skin in Relation to Various Methods of Storage. *Texas Rept. Biol. Med.* **10,** 3–21.

Barnes, R., Bacsich, P., Wyburn, G. M., and Kerr, A. S. 1946. A Study of the Fate of Nerve Homografts in Man. *Brit. J. Surg.* **34,** 34–41.

Billingham, R. E. 1953. Storage of Skin, in *The Preservation of Normal Tissues for Transplantation.* Ciba Foundation Symposium. In press.

Billingham, R. E., and Boswell, T. 1953. Sudies on the Problem of Corneal Homografts. *Proc. Roy. Soc. (London)* **141B,** 392–406.

Billingham, R. E., Krohn, P. L., and Medawar, P. B. 1951a. Effect of Cortisone on Survival of Skin Homografts in Rabbits. *Brit. Med. J.* **i,** 1157–1163.

Billingham, R. E., Krohn, P. L., and Medawar, P. B. 1951b. Effect of Locally Applied Cortisone Acetate on Survival of Skin Homografts in Rabbits. *Brit. Med. J.* **ii,** 1049–1053.

Billingham, R. E., and Medawar, P. B. 1952. The Freezing, Drying and Storage of Mammalian Skin. *J. Exptl. Biol.* **29,** 454–468.

Billingham, R. E., and Medawar, P. B. 1953. A Study of the Branched Cells of the Mammalian Epidermis with Special Reference to the Fate of their Division Products. *Phil. Trans. Roy. Soc.* **237B,** 151–171.

Blakemore, A. H., and Lord, J. W. 1945. A Nonsuture Method of Blood Vessel Anastomosis. Experimental and Clinical Study. *J. Am. Med. Assoc.* **127,** 685–691.

Boell, E. J. 1945. Cholinesterase Activity of Peripheral Nerves. *J. Cell. Comp. Physiol.* **25,** 75–84.

Briggs, R., and Jund, L. 1944. Successful Grafting of Frozen and Thawed Mouse Skin. *Anat. Record* **89,** 75–86.

Craigie, J. 1949. A Drying Apparatus for the Study of Tumour Transplantation. *Brit. J. Cancer* **3,** 250–255.

Deterling, R. A., Coleman, C. C., and Parshley, M. 1950. A Preliminary Report on Experimental Studies of Frozen Homologous Aortic Grafts. *N.Y. State J. Med.* **6,** 19.

Dmochowski, L., and Millard, A. 1950. Cellular Transmission of Mouse Sarcomata with Frozen-Dried Tumour Tissues. *Brit. Med. J.* **ii,** 1136–7.

Flosdorf, E. W., and Mudd, S. 1938. An Improved Procedure and Apparatus for Preservation of Sera, Microorganisms and Other Substances—the Cryochem Process. *J. Immunol.* **34,** 469–490.

Gersh, I. 1932. The Altmann Technique for Fixation by Drying while Freezing. *Anat. Record* **53,** 309–337.

Gibson, T., and Medawar, P. B. 1943. The Fate of Skin Homografts in Man. *J. Anat.* **77,** 299–310.

Greaves, R. I. N. 1946. The Preservation of Proteins with Special Reference to the Production of Dried Human Serum and Plasma for Transfusion. *Med. Research Council (Brit.) Spec. Rept. Ser.* **258.**

Gross, R. E. 1951. The Treatment of Certain Aortic Coarctations by Homologous Grafts. *Ann. Surg.* **134,** 753–768.

Gutmann, E., and Sanders, F. K. 1942. Functional Recovery Following Nerve Grafts and Other Types of Nerve Bridge. *Brain* **65,** 373–408.

Gye, W. E. 1949. The Propagation of Mouse Tumours by Means of Dried Tissue. *Brit. Med. J.* **i,** 511–515.

Gye, W. E., Begg, A. M., Mann, I., and Craigie, J. 1949. The Survival of Activity of Mouse Sarcoma Tissue after Freezing and Drying. *Brit. J. Cancer* **3,** 259–267.

Hanks, J. H., and Wallace, R. F. 1949. Relation of Oxygen and Temperature in the Preservation of Tissues by Refrigeration. *Proc. Soc. Exptl. Biol. Med.* **71,** 196–200.

Hoerr, N. L. 1936. Cytological Studies by the Altmann-Gersh Freezing-Drying Method: I. Recent Advances in the Technique. *Anat. Record* **65,** 293–313.

Holtfreter, J. 1948. Concepts on the Mechanism of Embryonic Induction and Its Relation to Parthenogenesis and Malignancy. *Symposia Soc. Exptl. Biol.* **2,** 17–49.

Hufnagel, C. A. 1953. Experimental and Clinical Observations on the Transplantation of Blood Vessels in *The Preservation of Normal Tissues for Transplantation.* Ciba Foundation Symposium. In press.

Hufnagel, C. A., and Eastcott, H. H. G. 1952. The Preservation of Arterial Grafts by Freezing. *Lancet* **i,** 531–537.

Hyatt, G. W., Turner, T. C., Bassett, C. A. L., Pate, J. W., and Sawyer, P. N. 1952. New Methods for Preserving Bone, Skin and Blood Vessels. *Postgrad. Med.* **12,** 239–254.

Kaliss, N., and Newton, O. 1949. The Effect of Injection Dosage Level of Lyophilized Mouse Tissue on the Subsequent Growth of a Tumor Homoiotransplant. *Anat. Record* **105,** 535.

Kaliss, N., and Snell, G. D. 1951. The Effects of Injections of Lyophilized Normal and Neoplastic Mouse Tissues on the Growth of Tumor Homoiotransplants in Mice. *Cancer Research* **11,** 122–126.

Katzin, H. M. 1947a. Contributions to the Technique of Corneal Grafting. *Arch. Opthalmol.* **37,** 379–382.

Katzin, H. M. 1947b. The Preservation of Corneal Tissue by Freezing and Dehydration. *Am. J. Opthalmol.* **30,** 1128–1134.

Kreutz, F. P., Hyatt, G. W., Turner, T. C., and Bassett, C. A. L. 1951. The Preservation and Clinical Use of Freeze-Dried Bone. *J. Bone and Joint Surg.* **33A,** 863–872.

Le Cocq, J. F., Le Cocq, E. A., and Anderson, K. J. 1950. Preliminary Report on the Use of Bone-Bank Bone. *Surg. Gynecol. Obstet.* **91,** 277–280.

Leopold, I. H., and Adler, F. H. 1947. Use of Frozen-Dried Cornea as Transplant Material. *Arch. Opthalmol.* **37,** 268–276.

Mann, I. 1949a. A Study of Cell Survival in Embryonic Tissue Grafts in Inbred Strains of Mice under Various Conditions. *Brit. J. Cancer* **3,** 255–259.

Mann, I. 1949b. Effect of Low Temperature on the Bittner Virus of Mouse Carcinoma. *Brit. Med. J.* **ii,** 251–253.

Mann, I. 1949c. Effect of Repeated Freezing and Thawing on Mouse Carcinoma Tissue. *Brit. Med. J.* **ii,** 253–255.

Mann, I., and Dunn, W. J. 1949. Propagation of Mouse Carcinoma by Dried Tumour Tissue. *Brit. Med. J.* **ii,** 255–257.

Marragoni, A. G., and Cecchini, L. P. 1951. Homotransplantation of Arterial Segments Preserved by the Freeze-Drying Method. *Ann. Surg.* **134,** 977–983.

Matthews, D. N. 1945. Storage of Skin for Autologous Grafts. *Lancet* **i,** 775–778.

Medawar, P. B. 1944. The Behaviour and Fate of Skin Autografts and Skin Homografts in Rabbits. *J. Anat.* **78,** 176–199.

Medawar, P. B. 1945. A Second Study of the Behaviour and Fate of Skin Homografts in Rabbits. *J. Anat.* **79,** 157–176.

Meeker, I. A., and Gross, R. E. 1951. Low Temperature Sterilization of Organic Tissue by High Voltage Cathode Ray Irradiation. *Science* **114,** 283–285.

Mider, G. B., and Morton, J. J. 1939. The Effect of Freezing *in Vitro* on Some Transplantable Mammalian Tumors and on Normal Rat Skin. *Am. J. Cancer* **35,** 502–509.

Parkes, A. S., and Smith, A. U. 1953. Regeneration of Rat Ovarian Tissue Grafted after Exposure to Low Temperatures. *Proc. Roy. Soc.* (*London*) **140B**, 455–470.

Passey, R. D., and Dmochowski, L. 1950. Freezing and Desiccation of Mouse Tumours. *Brit. Med. J.* **ii**, 1129–1134.

Passey, R. D., Dmochowski, L., and Lasnitski, I. 1950. Cultivation *in Vitro* of Frozen and Desiccated Mouse Tumours. *Brit. Med. J.* **ii**, 1134–1136.

Pate, J. W. 1953. Transplantation of Preserved Non-Viable Tissue, in *The Preservation of Normal Tissues for Transplantation.* Ciba Foundation Symposium. In press.

Paufique, L., Sourdille, G. P., and Offret, G. 1948. *Les greffes de la cornée.* Masson, Paris.

Peirce, E. C., Gross, R. E., Bill, A. H., and Merrill, K. 1949. Tissue-Culture Evaluation of the Viability of Blood Vessels Stored by Refrigeration. *Ann. Surg.* **129,** 333–348.

Peirce, E. C., Rheinlander, H. F., Moritz, A. R., Gross, R. E., and Merrill, K. 1949. Transplantation of Aortic Segments Fixed in 4 Per Cent Neutral Formalin. *Am. J. Surg.* **78,** 314–323.

Polge, C., Smith, A. U., and Parkes, A. S. 1949. Revival of Spermatozoa after Vitrification and Dehydration at Low Temperatures. *Nature* **164,** 666.

Reynolds, F. C., Oliver, D. R., and Ramsay, R. 1951. Clinical Evaluation of the Merthiolate Bone Bank and Homogenous Grafts. *J. Bone and Joint Surg.* **33A,** 873–883.

Rycroft, B. W. 1952. Second-Hand Sight. *Med. Ill.* **6,** 582–584.

Sanders, F. K., and Young, J. Z. 1942. The Degeneration and Re-innervation of Grafted Nerves. *J. Anat.* **76,** 143–166.

Seddon, H. J. 1947. The Use of Autogenous Grafts for the Repair of Large Gaps in Peripheral Nerves. *Brit. J. Surg.* **35,** 151–167.

Seddon, H. J., and Holmes, W. 1944. The Late Condition of Nerve Homografts in Man. *Surg. Gynecol. Obstet.* **79,** 342–351.

Smelser, G. K., and Ozanics, V. 1946. Effect of Quick Freezing at Very Low Temperatures of Donor Tissue in Corneal Transplants. *Proc. Soc. Exptl. Biol. Med.*, **62,** 274–277.

Smith, A. U., and Parkes, A. S. 1951. Preservation of Ovarian Tissue at Low Temperatures. *Lancet* **ii,** 570–572.

Snell, G. D., Cloudman, A. M., Failor, E., and Douglass, P. 1946. Inhibition and Stimulation of Tumor Homoiotransplants by Prior Injections of Lyophilized Tumor Tissue. *J. Natl. Cancer Inst.* **6,** 303–316.

Taylor, A. C. 1944. Apparatus for the Freeze-Drying of Tissue for Storage. *J. Lab. Clin. Med.* **29,** 657–663.

Warner, P. T. J. C. P., and Gostling, J. V. T. 1950. The Effect of Freezing and Freeze-Drying on the Transplantation of Sarcoma 37. *Brit. J. Cancer* **4,** 380–395.

Webster, J. P. 1944. Refrigerated Skin Grafts. *Ann. Surg.* **120,** 431–439.

Weiss, P. 1943a. Functional Nerve Regeneration through Frozen-Dried Nerve Grafts in Cats and Monkeys. *Proc. Soc. Exptl. Biol. Med.* **54,** 277–279.

Weiss, P. 1943b. Nerve Regeneration in the Rat Following Tubular Splicing of Severed Nerves. *Arch. Surg.* **46,** 525–547.

Weiss, P. 1943c. Nerve Reunion with Sleeves of Frozen-Dried Artery in Rabbits, Cats and Monkeys. *Proc. Soc. Exptl. Biol. Med.* **54,** 274–277.

Weiss, P. 1944. The Morphogenetic Properties of Frozen-Dried Tissues. *Anat. Record* **88,** *Suppl.* **4,** 48.

Weiss, P. 1950. Perspectives in the Field of Morphogenesis. *Quart. Rev. Biol.* **25,** 177–198.

Weiss, P., and Taylor, A. C. 1943a. Repair of Peripheral Nerves by Grafts of Frozen-Dried Nerve. *Proc. Soc. Exptl. Biol. Med.* **52,** 326–328.

Weiss, P., and Taylor, A. C. 1943b. Histomechanical Analysis of Nerve Reunion in the Rat after Tubular Splicing. *Arch. Surg.* **47,** 419–447.

Weiss, P., and Taylor, A. C. 1944. Transplantation of Frozen-Dried Cornea in the Rat. *Anat. Record* **88,** *Suppl.* **4,** 49.

Weiss, P., and Wang, H. 1945. Transformation of Adult Schwann Cells into Macrophages. *Proc. Soc. Exptl. Biol. Med.* **58,** 273–275.

Young, J. Z., and Medawar, P. B. 1940. Fibrin Suture of Peripheral Nerves. *Lancet* **ii,** 126–128.

## CHAPTER 12

# The Effects of Residual Moisture in Frozen-Dried Materials, and Its Measurement

L. G. BECKETT

*Research Laboratories, W. Edwards and Company Ltd., Crawley, Sussex, England*



## I. INTRODUCTION

"I regret to say that one still hears remarks such as: 'the material should be as dry as dust'; or 'less than 1% residual moisture is satisfactory' as though this applied to every material under all circumstances." R. I. N. Greaves, opening the first session of the symposium on Freezing and Drying, London, June 1951.

Gortner has stated (1949) that the determination of residual moisture in biological substances is a purely empirical procedure conditioned by the variables of temperature, pressure, and time. This statement is true when the various biochemical and physical changes which can take place during the analytical procedure are permitted to occur without control or notice. Many undetected changes probably take place in native proteins during such determinations, either because the change is reversible, or because only a small percentage of the substance undergoes a permanent change. Where the substance suffers permanent "denaturation," however, to a large extent these changes present obvious and fundamental difficulties for the determination of residual moisture. These difficulties have recently been briefly reviewed by Common (1951).

The technique of freeze-drying is being used increasingly and spectacular results have been obtained, yet the important factor of the residual moisture content of the dried materials has received comparatively little attention. It has rarely been doubted that the residual moisture content of the dried substance is of importance, but with few exceptions, reports of its magnitude or measurement are lacking, and it was probably this situation which prompted Greaves to pass the remarks quoted above.

The importance of measuring the moisture content is clearly indicated by the attention it receives in many spheres (*cf.* Marshall, 1953) outside freeze-drying, where frequently the end products described tolerate a much higher quantity of residual water than do materials for which freeze-drying is the only satisfactory method of preservation. Moreover such materials are frequently cheap and available in bulk, so that spoilage of a small percentage in testing for moisture is of little consequence. Unfortunately, detailed examination of much of this information proves disappointing, either because the sensitivity of the method described is much less than that required to detect the traces of moisture remaining in frozen-dried materials, or because of possible decomposition as a result of elevated temperatures or undesirable chemical reactions.

In freeze-drying it is frequently necessary to measure the residual water content of only a few milligrams of dried material. This usually requires the detection of only a few micrograms of water, a relatively difficult task which has hitherto involved tedious weighing of an extremely hygroscopic substance under difficult circumstances. Some alternative method to this is obviously desirable, and the need for such a method has frequently been stated in the literature (Seffinga, 1951; Makower and Myers, 1943).

## II. EFFECTS OF RESIDUAL MOISTURE ON NON-VIABLE MATERIALS

The study of the effects of residual moisture may be considered under two separate headings: (1) effects on non-viable substances such as sera, plasma, hormones, and foodstuffs; (2) effects on viable materials such as bacteria, viruses, and tissue cells.

There is no doubt that the best preservation of non-viable substances can be achieved only when they contain the lowest possible content of residual moisture. Because of the time necessary to reach such an ideal state of dryness, it is frequently necessary in practice to specify an upper limit for the ultimate residual moisture content. This value has, in the past, been decided as a result of general observation rather than by detailed examination. There are, of course, exceptions; Flosdorf (1949) reports that in the United States all frozen-dried products must, by law, have a moisture content below 1%.

Investigations concerned with the quantitative nature of the spoilage which can occur in non-viable substances having relatively high moisture contents have been reported by Lea and Hannan (1950). They showed that a pronounced interaction occurred between the components of a frozen-dried mixture of glucose and casein. It was shown that up to 7% or more of the glucose would react chemically with some of the casein without any obvious changes in the physical properties of the bulk protein. The predominant reaction was a combination of the free amino groups of protein with a reducing group of a sugar molecule. In the presence of more residual water further changes occurred, including loss of solubility and discoloration. Similar reactions in dried blood plasma between the proteins and glucose normally present or added to the whole blood as a preservative were demonstrated by Lea *et al.* (1950). These authors point out that in the complete absence of water interaction is negligible. Attention was also drawn to the fact that during the drying process, especially when the final drying temperature was 80°C. (Strumia and McGraw, 1943), the plasma would pass through moisture and temperature conditions, favorable to a fairly rapid reaction. The products of such reactions are insoluble, and this may be the first physical evidence that spoilage has occurred. Insolubility alone would prohibit the use of such plasma for transfusion purposes, but the toxic or immunological properties of these protein-glucose products have not yet been investigated.

Potency losses of various preparations as a result of high residual moisture content have been cited by Flosdorf (1949), who quotes as an example the loss in potency of diphtheria antitoxin. At 0.5% moisture, loss of potency over 3 years of storage was negligible, but at 5% to 8%, potency was nil after only 6 months' storage. Drying times and moisture content figures for plasma dried in Great Britain and the United States are also given by Flosdorf (1949), who, quoting Greaves, says that in Great Britain plasma was desiccated for 7 days in order to eliminate all moisture. Flosdorf's further statement that in the United States plasma is dried to leave moisture contents of 0.2% to 0.5% in from 8 to 20 hours is confusing, however. These figures cannot be doubted, but it would have been preferable to point out that the short time required, as compared with the 7 days quoted above, was due to a considerable difference in the physical conditions of drying, i.e., a smaller film thickness of frozen plasma, a bottle design offering less restriction to vapor flow, and a higher final drying temperature.

## III. EFFECTS OF RESIDUAL MOISTURE ON FROZEN-DRIED VIRUSES AND BACTERIA

The effects of residual moisture on the viability of desiccated virus and bacterial suspensions is not nearly so precisely defined as for the class of materials already considered. In general, it seems possible that viruses require much lower final moisture contents for successful preservation than do bacteria. It is interesting to note that Daubney (1951) states: "We tend to overdry our virus vaccines, as evidenced by the rapidity with which bacterial contaminants, never very numerous, die out during storage." Typical moisture contents quoted by Daubney vary between 0.03% and 0.7%.

Some experimental evidence exists (Naylor and Smith, 1946; Fry, 1951; Fry and Greaves, 1951; Hutton *et al.*, 1951) that for the successful preservation, i.e., with minimal loss in viability, of frozen-dried bacterial cultures it is essential to prevent overdrying. This, however, is in contradiction to the theories of others, such as Proom (1951).

Fry (1951) has reported a number of experiments in which aliquots of a suspension of paracolon bacilli were dried for short or long periods. In each case the suspension dried for the short period, and therefore having the higher moisture content, showed a higher survival rate. It was also shown that, if the solution in which the organisms were dried contained a sugar, the proportion surviving was increased. Fry and Greaves (1951), in describing an extension of these experiments, stated that one of the most important factors for bacterial survival in dried culture was the composition of the suspending medium. The addition of glucose or lactose to the medium greatly improved the survival rate. They attributed this improvement to the retention of water by the sugar during drying. Thus, when suspensions with and without added sugar were desiccated under identical conditions, on completion of desiccation those containing sugar should have had a higher residual moisture content than those without. This has been demonstrated by Sager (1952). It is interesting to note that Sager's results show that plasma containing 6% glucose (added before drying) loses its moisture below a residual moisture content of 4%, much more slowly than plasma containing 40% added glucose. These observations support the theory of Fry and Greaves that the addition of 5% to 10% of glucose or lactose will improve every drying medium for bacteria by acting as a water-retaining agent.

A quantitative and qualitative approach to the problem of optimum residual moisture content for maintenance of viability in frozen-dried *Brucella abortus* has been reported by Hutton *et al.* (1951). In this case the final moisture content of the dried suspension was regulated by exposure *in vacuo* to known pressures of water vapor. These authors showed that if the final drying temperature was kept below 40°C. (it is assumed that they refer to ambient temperature) there was a positive correlation between moisture content and viability. In further experiments, the residual moisture was adjusted to known values as described above, but before exposure to a known vapor pressure of water the suspensions had been "dried for an extended period at a temperature of 40°C." Having demonstrated a lack of correlation when the final drying temperature was 40°C., it is surprising that thereafter such drying was carried out before controlled hydration of the dry culture. It could well have been that considerable loss of viability occurred prior to rehydration because of this final drying temperature, or at least that such treatment might in some manner have affected the organisms' viability.

Tabulated data presented by these workers showed that when the suspensions dried at 40°C. were exposed for 2 hours in a system containing water vapor at a pressure of 1 micron (0.001 mm. Hg), which corresponds to a low final moisture content, then over a period of 90 days the count after storage at room temperature fell from a value of 78 to below 1. Optimum counts after storage were noted following 8 hours' exposure to water vapor at 50 microns. It is a pity that the methods (Levy *et al.*, 1945) used for determining the amount of water remaining did not have sufficient sensitivity for accurate measurement.

As the complexity of the cell or organism becomes greater, it would appear that the amount of residual moisture necessary for retention of viability must be higher than for the more simple organisms. Billingham and Medawar (1951), for example, showed that skin removed from rabbits, frozen, dried from the frozen state, reconstituted, and grafted back onto the rabbit lost viability if the residual moisture content was less than 24%.

## IV. METHODS OF MOISTURE DETERMINATION

Throughout references to work on freeze-drying there is the suggestion that difficulties arise whenever the problem of measuring residual moisture is concerned. A fundamental point is, of course, whether during the determination "free" or "bound" moisture is being measured and what degree of denaturation has taken place as the result of measurement.

The generally accepted standard method for moisture determination employs the vacuum oven. Typical methods for its use, as summarized by Flosdorf, are described here.

Current regulations of the National Institutes of Health in the United States specify a maximal moisture content of 1% for dried biological products. Weighing bottles, previously cleaned and vacuum-dried, are weighed to the nearest 0.1 mg. They are quickly filled with approximately 1 gram of the substance to be checked, their lids are rapidly replaced, and bottle and contents are reweighed. They are then transferred to a desiccator containing specially scraped phosphorus pentoxide, the bottle lids are tilted on their sides, and the desiccator is evacuated to a pressure of 50 to 100 microns. After 2 days the desiccator is opened, the bottle lids are closed, and the bottles are reweighed. The bottles are then returned to the desiccator for a further 24 hours. This procedure is continued until constant weight is obtained.

This is the procedure officially recognized in the United States, but

Flosdorf mentions a slight variation in which a vacuum oven maintained at a temperature of 50°C. ± 1°C. is substituted for the desiccator.

A difficulty common to both procedures is the number of accurate weighings which must be carried out, the limitations imposed by the possibility of error due to inaccurate weighing, and the minimum amount of water which may thus be detected. In addition, these methods do not establish that the loss in weight is due solely to removal of water. The second method is in one respect superior to the first in that the temperature for the determination is specified, but reference to Fig. 1A and B gives an indication of the increase in apparent moisture content for a slight

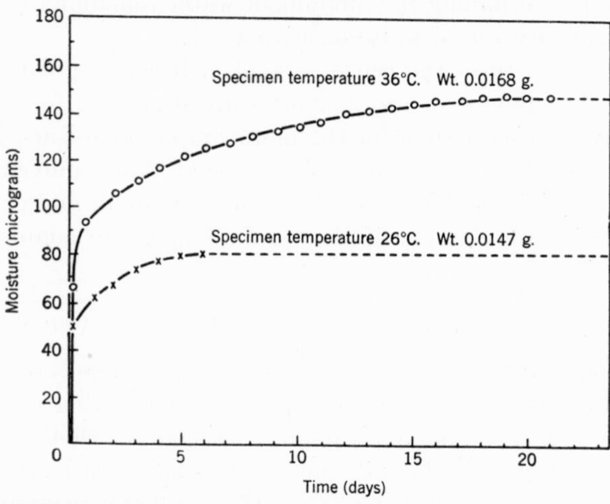


FIG. 1A. Drying curve for an ampoule containing a sample of plasma. Plasma obtained from citrated blood (420 ml. blood, 100 ml. 2% disodium citrate, 20 ml. 15% dextrose).

rise in temperature of plasma, under conditions of vacuum desiccation similar to those quoted.

The direct determination of moisture in dried biological material, by methods claimed to be rapid, has received considerable attention. Few of these methods are suitable, however, or have the requisite sensitivity for dealing with frozen-dried products. Those based on the Karl Fischer (1935) iodometric titration principle appear to be the most useful. The principle has the advantages of being a "chemical" one and, therefore, appeals to workers with experience in this field. By suitable modification it can be used to measure quantities of moisture in the microgram range, and it is reasonably rapid. The inherent disadvantages of the technique are: (a) the difficulty of retaining the reagents in the required state (atmospheric moisture must be rigidly excluded) and, when extreme sensitivity is required, the necessity for rechecking them before use; (b) the possibility of side reactions between the reagent and the material being examined (Schroeder and Nair, 1948; De Whalley, 1951); and, finally, (c) the fact that specimens, after treatment with the reagents, have no further value as biological material.

The Karl Fischer reagent consists of a solution of iodine and anhydrous sulfur dioxide in an anhydrous mixture of pyridine and methanol. The solution is dark brown in color and changes to yellow in the presence of water. The usual procedure in a determination is to mix a dried specimen of known weight with anhydrous methanol (which must previously

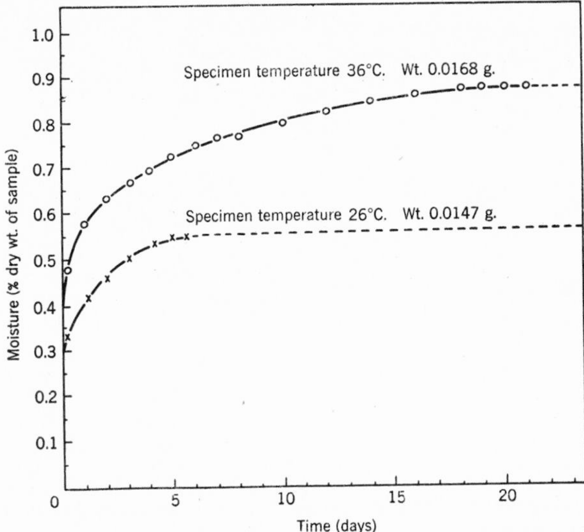


Fig. 1B. Percentage residual moisture curve derived from Fig. 1A. These curves have been corrected for diffusion of extraneous water into the apparatus, as described on p. 298.

be tested for water content) and then to titrate this with the reagent. If the specimen solution is colorless the end point can be detected visually, the yellow solution initially produced turning brown. It is claimed that quantities of water down to 0.5 mg. can thus be detected (Mitchell, 1951).

A method using an electrometric end point, based on the technique of Foulk and Bawder, depends on the hydrogen polarization of a platinum cathode in the absence of iodine from the solution. A micromethod based on this technique has been described by Levy *et al.* (1945). A penicillin bottle is the titration vessel, and 0.25 to 1.00 mg. of water may be detected with a precision of 0.02 mg. to 0.1 mg. The method was originally devised to measure the residual moisture content of penicillin salts.

Determinations using an electrometric end point are, however, somewhat tedious. With a view to overcoming this, Johansson (1949) devised an automatic titration apparatus, consisting of a hypodermic syringe driven through reduction gearing by an electric motor controlled from relays operated by platinum electrodes in the titration flask. Reagent is automatically added from the syringe to the titration vessel until the end point is reached, when the syringe motor automatically stops. The amount of reagent which has been delivered is then read from suitable scales connected to the syringe drive mechanism, and from this the moisture content may be calculated.

Two references to the use of the Karl Fischer method for determining the residual moisture of frozen-dried preparations are found in the work of Hutton *et al.* with *Brucella abortus* (1951) and Sager (1952) with dried blood plasma. The latter article contains a detailed account of the exact methods employed both for carrying out the titrations and for the preparation of the reagents.

Early in 1947 the need was felt in the research laboratories of W. Edwards & Co. (London) Ltd. for a method of determining the residual moisture content of small amounts of biological materials after centrifugal freeze-drying (Greaves, 1944). This led to a survey of *physical* methods of moisture detection, requiring the minimum of weighing and having the requisite sensitivity for examination of amounts of dried materials of only a few milligrams.

Because of the availability of vacuum pumping and measuring equipment, attention was directed to the possibility of utilizing the vapor pressure characteristics of the material as an index of moisture content. Apparatus and methods for such comparisons had previously been described. The apparatus of Makower and Myers (1943) required calibration, whereas that of Vincent and Simons (1940) was absolute within its working range. The procedure consisted in exposing the dried material in a vacuum system containing a manometer. After evacuation the system was isolated and allowed to equilibrate, the vapor pressure of water being indicated by the manometer.

Although the apparatus of Makower and Myers is similar in construction to that developed by W. Edwards & Co., its method of operation is different. It is therefore instructive to examine in detail the method of operation. The substance to be examined was contained in the flask S (Fig. 2), which was surrounded by a bath Z maintained at constant temperature. With taps A, B, and C open and the U-trap T immersed in a mixture of solid carbon dioxide and alcohol, the system was evacuated by the two-stage mechanical pump. During this period, water evaporating from the specimen was collected in the trap T. After evacuation to low pressure (below 0.1 mm. Hg) the tap B was closed and the refrigerant mixture removed from the trap T. Water frozen out in this trap re-evaporated and was then reabsorbed by the specimen until equilibrium was reached, usually in ½ to 2 hours. The equilibrium pressure was read on the manometer M, which was filled with Octoil, a low vapor pressure diffusion pump fluid. It should be noted that one limb of the manometer was continually pumped by the vacuum pump to maintain a stable zero.

Considerable difficulty was experienced in calibrating the apparatus because: (a) the vapor pressures exerted by frozen-dried materials of low final moisture content and at temperatures of 20°C. were too low to be read with any degree of accuracy; and (b) the fundamental problem, already mentioned, of providing a calibration curve, obtained by

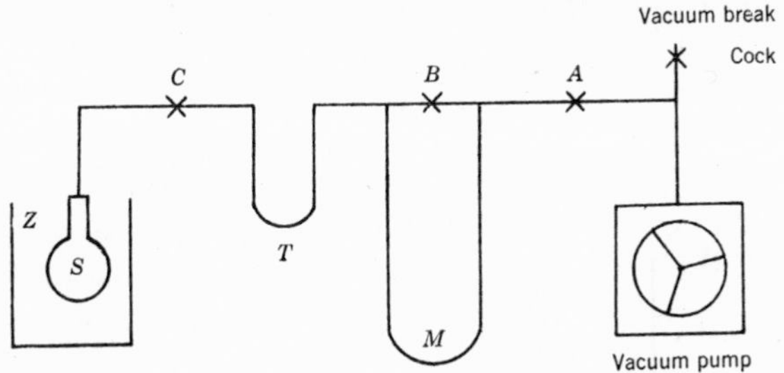


FIG. 2. Apparatus of Makower and Myers.

comparison with substances examined by the vacuum-oven method presented difficulties.

The second of these difficulties was overcome by making the apparatus absolute and therefore independent of calibration. This is fairly easily and conveniently carried out by accurately determining the volume of the system between the tap C up to the tap B and including the space above the oil in the manometer. Now, for a given pressure rise in the system, entirely due to water vapor, the mass of water contained in the apparatus to produce this rise is given by

$$M = PV\left(\frac{1}{760} \cdot \frac{273}{T} \cdot \frac{S_o}{S_{\text{Hg}}} \cdot \frac{18}{22{,}400}\right) \tag{1}$$

where $M$ = mass of water in grams.
$V$ = volume of system in cubic centimeters.
$T$ = temperature of measuring system in °K. (not to be confused with the temperature of the specimen).
$P$ = pressure in millimeters of oil.
$S_{\text{Hg}}$ = density of mercury at temperature $T$.
$S_o$ = density of oil at temperature $T$.

Thus, for a measuring system having a volume of 10 cm.³ and a manometer fluid having a specific gravity of 0.8, the increase in pressure within the system for 10 micrograms of water at ambient temperature 20°C. is determined as follows: When $M = 10^{-5}$ gram, $V = 10$ cm.³, $T = 293$°K., $S_{Hg} = 13.55$, and $S_o = 0.83$, then from eq. 1,

$$10^{-5} = \frac{P \times 10 \times 1 \times 273 \times 0.83 \times 18}{760 \times 293 \times 13.55 \times 22{,}400}$$

$$P = \frac{10^{-5} \times 760 \times 293 \times 13.55 \times 2240}{10 \times 1 \times 273 \times 0.83 \times 18}$$

$$= 16.57 \text{ mm. oil} \tag{2}$$

By a modification of the technique of Makower and Myers it then became possible to plot drying curves by measuring the mass of water

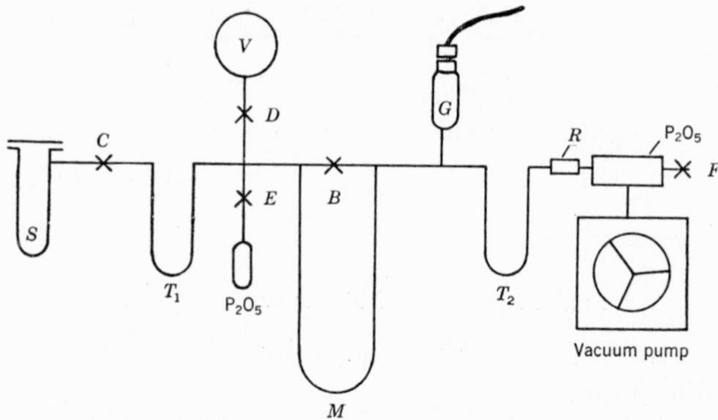


FIG. 3. Apparatus developed by W. Edwards & Co.

vapor and the time taken for its extraction from the specimen. The procedure is greatly simplified by calibrating the manometer directly in divisions equal to $10^{-5}$ gram of water.

A number of necessary refinements were added to the apparatus which is shown in Figs. 3 and 4. To accommodate ampoules and small vials, the specimen tube S was fitted with a metal cover, vacuum-sealed to the glass flange of the tube S by a trapped, synthetic rubber O ring. This cover was also arranged to support an ampoule and to break off its neck while under vacuum in the measuring system, a proved advantage when extremely small amounts of hygroscopic materials are being examined. The cock C and the trap T are positioned similarly to those of Makower and Myers. The volume V with its isolating cock D is used to extend the upper range of the apparatus, which, of course, is directly dependent on total volume. The phosphorus pentoxide trap and the isolating cock E are used to absorb water vapor on completion of each reading and by this means to indicate the presence of any permanent gases. In the absence of gases the apparatus may be operated with the stopcock B closed throughout the readings, thereby minimizing the risk of extraneous moisture entering the measuring system *via* the vacuum pump and its connections. The manometer M is filled with a thoroughly degassed and dehydrated mechanical pump oil. The Pirani-type thermal conductivity gauge is used to ensure that low pressures exist in the system. For routine work, pressures are never permitted to rise above 0.05 mm. Hg (50 microns) and generally are below 0.01 mm. Hg (10 microns). The trap $T_2$, which is refrigerated constantly throughout an observation, prevents moisture or other volatile substances from reaching the measuring system from the vacuum pump or the rubber connecting tube R. This trap can also be used to collect moisture from the measuring system following an observation, if, for any reason, the phosphorus pentoxide trap and its cock E are not used. As an additional precaution, to prevent moisture from the vacuum pump reaching the system, and also as a means of clearing water from trap $T_2$ while under vacuum, the vacuum pump itself is fitted with a phosphorus pentoxide trap. The vacuum-break valve F, serving to admit gas to the specimen on completion of dehydration, is so arranged that air, nitrogen, etc., must pass first over the phosphorus pentoxide and then through the refrigerated trap $T_2$ before reaching the specimen. This is a necessary precaution when the dried contents of the specimen tube have to be weighed on completing the determination. An additional air admittance valve is fitted to the specimen-tube cover.

The procedure for determining the residual moisture content of a specimen contained in an ampoule sealed by fusing its glass stem is as follows: A nick is made near the top of the ampoule stem, and fitted circumferentially around this is a loop of fine-gauge Nichrome wire. The ampoule is inserted into a spring clip attached to the cover of the specimen tube, and the Nichrome loop is connected to two adjacent terminals. The cover supporting the ampoule is then placed on the flange of the specimen tube S, and the apparatus, already evacuated by the mechanical pump, is cautiously connected to it by opening the stopcock C. At this stage the trap T is not refrigerated, and the volume V is open to the system. A short period of pumping rapidly removes air from the tube S and dries out the system before readings are taken. To begin observations, the cock E is momentarily opened to equalize the pressure in the phosphorus pentoxide trap, the trap T is refrigerated, cock D is closed, and the Nichrome wire surrounding the ampoule neck is heated until the glass cracks. The top of the ampoule is then displaced by lightly tapping with a plunger operated by an external magnet. Moisture evolved from the specimen condenses in the trap T. After a few seconds, or minutes,

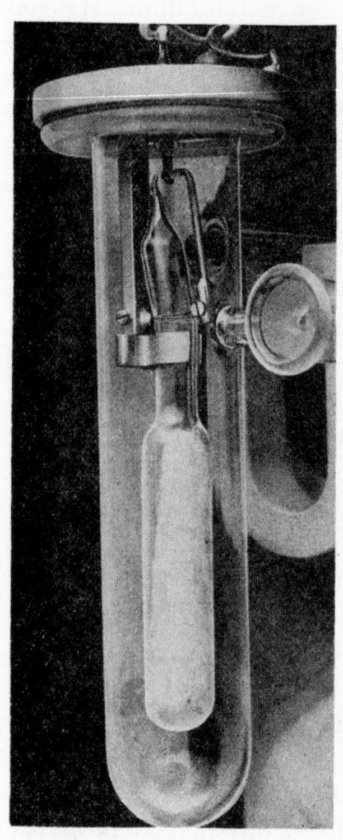

A

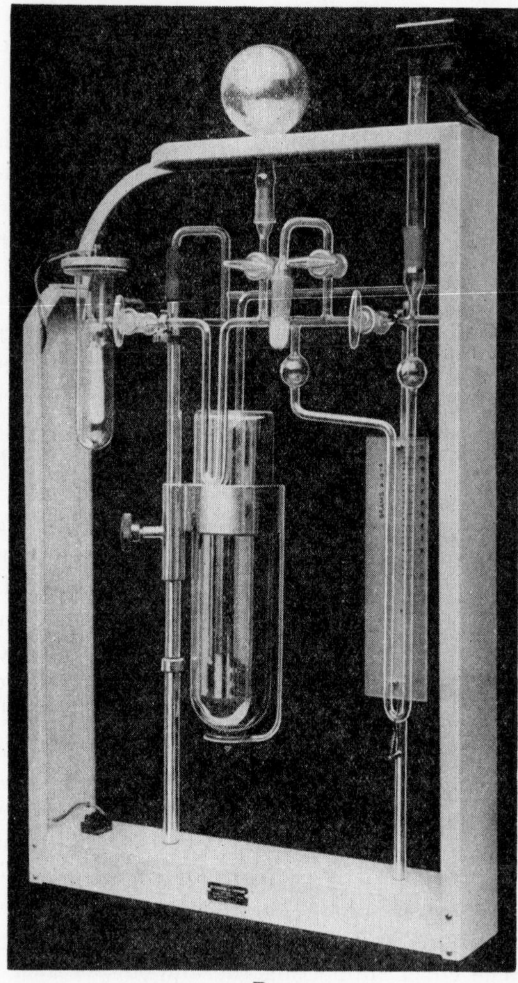

B

Fig. 4. Micro moisture determination apparatus developed by W. Edwards & Co. The specimen tube is to the left, the calibrated manometer to the right. The volume, V, is on top of the apparatus (see Fig. 3). The parallel tube surmounted by a small horizontal rectangular box, mounted above the right limb of the manometer (which is the pumped reference limb), is the measuring head of a thermal (Pirani type) of vacuum gauge. The inset shows an enlarged view of the specimen holder, with the severed ends of the ampoule being displaced by a magnetically operated plunger.

depending upon the speed with which water is released, the cocks C and B are closed and the refrigerant is removed from the trap T. Ice condensed therein evaporates, and the resulting rise in pressure is read from the manometer M, which is calibrated directly in terms of mass of water. Water vapor is removed from the measuring system either by chemical absorption by opening cock E or by condensation in trap $T_2$ after opening cock B. The former provides a check on the presence of non-absorbable gases or vapors, since the manometer would not in their presence return to zero. Closing cock B and/or E and replacing the refrigerant around trap $T_2$ prepares the system for the next observation. The readings are continued until no further water is released by the specimens. The sum of the amounts of water represents the moisture content of the specimen for the given conditions of vacuum and specimen temperature. The apparatus is then filled with dry air or other gas (dried by the built-in drying traps), the open ampoule is removed and weighed, the contents are washed out, and the ampoule is dried and reweighed; by subtraction the weight of the dry material is thus obtained.

The percentage moisture content is given by

$$\frac{\text{Total weight of moisture removed in apparatus}}{\text{Weight of dry specimen}} \times 100$$

The volume V is used when masses of water exceeding the calibration range of the manometer have to be measured. It should be noted that the calibration applies only for water vapor pressures less than the saturation vapor pressure of water at the temperature of the measuring system. The effect of this volume will be appreciated if reference is made to the equation on page 293. It is standard practice always to include this volume when taking the first of a series of observations. For convenience, to simplify the scale correction factor when V is included in the system, its volume is made 10 or 100 times as large as the volume of the measuring system. If the quantity of water in the measuring system with the volume V connected is too small to be read on the manometer, the water vapor can be removed from V simply by replacing the refrigerant around the trap T and then after 5 or 6 minutes closing cock D and removing the refrigerant from the trap, when the moisture will be released into the measuring system and an increased manometer reading obtained.

This description outlines a method of determination which necessitates destruction of the specimen. Where non-viable specimens are concerned, and where the container or ampoule can ultimately be obtained for weighing, the ampoule and contents are weighed prior to insertion in the measuring apparatus. Of course it is then necessary to retain the end of the ampoule removed to expose the specimen. Where specimens are contained in vials, or similar open-top containers, loss of moisture from the specimen during initial evacuation of the tube S is prevented by surrounding it with a refrigerant mixture of solid carbon dioxide and alcohol. It is, of course, then necessary to ensure that the apparatus is filled with dry gas at, or slightly above, atmospheric pressure before removing the cover of the tube S to insert the vial. Various methods operating *via* metallic bellows or through vacuum seals are available for opening stoppered and metal ring sealed vials.

The plotting of drying curves, such as those shown in Figs. 1A, 1B and 5, is most valuable in predicting end points. The curves are particularly

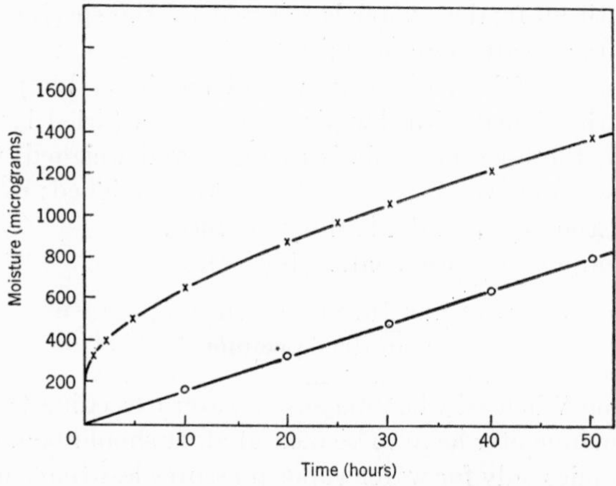


FIG. 5. Drying curve for an ampoule containing a sample of frozen-dried human plasma. Plasma obtained from citrated blood (420 ml. blood, 100 ml. 2% disodium citrate, 20 ml. 15% dextrose). Weight of sample, 0.1472 gram; temperature of sample, 26°C. "O" plot, observed values of diffusion of extraneous moisture into apparatus. "X" plot, observed values of moisture extracted from plasma plus extraneous moisture.

useful when dealing with open-neck vials, initially frozen as described in the previous paragraph, when they indicate whether the first one or two observations consist only of water removed from the specimen, or whether they include extraneous moisture in or on the vial or from specimen tube T. Close inspection of Fig. 5 discloses near the base line a plot entitled "Correction Curve." This is the amount of water which diffuses into the apparatus through the synthetic rubber O ring forming a vacuum seal between the cover and the specimen tube S. When this seal ring is being used a blank run is carried out periodically on the apparatus to verify that the rate of diffusion of water through it has remained constant. So far it has been the writer's experience that within the life of the ring this is so. When taking a series of readings for a moisture determination, an appropriate mass of water obtained from this curve must be subtracted from the mass indicated by the manometer readings. A curve so corrected and derived from Fig. 5 is shown in Fig. 6. The diffusion of water into the measuring system can be prevented by replacing the O ring by a vacuum grease seal.

It will be appreciated that the specimen tube S on the apparatus can be held at any desired temperature during an observation. Thus, it is possible to simulate the vacuum-oven methods without the necessity for tedious weighing or the possibility of attendant inaccuracy.

The determinations and the methods of obtaining them with this apparatus, although satisfying the conditions of controlled specimen temperature, high sensitivity, and preclusion of oxidizing or chemically

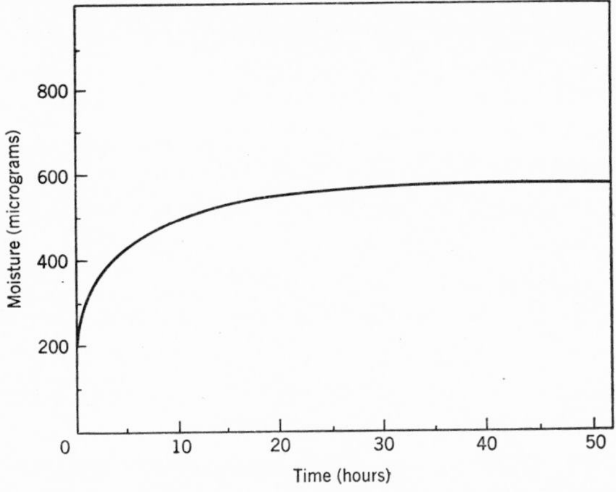


FIG. 6. Drying curve of Fig. 5 corrected for extraneous moisture.

active atmospheres or substances, have the disadvantage of the time required for completion. The method and suggestions of Makower and Myers (1943) and Seffinga (1951) may also be carried out with this apparatus. Not only is it possible to measure the equilibrium pressure of water vapor directly, but where this is too small to be read on the manometer, the vapor pressure can be magnified as follows. With the system evacuated and cocks C and D open, E, B, and F closed, and the system in equilibrium, cock C is closed, trap T is refrigerated, and after some 10 to 12 minutes cock D is closed and all water vapor in the measuring system is condensed in the trap T. If the refrigerant is now removed from this trap, the pressure in the measuring system, because of the water vapor, will be increased in direct relation to the ratio of the volume V to the volume of the measuring system. If we assume this to be 60:1 and the sensitivity of the oil manometer equal to 0.06 mm. Hg, then clearly it is possible to measure water vapor pressures of 0.001 mm. Hg (1 micron).

A calibration in terms of water vapor pressure is readily accomplished. Typical specimens of material are exposed in the apparatus. Their vapor pressures are determined by one of the methods described above, and simultaneously the mass of water in the apparatus is noted. From this data, a drying and vapor pressure curve are readily plotted.

When using the method of vapor pressures for determining moisture contents, it is of course necessary that a separate calibration curve be prepared for each type of substance or specimen; e.g., a calibration curve for dried peptone would be next to useless for determinations on mammalian skin. A further factor which must be kept in mind is the mass of water necessary for an observation. If this should represent a large fraction of the residual moisture content of the specimen, its extraction will mean a large change in the equilibrium conditions of the specimen, with consequent inaccuracy.

This difficulty may be overcome either by increasing the size of the specimen or by taking the average of a large number of plots obtained from specimens as nearly identical as possible and using this as the source of calibration. It must be appreciated that such a calibration curve is applicable only to specimens of identical weight to those used for calibration.

In addition to its use for determining moisture in biological materials the apparatus described can be used for many other purposes. One such purpose, of interest to the biologist, is the rate of diffusion of moisture through packing materials.

## V. CONCLUSION

The aim of this article has been to present a summary of typical results and of methods and apparatus by which they can be obtained, and to describe a new piece of equipment developed for the specific purpose of moisture determination in dried biological materials. It is to be hoped that when workers present data on frozen-dried products they will appreciate the importance of residual moisture, make some effort to determine it, and, above all, to state precisely the method used for its measurement.

The author is indebted to Mr. A. S. D. Barrett, Technical Director of W. Edwards & Co. (London) Ltd., for permission to publish this article, and for the assistance of Miss. E. Elger and Mr. T. W. Rowe in its preparation.

## REFERENCES

Billingham, R. E., and Medawar, P. B. 1951. The Viability of Mammalian Skin after Freezing, Thawing and Freeze-Drying, in *Freezing and Drying*. Edited by R. J. C. Harris. The Institute of Biology, London. Pp. 55–62.

Common, R. H. 1951. Moisture Determination. Some Basic Difficulties in Testing for Moisture. *Can. Food. Inds.* **22,** 6.

Daubney, R. 1951. The Freeze-Drying of Living Virus Vaccines for Veterinary Use, in *Freezing and Drying.* Edited by R. J. C. Harris. The Institute of Biology, London. Pp. 143–153.

De Whalley, H. C. S. 1951. Determination of Water in Molasses with the Karl Fischer and Other Methods. *Intern. Sugar J.* **53,** 157.

Fischer, K. 1935. A New Method for the Analytical Determination of the Water Content of Liquids and Solids. *Angew. Chem.* **48,** 394–396.

Flosdorf, E. W. 1949. *Freeze-Drying.* Reinhold Publishing Corp., New York.

Fry, R. M. 1951. The Influence of the Suspending Fluid on the Survival of Bacteria after Drying, in *Freezing and Drying.* Edited by R. J. C. Harris. The Institute of Biology, London. Pp. 107–115.

Fry, R. M., and Greaves, R. I. N. 1951. The Survival of Bacteria before and after Drying. *J. Hyg.* **49,** 220–246.

Gortner, R. A. 1949. *Outlines of Biochemistry.* John Wiley and Sons, New York.

Greaves, R. I. N. 1944. Centrifugal Vacuum Freezing. Its Application to the Drying of Biological Materials from the Frozen State. *Nature* **153,** 485–487.

Hutton, R. S., Hilmoe, R. J., and Roberts, J. L. 1951. Some Physical Factors that Influence Survival of *Brucella abortus* during Freeze-Drying. *J. Bacteriol.* **61,** 309–319.

Johansson, A. 1949. The Microdetermination of Water. *Acta Chem. Scand.* **3,** 1058–1066.

Lea, C. H., and Hannan, R. S. 1950. Biochemical and Nutritional Significance of the Reaction between Proteins and Reducing Sugars. *Nature* **165,** 438–439.

Lea, C. H., Hannan, R. S., and Greaves, R. I. N. 1950. The Reaction between Proteins and Reducing Sugars in the "Dry" State. Dried Human Blood Plasma. *Biochem. J.* **47,** 626–629.

Levy, G. B., Murtaugh, J. J., and Rosenblatt, M. 1945. Microdetermination of Water. *Ind. Eng. Chem. Anal. Ed.* **17,** 193–195.

Makower, J., and Myers, S. 1943. A New Method for the Determination of Moisture in Dehydrated Vegetables. *Proc. Inst. Food. Technol.* Pp. 156–164.

Marshall, W. R., Jr. 1953. Drying. *Ind. Eng. Chem.* **45,** 47–54.

Mitchell, J., Jr. 1951. Karl Fischer Reagent Titration. *Anal. Chem.* **23,** 1069–1075.

Naylor, H. B., and Smith, P. A. 1946. Factors Affecting the Viability of *Serratia marcescens* during Dehydration and Storage. *J. Bacteriol.* **52,** 565–573.

Proom, H. 1951. Some of the Factors Affecting the Viability of Bacterial Cultures Subjected to the Freeze-Drying Process, in *Freezing and Drying.* Edited by R. J. C. Harris. The Institute of Biology, London. Pp. 117–126.

Sager, H. 1952. The Water Content of Dried Plasma and Its Determination. *Pharm. Acta Helv.* **27,** 121–149.

Schroeder, C. W., and Nair, J. H. 1948. Determination of Water in Dry Food Materials. Karl Fischer Method. *Anal. Chem.* **20,** 452–455.

Seffinga, G. 1951 (quoted by Sager, 1952).

Strumia, M. M., and McGraw, J. J. 1943. Method and Apparatus for Shell Freezing and Rapid Drying of Plasma and Other Products from the Frozen State by Low Temperature Water Vapor Condensation *in Vacuo. J. Lab. Clin. Med.* **28,** 1140–1155.

Vincent, R. S., and Simons, A. 1940. Sensitive Method for the Determination of Water applied to Electrical Insulating Materials. *Proc. Phys. Soc.* (*London*) **52,** 489–500.

CHAPTER 13

# The Application of Freeze-Drying to Electron Microscopy

ROBLEY C. WILLIAMS

*Virus Laboratory, University of California, Berkeley, California*



## I. INTRODUCTION: GENERAL REMARKS

Although the techniques of vacuum sublimation had been well known for some time preceding the early developmental years of electron microscopy, only quite recently have these methods been employed in the preparation of electron microscopic specimens of biological materials. The primary reasons for this delay in the application of an older technique are fairly evident: so much completely novel and exciting information has been quickly and easily secured from even the crudest kinds of preparation that the adoption of a more refined, and complicated, method has had to await the maturing influence of time. In addition, the older, unshadowed micrographs did not permit a demonstration of three-dimensional relief, and consequently it has been only after the general acceptance of the methods of shadowing (Williams and Wyckoff, 1944, 1946) that an appreciation could be gained of the seriousness of the artifacts introduced into specimens by improper preparation.

An electron microscopist is likely to be so inured to the existence of preparative artifacts in his specimens that he must stop and re-examine his micrographs with the fresh eye of a novice in order to gain an adequate appreciation of the ubiquity and magnitude of these artifacts. Seldom is there seen in an electron micrograph a biological object which appears

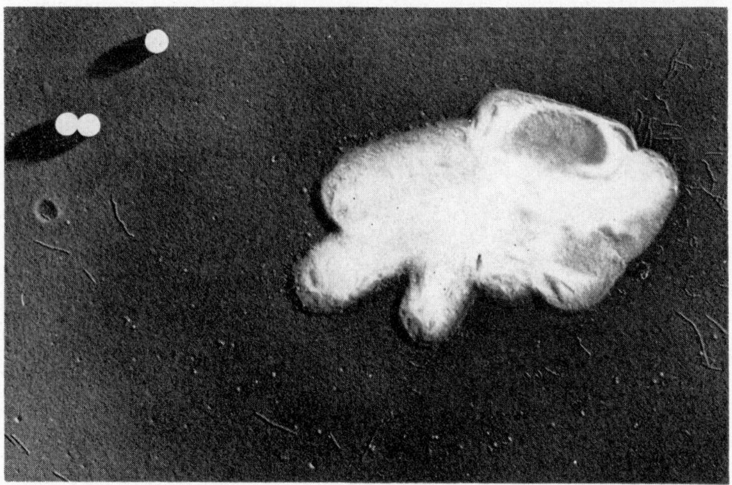

FIG. 1. Group of *E. coli* organisms, dried in air from a microdroplet of distilled water. The great degree of flattening is evidenced by the shortness of the shadows. The spherical objects in the upper left corner of the micrograph are polystyrene latex particles; the ratio of their shadow lengths to their diameters gives the local shadow angle (3.3/1 in this micrograph). This preparation, and all others shown in this chapter, is shadowed with uranium upon a collodion substrate film. 11,500×.

even fairly similar to what our corollary experience would tell us the object must look like. The appearance of a bacterium like *E. coli* is a good illustration of this statement. Observations with light microscopes, particularly the phase contrast microscope, indicate clearly that the overall shape of this object must be approximately cylindrical with rounded ends. A conventional electron micrograph (Fig. 1), however, shows these organisms to be wide and flat, with practically no intimation of cylindrical form. It is an interesting commentary upon our willingness to disbelieve what we directly see to recall that for over ten years we have accepted this sort of micrograph as an adequate representation without great mental qualms. It may be maintained, of course, that the overall shape of such a large object will be of little concern to most electron microscopists. They may be interested instead in the fine detail of structure upon the surface of the organism or within it, or they may be interested in the shape and size of smaller objects, such as fibrils, viruses, and protein molecules. But the obvious failure of a micrograph to exhibit an object such as a bacterium with an overall shape in even approximate agreement with what must be its real shape in the living state should excite a reluctance toward accepting literally electron microscopic evidence of morphology on any scale of detailed fineness. An air-dried bacterium shows a surface detail which is wrinkled and mottled. Is this because the surface of the living organism is wrinkled, or has the wrinkling been introduced partially or wholly as an artifact due to drying? This is the kind of question which, until recently, could not be proposed with any degree of relevancy, nor could it be answered in other than a hypothetical way.

### 1. *Effects of Surface-Tension Forces upon Small Biological Objects*

An ordinary air-dried preparation of biological material ready to be examined in the electron microscope has been subjected to a notably damaging set of foreign environments. The material, customarily contained within a drop of isotonic, aqueous salt suspension, is deposited upon a small specimen grid prefilmed with collodion. The drop dries in a few minutes, during most of which time the solvent is strongly hypertonic. After complete drying the salt is rinsed off the film with distilled water, thus exposing the biological material to a severely hypotonic environment, and the residual distilled water is allowed to evaporate completely. During both drying phases the material is subjected to the forces of aqueous surface tension, having been "softened up" for this experience by exposure to solvents ranging through a full gamut of tonicity.

The pressure of surface tension acting upon the exposed surface of a very small object while drying is larger than one might expect. Anderson (1952) has given a calculation of this pressure and has shown it to be approximately 1 ton per square inch acting over the surface of a virus of average size. When it is recalled that such an object is usually in a hydrated condition when exposed to this pressure, it is to be anticipated that great flattening will ensue upon drying. As a matter of fact, only one biological object has so far been shown to be capable of resisting the flattening forces of surface tension; the particles of tobacco mosaic virus appear (Williams, 1952a) to be as high as they are wide when either air-dried or frozen-dried. Apart from the flattening effect, there is another influence of surface tension forces which may result in either aggregation or disruption, particularly when acting upon small particles. An example of the aggregative effect is shown in Fig. 2, an electron micrograph of a partially ordered array of purified bushy stunt virus. An effect tending toward order is desirable, of course, if one is studying the crystallization habit of a purified virus, but is hardly desirable if one is examining the virus for the purpose of learning something of its most likely morphology while *in vivo*. A breakage of individual particles, particularly if they are of linear shape like those of tobacco mosaic virus, can also occur upon drying. Williams and Steere (1951) have concluded that particles of

FIG. 2. An ordered array of purified tomato bushy stunt virus. The virus particles are of uniform size and have been clustered into a two-dimensional close-packing by the forces of surface tension during drying from a water suspension. 21,000×; 2.6/1 shadow angle.

tobacco mosaic virus are more uniform in length, and are generally longer, as they exist in suspension than following deposition upon films for electron microscopy.

### 2. *Preservation of Three-Dimensional Structure by the Critical-Point Method*

The preservation of three-dimensional structure in specimens to be photographed in the electron microscope can be achieved only if drying is accomplished without the action of any interfacial surface tension of a magnitude even remotely approaching that of a water-air interface. An imaginative solution to this problem of structural integrity is to desiccate the objects from a suspending medium which is in a state above its critical point. Anderson (1951) has initiated the use of carbon dioxide for this method and has developed it particularly in the preparation of cell membranes and bacteria. The essence of the technique is that the specimen material is brought from its initial aqueous surroundings to a suspension in liquid carbon dioxide, following which step the carbon dioxide is raised to a temperature above its critical point (45°C.) and allowed to leave the specimen material as a gas.

Anderson has pointed out the liabilities of this technique as well as demonstrating beautifully its success in preserving three-dimensional structure. The disadvantages are primarily these: (1) the material must be chemically fixed (with attendant uncertainties as to effects upon small-scale structure) prior to immersion in liquid carbon dioxide; (2) the effects of an environment as strange as liquid carbon dioxide may be harmful; (3) the specimen material is exposed to the viscous forces of moving liquids during the preparative steps, and spatial relationships among quasi-separate particles, such as bacteria with bacteriophages, may become altered.

## II. FREEZE-DRYING FOR ELECTRON MICROSCOPY: GENERAL CONSIDERATIONS

The preparation of electron microscope specimens by quick freezing and subsequent vacuum sublimation would appear to have both advantages and disadvantages compared with the critical-point preparative method. The advantages are, at least in principle: (1) specimen objects can be physically "fixed" almost instantaneously, with lessened risk of changes that may occur in relatively slow chemical fixation; (2) the only foreign environment experienced by the object prior to desiccation is that of ice, but the object is locked in a solid matrix during this exposure; (3) the spatial relationships of quasi-separate objects may be fairly well preserved, since the physical fixation is quick and complete; (4) the dried material can be readily shadowed for electron microscopy, if desired.

Some disadvantages of freeze-drying are: (1) the medium in which the specimen material is suspended must be relatively free of non-volatile components; (2) even when freezing is extremely rapid, the formation of ice crystals within the specimen objects must certainly take place; (3) interfacial forces at the receding ice edge during sublimation must exist, but their effects are unpredictable.

With either the critical-point or the freeze-drying method there must be some distortion of spatial relationships among small objects as sublimation proceeds. Objects initially suspended throughout the liquid carbon dioxide, or the ice, must finally come to rest upon the surface of the substrate film or upon other particles and thus form aggregations or clumps whose size depends upon the concentration of the suspended objects (see Fig. 12). This clumping is three-dimensional and random, quite distinct from the essentially two-dimensional aggregation resulting from surface tension forces during ordinary air drying. The latter kind of aggregation is established while the particles are still in semi-suspension and relatively free to move short distances under the impact of thermal collisions (Brownian motion). As a result of this circumstance well-ordered arrays of particles are produced if they are of uniform size. On the other hand, during vacuum sublimation the particles are always in solid-solid contact with the ice, or with other particles, or with the substrate film, and the thermal collisions cannot jostle the particles enough to allow them to fit into ordered arrays.

## III. EARLIER METHODS OF FREEZE-DRYING ELECTRON MICROSCOPE SPECIMENS

The first description of a freeze-drying technique with specific application to electron microscopy is due to Wyckoff (1946). Subsequent to this publication Wyckoff (1947) has shown, with micrographs, the results of some experiments on frozen-dried, concentrated suspensions of tobacco mosaic virus. Pease (1947) has described the effects of quick freezing and vacuum sublimation upon preparations of a myosin sol in potassium chloride and has shown a micrograph from which he has concluded that ionic constituents in solution can be frozen in place without crystallization. These three reports, in addition to those recently made by the author (Williams, 1952b, 1953), appear to be the only ones dealing primarily with freeze-drying for electron microscopy. Wyckoff's technique involves placing a small drop of suspension upon a cooled, collodion-filmed specimen grid which is resting upon a massive block chilled to approximately the temperature of solid carbon dioxide. The drop is immediately aspirated, and that portion of the drop which congeals in the time between deposition and aspiration remains upon the collodion film. The chilled block, with specimen screen still resting upon it, is placed in a vacuum apparatus, such as a shadowing unit, and sublimation is carried out while the block comes to room temperature. At the end of the sublimation period the specimen screens are removed for direct microscopic examination, or they are left in the same vacuum and shadowed. Although this technique has been occasionally used by several investigators, it has certain fundamental defects (to be discussed later) which prevent it from being adequate for complete freeze-drying.

The physical principles involved in freeze-drying for electron microscopy are essentially the same as those underlying the method as applied to larger quantities of biological materials: a quick and hard freezing, a fairly rapid sublimation at a temperature below any eutectic point that might be reached as the ice evaporates, and a final completion of desiccation at a slightly elevated temperature. The interrelations of temperature, pressure, and geometry in the sublimation process have recently been discussed succinctly in a paper by Malmstrom (1951), who emphasizes that the speed of sublimation is enhanced by a low partial pressure of water vapor, a specimen temperature as high as is safe, and a short and direct route between specimen and cold trap. Freeze-drying for the specialized purpose of electron microscopy is in one fundamental respect simpler than the more usual types of freeze-drying in that only extremely small quantities of suspension are needed. This circumstance allows extremely rapid freezing and fairly rapid sublimation to be achieved. A difficulty associated with freeze-drying for electron microscopy resides in the requirement that the specimen objects be micrographed when on a thin and delicate film, and hence, for technical reasons, must be frozen and sublimed upon that film. This latter requirement presents serious troubles in securing adequate thermal transfer during the vacuum sublimation.

## IV. DESCRIPTION OF A NEW FREEZE-DRYING METHOD

A new technique has recently been developed in this Laboratory for the preparation of electron microscope specimens by freeze-drying. In this method extremely small droplets of suspended material are made to impinge at high velocity upon a thin collodion film which is in intimate thermal contact with a massive heat reservoir maintained at a low temperature. The droplets flatten considerably upon impingement and freeze almost instantaneously. Vacuum sublimation is then carried out, the frozen-dried objects are shadowed *in situ* on the collodion film, and the film (with shadowed objects) is transferred to a specimen grid for electron microscopy.

### 1. *Apparatus: Deposition of Material*

The apparatus for freeze-drying is shown schematically in Fig. 3. In detail the technique is as follows: A substrate film about 0.1 micron thick is prepared in the usual way by spreading upon water a solution of collodion in amyl acetate. A portion of this film is picked up on a ring about 1.5 cm. in diameter and is transferred to the top surface of the heat reservoir, shown in Fig. 3 as the copper support. The transference is made by first placing the filmed ring on the support and dampening it with condensed breath moisture. Intimate contact is fairly well assured if the interference film of air initially seen between film and copper surface disappears as the collodion drys from its temporary moistening. The ring is then pushed down until the film breaks; this leaves a tightly stretched film covering the copper surface. This surface should be slightly convex and polished with emergy paper as fine as No. 0000. The copper support is then lowered into place at the bottom of the sublimation tube and stuck to the bottom of the tube with a patch of Dow-Corning high-vacuum grease. This affords satisfactory thermal conduction between the wall of the glass tube and the support and allows the temperature of the latter to be readily and promptly controlled by immersion of the tube into liquids of known temperature. The open end of the sublimation tube is then covered to exclude dust, and the tube is placed for about 5 minutes in a bath of solid carbon dioxide–alcohol mixture. Difficulties

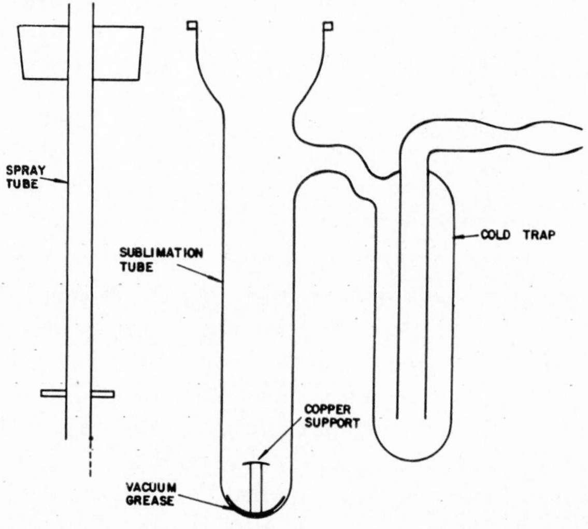


FIG. 3. Outline drawing of part of the apparatus used for freeze-drying biological materials for electron microscopy. The operation of the apparatus is described in the text. Drawing is about ¼ actual size.

are encountered if a bath of liquid nitrogen is used, owing to the condensation of atmospheric oxygen at the bottom of the tube. If a bath colder than carbon dioxide–alcohol is needed, it is convenient to use cold *iso*-pentane since this can be easily maintained at any temperature above −150°C.

### 2. *Sublimation*

After the tube and support have come to a temperature in equilibrium with the cooling bath, a tube (shown separately as a spray tube in Fig. 3) is inserted into the sublimation tube to within 3 cm. of the top of the copper support. About 0.01 ml. of the specimen suspension is sprayed (see below) through the tube and upon the collodion surface. The top of the sublimation tube is then covered with a lid with a vacuum-tight seal, the vapor trap is surrounded with liquid nitrogen, and the apparatus is connected to a high-vacuum system. During sublimation the temperature of the bath surrounding the tube can easily be kept at any reasonable value, but it has been found that about −45°C. is generally satisfactory, both for the preservation of a hard ice structure during sublimation and for the realization of a sufficiently rapid rate of sublimation.

After 15 to 20 minutes, with a vacuum gauge reading of about $10^{-4}$ mm. Hg, the sublimation at low temperature is essentially complete and the temperature of the dried specimen material can be raised by surrounding the tube with hot water. Trial has shown that thoroughly desiccated biological objects can be heated to 65°C. without any structural alteration apparent in the electron microscope. This elevated temperature brings about further drying and additional sublimation of slightly volatile constituents and also ensures that air can be admitted to the sublimation tube without any liability of moisture condensing upon the specimen.

### 3. *Transfer of Specimen Film*

After air is admitted slowly to the system through a stopcock in the lid of the sublimation tube, the copper support is removed, the grease is cleaned from its under surface, and if desired, it is placed in an ordinary shadow-casting unit. The collodion film must now be transferred to an electron microscope specimen grid. This transfer is done in two steps, each similar in technique to replication (Schaefer, 1942), since a one-step replication would bring the specimen objects on the "wrong side" (i.e., the side uppermost in the electron microscope) of the grid wires. The first transfer is made with the aid of a piece of Scotch tape in which two holes, 3/16 to 1/4 in. in diameter, have been punched. The tape is placed carefully upon the collodion-filmed surface and gently pressed into close contact. When the tape is slowly pulled away, the collodion film is found stretched across the two holes. This effects the first transfer. Another piece of Scotch tape is now laid, adhesive side up, upon a flat piece of glass; this tape is conveniently held in place by means of a piece of double-coated Scotch tape positioned beforehand upon the glass. Two 200-mesh microscope grids are placed upon this second piece of tape with pieces of paper, 1 mm. square, between the grids and the tape. The first piece of tape (containing the two filmed holes) is now placed, adhesive side down, upon the second piece of tape, with the collodion-covered holes centered over the two grids. The collodion surrounding the 1/8-in. grids is gently stuck to the adhesive of the underlying tape with the aid of a dull needle. The collodion film is now in good contact with the 200-mesh grids, and they can be removed from the tape with a pair of forceps. Both of these transfer processes should be done, of course, in a relatively dry atmosphere to prevent hydrating the highly desiccated biological material.

### 4. *Discussion of Spraying Methods*

Spraying of the suspension is accomplished with the aid of either a low-velocity nebulizer (commercially available as a Vaponefrin Vaporizer from the Vaponefrin Co., Upper Darby, Pennsylvania), or a high-velocity spray gun like the one developed by Backus and Williams (1950). If the biological material to be sprayed consists of fairly large and delicate objects, such as cells, the lower velocity of droplet impact provided by the nebulizer may be preferable in order to minimize any damage to the objects. But the frozen-droplet patterns resulting from the high-velocity gun are generally preferable, since the droplets are greatly flattened upon impact and provide a more widely spread field in which smaller objects, such as viruses, can be found quite well separated. In addition, the greatly flattened droplets will freeze more rapidly than will those deposited from the nebulizer. If the nebulizer is used, the spray tube must be of metal and be electrically connected to the copper support with something like a light chain (shown as a dotted line at the bottom of the spray tube in Fig. 3). If this is not done the electrostatic charge developed between support and tube during spraying will prevent the low-velocity droplets from impinging in satisfactory numbers upon the surface of the copper support. A glass tube, without grounding chain, is satisfactory for use with the high-velocity spray gun.

## V. CRITICAL EXAMINATION OF EARLIER FREEZE-DRYING METHODS

The description of the freeze-drying technique developed in this laboratory helps one to understand why any method closely like the one described earlier (Wyckoff, 1946) will fail to accomplish an adequate freeze-drying of biological specimens. The primary misconception underlying such a method is the supposition that heat will be transferred readily from one rigid body to another when they are held together by resting contact only. As a matter of fact two rigid bodies (such as a microscope specimen grid resting on a chilled block) are likely to be in contact at only three points, and the rate of heat transfer across these points is slow indeed. In air the heat transfer between two solid bodies in resting contact is primarily by means of convection and conduction of the air, whereas in a vacuum the heat transfer is almost solely by radiation. These aspects of thermal transfer are matters for consideration at two stages in the earlier method of freeze-drying: (1) the time taken for the bottom layer of a drop of suspension to freeze, when placed upon a specimen screen in resting contact with a block chilled to as low a temperature as −190°C., can be calculated to be quite long, of the order of half a second; (2) near the conclusion of vacuum sublimation the temperature of the specimen is determined almost solely by the radiative equilibrium established by the presence of the chilled block under the specimen and by the bell jar at room temperature above it. If the reasonable assumption is made that the temperature of the block at this critical time is approximately −75°C., a calculation shows that the temperature of the specimen will be about −5°C., an obviously unsafe temperature for vacuum sublimation.

## VI. EVALUATION OF THE NEW FREEZE-DRYING METHOD

### 1. *Rate of Cooling of the Deposited Material*

The method of freeze-drying here described provides for a rapid rate of cooling of the droplets owing to their small volumes, the thinness of

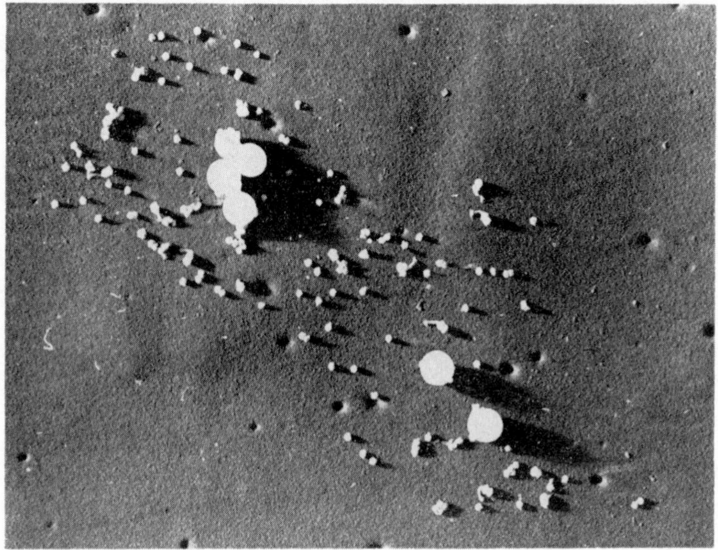

FIG. 4. A frozen-dried droplet pattern of a mixed preparation of $T_2$ and $T_3$ bacteriophage particles. This micrograph shows the extent to which a very small droplet of material is spread by the forces of impingement before it freezes. The maximum thickness of the frozen droplet can be calculated from the area covered by the virus particles, as explained in the text. 18,000×.

their flattened form as they impinge upon the copper support, and the excellence of the thermal contact between the flattened droplets and the heat reservoir (the cold copper support). The volume and thickness of a frozen droplet pattern can be calculated from the information provided by a micrograph like that shown in Fig. 4. The bacteriophage virus particles shown here were sprayed at a total concentration of $10^{12}$ per milliliter, and since there are about 100 of them in the pattern, the volume of this droplet is $10^{-10}$ ml. The area of the pattern is about $10^{-7}$ cm.$^2$; consequently, the thickness of the initial frozen droplet must have been less than 10 microns. On the average, droplets sprayed from the high-velocity gun are found to form frozen patterns about 4 microns thick. If it is assumed that the thermal conduction between the top of the flattened droplet and the cold copper support is due only to the bulk thermal properties of the water droplet and the collodion film, i.e., that there is no significant thermal resistance in the contact surfaces between water and collodion and between collodion and copper, the rate of cooling of the droplet can be calculated by the elementary formula of thermal conduction. If the initial difference of temperature between water and copper is taken as 95°C., the upper surface of a flattened droplet 4 microns thick should cool at a rate of approximately $10^6$ degrees per second, and the entire droplet should change from the liquid to the ice phase in about $3 \times 10^{-5}$ sec. It is important to note that this rate of cooling can be increased only by lowering the temperature of the copper support or by decreasing the thickness of the spread-out droplet. If the copper is cooled by liquid nitrogen, the cooling rate will be twice the rate achieved by cooling with alcohol-carbon dioxide. Extremely thin frozen droplet patterns are possible, but if the thickness is made much less than 3 to 4 microns the distortion of biological materials by droplet impingement may be serious. When the low-velocity nebulizer is employed for creating spray droplets, their thickness when flattened and frozen is of the order of 10 microns, and the rate of cooling is about one-fifth that of the more completely flattened droplets provided by the high-velocity spray.

### 2. *Speed of Sublimation*

The speed of the low-temperature sublimation *in vacuo* is determined by the mass and surface area of the frozen droplets, the temperature and vapor pressure of sublimation, and the efficiency of the net transfer of water vapor from the sublimation surface to the cold trap. The technique described here provides for rapid sublimation, owing to the low mass and large surface area of the separate frozen droplets. Not much choice can be exercised about the temperature to be maintained during sublimation, since a temperature higher than about −35°C. is generally considered unsafe, while the rate of sublimation approaches vanishingly small values at temperatures below about −80°C. The efficiency of transfer of the water vapor is maximized by maintaining a large temperature differential between the surface of the subliming material and of the trap, and by providing for minimal impedance to the diffusion of vapor between these surfaces. The apparatus shown in Fig. 3 provides for the maintenance of as large a temperature differential as is practically feasible, but the pathway for molecular diffusion could be improved by using glass tubing of larger bore and with less abrupt turns. However, since the sublimation time is only 10 to 15 minutes in the apparatus shown (at a subliming temperature of $-45°C.$ and a pressure of $5 \times 10^{-4}$ mm. Hg), a saving of 5 minutes or so per run, at best, would be the limit of the practical advantage that could be gained by redesigning the apparatus.

### 3. *Problem of Non-Volatile Salts*

Serious difficulties arise in the vacuum sublimation of any biological material on account of the non-volatile salts which are almost always in solution in the natural tissue liquids or are incorporated in any medium in which particulate objects are to be suspended. The effect of the presence of a salt in solution, of course, is to lower its freezing point. But, as the ice sublimes, the salt concentration ranges from an initially dilute one (around 1%) to an infinitely concentrated one, and the concentration corresponding to the eutectic point will be encountered sometime during the sublimation. In the case of vacuum sublimation for electron microscopy the further difficulty arises that the effect of very small quantities of non-volatile salt will alter seriously the apparent morphology of the minute objects generally observed. Of course, some small biological objects, such as most of the plant viruses, can be readily suspended in distilled water, but most require a suspending medium containing an electrolyte. A preparation of purified virus particles suspended at a concentration suitable for freeze-drying for electron microscopy, and in a 1% solution of, say, sodium chloride, contains from 100 to 1000 times as much salt as viral material. One of the classical methods of preparation of air-dried specimens involves rinsing the salt from the specimen after drying, but, of course, rinsing should not be performed on a specimen after it has been frozen and vacuum sublimed.

A satisfactory suspending material, ammonium acetate, has been described by Backus and Williams (1950) for air-dried preparations in which complete volatility of solvent at room temperature is desired. Unfortunately, ammonium acetate cannot be easily used for vacuum sublimation inasmuch as its eutectic temperature is below $-75°C.$ Two electrolytes which possess the desired properties of sufficient volatility, a reasonably high eutectic temperature, and a biologically acceptable chemical composition have been found to be satisfactory. They are ammonium benzoate and ammonium succinate, of which the former is the more satisfactory when made up as a 2% solution at a pH of 7.0. Its eutectic point is about $-10°C.$ Its volatility at room temperature is low, but if it is heated to about 60°C. for 15 minutes at the end of the low-temperature sublimation period, it leaves no non-volatile residue observable in the electron microscope.

Pease (1947) has stated that he has frozen-dried a myosin sol in 0.5 *M* potassium chloride without any electron microscopic evidence of salt being present in the final preparation. The sol was frozen rapidly in liquid air and vacuum sublimed at −72°C. It is difficult to accept Pease's conclusions that the $K^+$ and $Cl^-$ ions have literally evaporated away, and his two published electron micrographs are not convincing evidence that there is no salt present in the material. In fact, the micrographs remind one of the structures commonly encountered in the electron microscopy of salt-containing materials, generally called "salt-trees." The evidence regarding the fate of the potassium chloride has unfortunately been obscured in Pease's micrographs by the presence of the myosin; a conclusive demonstration of the disappearance of ionic salt during freeze-drying will have to be obtained from a preparation that is solely, or primarily, a salt solution. Some investigation has been made in this Laboratory toward securing salt-free, frozen-dried specimens from starting materials which contain non-volatile salt. Although no desiccation has been tried at temperatures lower than −50°C., it is our universal experience that the sublimed droplet patterns contain salt.

## VII. DIFFICULTIES IN THE ELECTRON MICROSCOPY OF FROZEN-DRIED MATERIALS

### 1. *Electron Opacity of Specimens*

The electron microscopy of specimens which have retained their three-dimensional shape involves in an acute fashion a few of the problems encountered less severely in the microscopy of air-dried material. The most noticeable problem encountered with such three-dimensional specimens, when they are as large as bacteria, is their great opacity to electrons, which makes it difficult to obtain any information about structural detail of their surfaces or interiors. The cause of this large opacity probably resides in the greater line-of-sight thickness of the frozen-dried objects compared with the relative thinness of the flattened air-dried specimens. A frozen-dried *E. coli*, for example, such as may be seen in Fig. 8, is about 0.6 micron thick, while the flattened objects shown in Fig. 1 are less than 0.2 micron thick. If the enhanced opacity is due primarily to increased thickness, and if the freeze-drying of organisms the size of bacteria becomes common practice, it would seem that satisfactory electron micrographs will be secured only with the aid of electron microscopes of accelerating voltage much higher than the present 50,000 to 60,000 volts used in the RCA instrument.

Even with very small particles, such as those of tobacco mosaic virus, there is a noticeable enhancement of the electron opacity of those particles which are not in full contact with the collodion substrate film. In the case of shadowed preparations this effect can probably be explained by the circumstance that the electrons must penetrate three films of shadowing metal: the film on the collodion, and a film on both the under and upper surface of the virus particle. On the other hand, only one film of metal has to be penetrated when the particle is in close and full contact with the collodion.

### 2. *Heating of Specimen Objects*

A second problem in the electron microscopy of frozen-dried materials results from the slowness of heat transfer in a vacuum. The frozen-dried objects, desiccated and rigid, are in very tenuous thermal contact with the substrate film and must dissipate by radiation alone the heat gained from inelastic electron collisions in the microscope. Air-dried specimens are much easier to keep cool, since they have dried with good thermal contact to the collodion film, which in turn is in good thermal contact with the metal specimen grid. The consequence of the poor heat-dissipative properties of the larger frozen-dried specimens (such as cells) is that they shrivel and curl under bombardment by what would ordinarily be called only a moderately intense electron beam. Small specimens, such as most virus particles, are not as severely affected in this manner. In the photography of such objects the intensity of the electron beam striking the specimen must be kept at a value much less than would be normally employed.

### 3. *Growth of Contaminating Film*

A third difficulty encountered in the electron microscopy of small frozen-dried objects not in full contact with the substrate film is associated with the growth of a contaminating film upon the objects during exposure to the electron beam. As Williams (1952a) has demonstrated, this film is always formed when objects are exposed to the electron beam, but usually it is not particularly noticed on shadowed specimens of air-dried material. This is because the shadowing is accomplished prior to the growth of the contaminating film, and inasmuch as the film is quite uniform in thickness and of relatively low electron opacity, it cannot be seen against the higher contrasts produced by the shadowing. But wherever a small object is supported by other objects at some distance from the collodion film, the contaminating growth is seen to encircle the object like a halo. Figure 5 shows some frozen-dried particles of tobacco mosaic virus, most of which are held completely away from the underlying collodion. It is apparent that a halo of relatively transparent material has formed around the particles upon prolonged exposure to the electron beam.

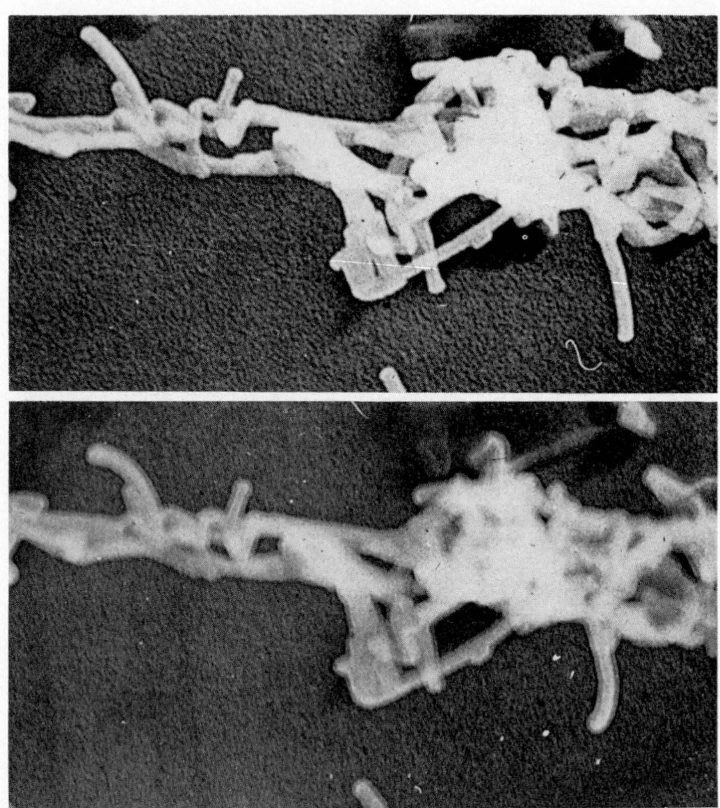

Fig. 5. A portion of a frozen-dried preparation of tobacco mosaic virus in which most of the virus particles are not touching the collodion substrate film. The upper micrograph was secured with minimal exposure to the electron beam in the microscope; the lower micrograph was taken after 5 minutes' exposure to a moderately intense beam. The halos seen around the particles in the latter picture are due to a contaminating film deposited during the exposure to this beam. 130,000×.

## VIII. EXAMPLES OF ELECTRON MICROGRAPHS OF FROZEN-DRIED SPECIMENS

The electron micrographs shown in Figs. 6 to 14 illustrate some of the types of biological objects which have been prepared by the freeze-drying technique discussed here. In some cases the morphology of the frozen-dried material differs considerably from that of the same material air-dried. On the other hand, particles of tobacco mosaic virus and of tomato bushy stunt virus appear almost the same when prepared by either method.

Figures 6 and 7 exhibit two kinds of objects whose appearance is particularly sensitive to the degree of excellence of the freeze-drying procedure. In Fig. 6 are shown two human erythrocyte ghosts, initially lysed in distilled water and then fixed in osmic acid prior to freeze-drying. When air-dried these cell membranes are completely flattened (Dawson and Elford, 1949) and exhibit a double membrane thickness of only about 30 mμ. Anderson (1952) has shown some red-cell ghosts prepared by the

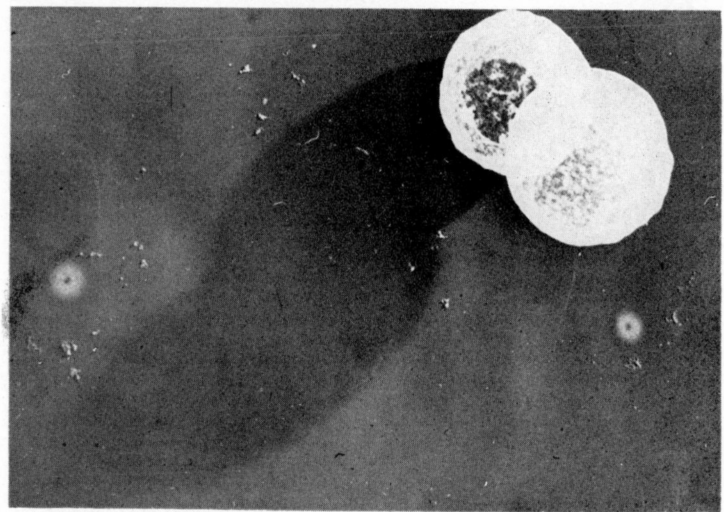

FIG. 6. Two frozen-dried "ghosts" of human erythrocytes, prepared by lysis in distilled water and followed by fixation in 1% osmic acid. The ghost at the lower right is wholly supported by the other one, as is evidenced by the shadows. 4000×.

critical-point method which are spherical and appear smoother than those seen in Fig. 6. This difference in appearance may be a reliable indication that Anderson's method preserves delicate structure better than does freeze-drying; on the other hand, it may be the result of differences in handling the red cells through lysis and fixation, or of differences in heating effects during the electron microscopy. Figure 7 illustrates the degree to which linear particles, such as those of tobacco mosaic virus, intermesh in a fluffy, tenuous form upon sublimation of the ice. Previous micrographs of frozen-dried tobacco mosaic virus (Wyckoff, 1947) fail to show a comparable degree of three-dimensional structure. However, it should not be inferred that the virus particles, in suspension, were arrayed necessarily in a form like that shown by the micrograph. A particle must be supported by something (in this case, other particles) to remain in the vicinity of the collodion film, and hence a certain amount of clumping and coalescence doubtless occurs.

Figures 8 and 9 are of a typical bacillus (*E. coli*) and of a spirillum (*Rhodospirillum rubrum*). Figure 8 is to be compared with Fig. 1, a micrograph of some members of the same culture. The *E. coli* organisms, when frozen-dried, appear generally cylindrical with rounded ends—the appearance that would be ascribed to them from observations with the phase

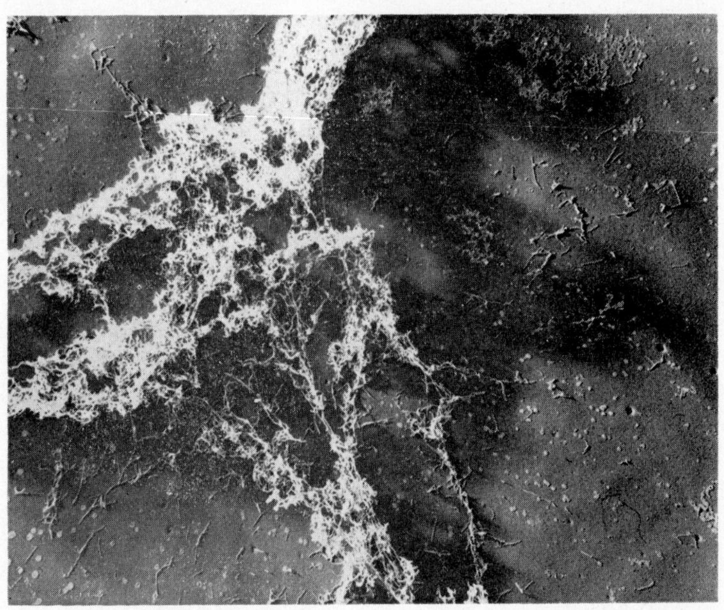

FIG. 7. A concentrated suspension of frozen-dried tobacco mosaic virus particles. Most of the particles are considerably removed from the substrate and form a fluffy-appearing deposit. Note the extreme length of the shadows, in this case indicating that the higher portions of the deposit are about 3 microns above the collodion film. 6000×; 3/1 shadow angle.

contrast microscope upon living organisms. The electron opacity of the objects is dismaying, preventing as it does any observation of surface detail or inner structure. Electrons of higher accelerating voltage will probably have to be employed to allow satisfactory penetration of this and similar objects. Figure 9 shows objects quite comparable with those shown by Anderson (1952) and clearly demonstrate the true helical nature of the *Spirillum rubrum* organism. When air-dried, these spirilla retain a two-dimensional form only and appear as short, flat sine waves.

Figure 10 is an electron micrograph, at two different magnifications, of some collagen fibers from chrome-tanned leather. This type of fibril, in air-dried form and both stained and unstained, has been extensively

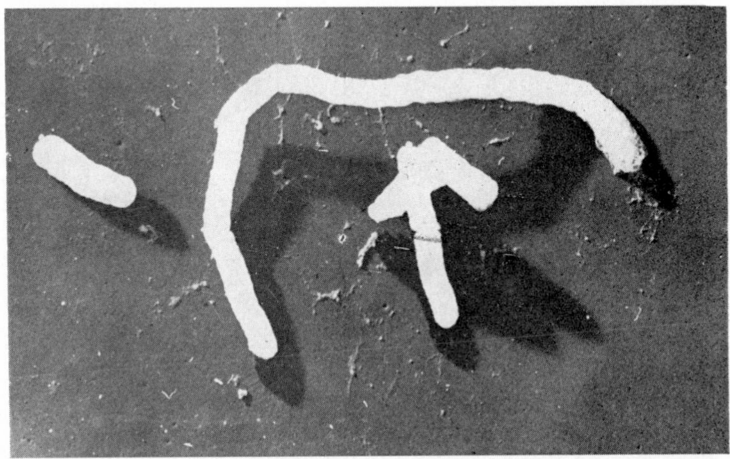

FIG. 8. Some organisms of *E. coli* prepared for electron microscopy by freeze-drying from a distilled water suspension. The long, bow-shaped object is probably an end-to-end string of several bacteria. The frozen-dried objects are so thick that no detail of their surface or inner structure can be discerned. The isolated organism on the left evidently has the shape of a cylinder with rounded ends. 10,000×; 2/1 shadow angle. This micrograph is to be contrasted with Fig. 1.

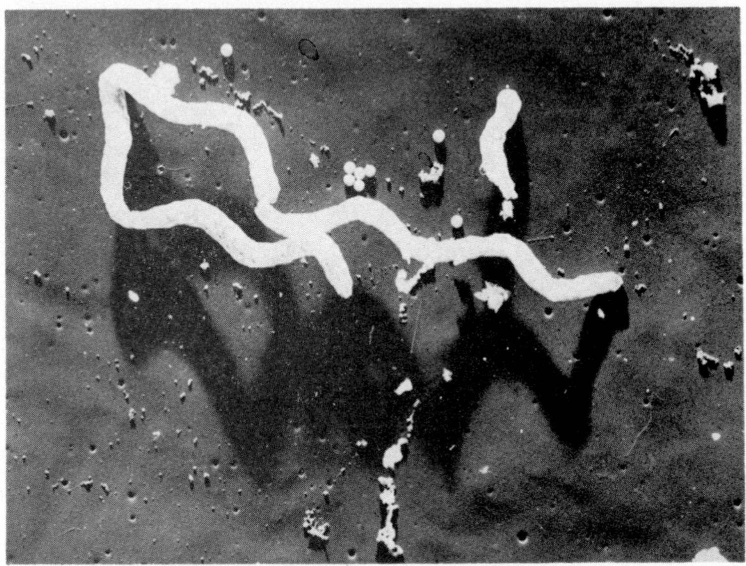

FIG. 9. A group of the helical-shaped organisms of *Rhodospirillum rubrum*. When air-dried, these objects appear two-dimensionally sinuous without any evidence of helical form. The eight spherical objects in the micrograph are polystyrene latex particles. 6000×.

investigated by electron microscopy (Schmitt and Gross, 1948; Nutting and Borasky, 1948) and exhibits a major periodicity of structure of about 65 m$\mu$. There has been some doubt, however, as to whether the periodicity of surface structure seen in shadowed electron micrographs of untanned

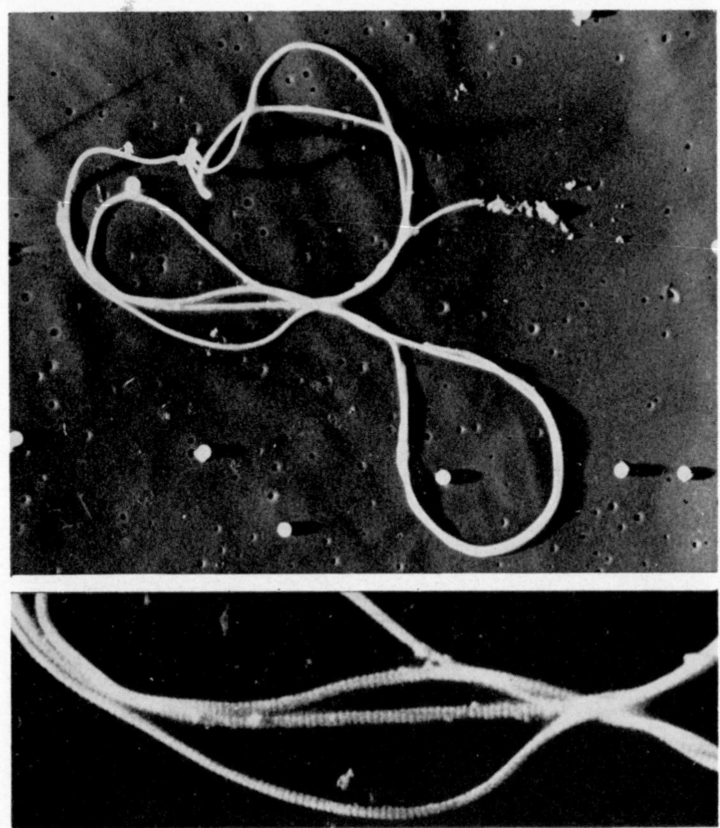

FIG. 10. Fibrils of chrome-tanned leather frozen-dried from an aqueous suspension. The shadows indicate that the fibers are in contact with the collodion film over most of their length, but in the upper portion of the micrograph the very long shadows show that the fibers are projecting well above the collodion film. 7500×. The lower micrograph is an enlarged portion (18,000×) of the upper one, showing that the typical cross striations are present in the frozen-dried material.

material is solely due to the drying of the fibers or is a three-dimensional surface irregularity present initially in the wet material. The work of Gross and Schmitt (1948) indicates that the banded appearance is only faintly present in replicas of damp collagen from human skin, if one grants that the damp replication process is sufficiently faithful to render the results definitive. The frozen-dried tanned fibers appear to have the same general sort of periodic structure as do the air-dried ones, however, and it can be stated that for the tanned material, at least, the surface banding is doubtless present in the wet fibers.

A solution of highly polymerized sodium desoxyribonucleate prepared for electron microscopy by freeze-drying is shown in Fig. 11. Many lines of physical evidence suggest that the long polymeric chains exist in dilute solution as an extremely tenuous network, and the electron micrographs of frozen-dried material substantiate this viewpoint (Williams, 1952b).

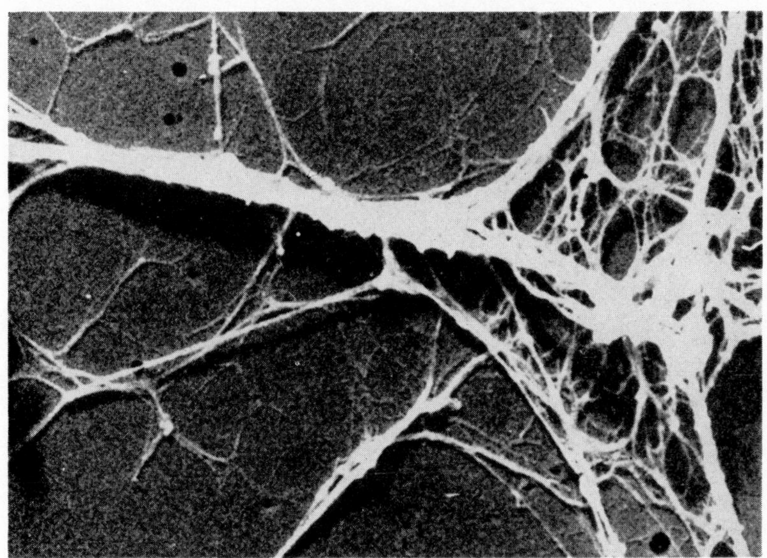

FIG. 11. A network of fibrils of frozen-dried sodium desoxyribonucleate. There is evidence that considerable aggregation of the fibrils has taken place, presumably during vacuum sublimation. In the lower center of the micrograph is a long fiber which appears to have been stretched and has been left in a position somewhat removed from the substrate film. 18,000×; 2/1 shadow angle.

There is no question, however, but that a certain amount of aggregation has occurred during the preparative cycle, probably during the vacuum sublimation. Very tenuous fibers of great length suspended in air doubtless wave in the fitful gusts of Brownian motion and adhere to other fibers upon touching them. Micrographs of air-dried material (Scott, 1948) have indicated the existence of fibers of varying thickness and flatness but have not shown such delicate tracery.

In Fig. 12 is demonstrated the degree of flattening experienced by an air-dried virus of medium size, the Shope papilloma virus of wild rabbits. The comparison in shape between the air-dried virus (upper photograph) and the frozen-dried virus (lower photograph) has been facilitated in this

FIG. 12. Particles of the virus of rabbit papilloma both air-dried and frozen-dried on the same specimen film. Upper picture shows the considerable flattening of the particles, which results from direct drying from an aqueous suspension. Lower picture is another portion of the same original micrograph and shows individual and clustered frozen-dried particles. These particles are almost spherically shaped, except for the distorting effect of a thick uranium coating. Although the air-dried particles are $\frac{4}{3}$ the diameter of the frozen-dried ones, the volumes of both kinds of particles are the same. 50,000×.

instance by spraying both the droplets to be air-dried and the droplets to be frozen-dried upon the same collodion-coated copper support. This provides for identical shadowing and micrography of both virus samples. Both halves of Fig. 12 are taken from the same electron micrograph and reassembled here to show a favorable juxtaposition of the two kinds of preparation. It can be seen that the air-dried virus particles are flattened considerably; their height-to-diameter ratio is about 0.6. The frozen-dried particles appear to be almost exactly spherical, with a height-to-width ratio of more than 0.9.

Figure 13 is a micrograph of a frozen-dried preparation of $T_2$ bacteriophage of *E. coli*. Although air-dried preparations of this virus consist of objects generally similar in appearance to the ones shown here, their "heads" have usually been described as ellipsoidal or egg-shaped (Wyckoff, 1949). Anderson (1952), however, concluded that these objects are hexagonal in cross section, with a morphology like that shown in

FIG. 13. Preparation of $T_2$ bacteriophage frozen-dried from suspension in ammonium benzoate. The heads of the particles can be seen to be shaped with sharply drawn angularities. The club-like ends of the tails are particularly noticeable in frozen-dried preparations. 50,000×; 2.5/1 shadow angle. Insert: a $T_6$ particle which is presumably standing vertically upon the end of its tail. Its cross-sectional shape is approximately hexagonal. 80,000×; 2.0/1 shadow angle.

Fig. 13. The general external shape of the head appears to be that of a hexagonal prism with pyramidal ends. When frozen-dried, the tail appears as a well-integrated appendage, devoid of any of the signs of "fraying" so commonly seen in air-dried preparations. Its end exhibits a pronounced club. The insert in Fig. 13 shows an unusual case where only the end of the tail of the bacteriophage is evidently in contact with the collodion, causing the object to point directly at the observer. The object shown in the insert is a $T_6$ bacteriophage, morphologically identical with the $T_2$ and $T_4$ bacteriophages.

Another frozen-dried bacteriophage, $T_3$ of *E. coli*, is seen in Fig. 14. This phage (and $T_7$ of *E. coli*) has generally been believed to have a spherical head and no tail. As can be seen in Fig. 14 the head frequently has a hexagonal shape which is particularly well brought out by the virus particle shown in the insert. Furthermore, most particles have stubby appendages which might be called "tails" or "snouts"; it appears that the surface tension forces in air-drying are sufficiently great to cause the

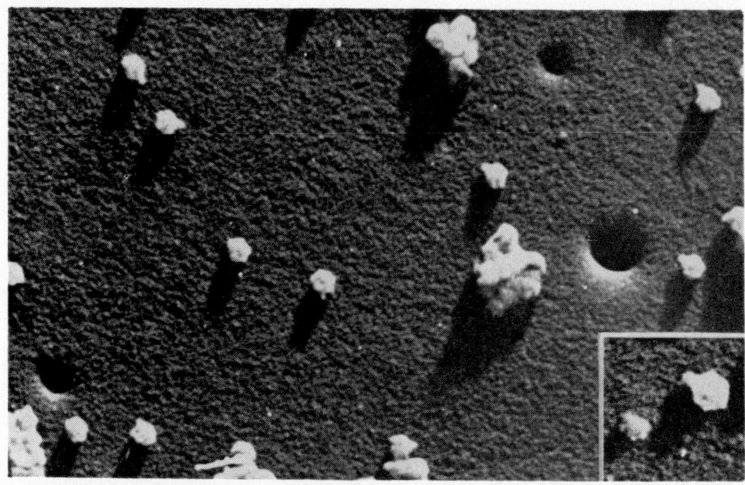

FIG. 14. $T_3$ bacteriophage particles prepared for electron microscopy by freeze-drying from an ammonium benzoate suspension. The particles appear approximately six-sided, with a short appendage attached at one corner. The larger masses are clumps of individual virus particles. 60,000×; 3/1 shadow angle. Insert: a particularly beautiful specimen exhibiting symmetry of form. 100,000×.

short tail to disappear as a projection and to round off the hexagonal contour into an approximate sphere.

## IX. SUMMARY

The ordinary practice of electron microscopy of biological materials is beset with uncertainties in the interpretation of structures, owing to the severe effects of surface tension forces during the time in which an object is drying from its suspending fluid. The result of the action of these forces is generally to flatten particles such as cells and viruses. Two methods have been employed to reduce the magnitude of the surface tension effects: the critical-point method, in which objects are "dried" from a fluid under conditions above its critical point, and the freeze-drying method, in which the specimen material is rapidly frozen and vacuum sublimed. Both techniques have advantages and disadvantages, but both appear to be successful in retaining the three-dimensional structure of biological materials.

Freeze-drying of biological specimens has been employed for electron microscopy for several years, but its results have been on the whole disappointing. A reconsideration of the thermal factors involved in the existing technique indicates that an adequate freeze-drying has probably not been achieved. A new technique has been recently developed in which thorough consideration has been given to problems of thermal transfer. Rapid freezing is accomplished by utilizing extremely small droplets of specimen material which are made to impinge upon a cold surface of copper. Vacuum sublimation is accomplished fairly rapidly, even at a low temperature, for the reason that the volumes of the individual frozen droplets are small and their areas large. The new method has been applied to the examination of cells, fibers, and viruses, and the results appear to vindicate the belief that many of the morphological distortions implicit in the practice of air-drying such objects can be largely avoided.

Most of the biological preparations used in testing the applicability of the new free-drying technique have been supplied by colleagues of the author. It is a great pleasure to acknowledge the generous cooperation of Drs. Dean Fraser, C. A. Knight, and Arthur B. Pardee of this Laboratory, and of Dr. Mortimer P. Starr of the University of California at Davis.

## REFERENCES

Anderson, T. F. 1951. Techniques for Preservation of 3-Dimensional Structure in Preparing Specimens for the Electron Microscope. *Trans. N.Y. Acad. Sci.* **13,** 130–134.

Anderson, T. F. 1952. Stereoscopic Studies of Cells and Viruses in the Electron Microscope. *Am. Naturalist* **86,** 91–100.

Backus, R. C., and Williams, R. C. 1950. The Use of Spraying Methods and of Volatile Suspending Media in the Preparation of Specimens for Electron Microscopy. *J. Appl. Phys.* **21,** 11–15.

Dawson, I. M., and Elford, W. J. 1949. The Investigation of Influenza and Related Viruses in the Electron Microscope, by a New Technique. *J. Gen. Microbiol.* **3,** 298–311.

Gross, J., and Schmitt, F. O. 1948. The Structure of Human Skin Collagen as Studied with the Electron Microscope. *J. Exptl. Med.* **88,** 555–568.

Malmstrom, B. G. 1951. Theoretical Considerations of the Rate of Dehydration by Histological Freeze-Drying. *Exptl. Cell Research* **2,** 688–692.

Nutting, G. C., and Borasky, R. 1948. Electron Microscopy of Collagen. *J. Am. Leather Chemists' Assoc.* **43,** 96–110.

Pease, D. C. 1947. The Disappearance of Salt from Glass Ice during Low-Temperature Dehydration, and Its Implications in Electron Microscopy. *Science* **106,** 543.

Schaefer, V. J. 1942. New Methods for Preparing Surface Replicas for Electron Microscopic Observation. *Phys. Rev.* **62,** 495–496.

Schmitt, F. O., and Gross, J. 1948. Further Progress in the Electron Microscopy of Collagen. 1948. *J. Am. Leather Chemists' Assoc.* **43,** 658–675.

Scott, J. F. 1948. Electron Micrograph Studies on Sodium Desoxyribose Nucleate. *Biochim. et Biophys. Acta* **2,** 1–6.

Williams, R. C. 1952a. High-Resolution Electron Microscopy of the Particles of Tobacco Mosaic Virus. *Biochim. et Biophys. Acta* **8,** 227–244.

Williams, R. C. 1952b. Electron Microscopy of Sodium Desoxyribonucleate by Use of a New Freeze-Drying Method. *Biochim. et Biophys. Acta* **9,** 237–239.

Williams, R. C. 1953. A Method of Freeze-Drying for Electron Microscopy. *Exptl. Cell Research* **4,** 188–201.

Williams, R. C., and Steere, R. L. 1951. Electron Microscopic Observations on the Unit of Length of the Particles of Tobacco Mosaic Virus. *J. Am. Chem. Soc.* **73,** 2057–2061.

Williams, R. C., and Wyckoff, R. W. G. 1944. The Thickness of Electron Microscopic Objects. *J. Appl. Phys.* **15,** 712–716.

Williams, R. C., and Wyckoff, R. W. G. 1946. Applications of Metallic Shadow-Casting to Microscopy. *J. Appl. Phys.* **17,** 23–33.

Wyckoff, R. W. G. 1946. Frozen-Dried Preparations for the Electron Microscope. *Science* **104,** 36–37.

Wyckoff, R. W. G. 1947. Electron Micrographs from Concentrated Solutions of the Tobacco Mosaic Virus Protein. *Biochim. et Biophys. Acta* **1,** 139–146.

Wyckoff, R. W. G. 1949. *Electron Microscopy,* Interscience Publishers, New York. P. 166.

## Chapter 14

# Freezing and Drying of Tissues for Morphological and Histochemical Studies*

ISIDORE GERSH and JOHN L. STEPHENSON

*Department of Anatomy, University of Chicago, Chicago, Illinois*



* Aided by a grant from the Wallace C. and Clara A. Abbott Memorial Fund of the University of Chicago and from the Commonwealth Fund of New York.

## I. INTRODUCTION

In 1890, Richard Altmann introduced an ingenious method for the preparation of tissues for use in microscopic anatomy. He froze blocks of organs and tissues and dehydrated them at a low temperature in a vacuum. In the resulting dry state, the specimens were infiltrated with paraffin and sectioned (Fig. 1). With great vision, he foresaw the major advantages of such a method for cytology. He believed that tissues prepared in this way would be free of shrinkage and that cell components or substances introduced into the body could be retained and identified microscopically, especially intravital dyes.

It is rather ironical that what would seem to have been his chief hope was in fact ill-founded. His great expectation was that treatment of a series of sections of a single frozen-dried specimen with a number of fixatives would quickly give information on the best fixative to employ for optimal fixation in fresh tissues of any cell component. The fact is that frozen-dried tissues are not subject to the same kinds of fixation artifacts as are fresh tissues. For example, fixatives which fail to preserve mitochondria when the organ is preserved by immersion do not destroy them when applied to sections of frozen-dried material (Bensley and Gersh, 1933a). Again, immersion agents which preserve glycogen poorly are quite innocuous when applied to sections of the same material fixed by freezing and drying (Gersh, 1932). The same lack of correspondence of fixation by immersion and by freezing and drying also holds for extracellular components, as, for example, the colloid of the thyroid acini or the ground substance of connective tissues. Be that as it may, Altmann found the technical details to be discouragingly laborious and was unable to develop or exploit his method fully. The method with its many possibilities for the histologist was familiar to Mann, Mathews, Bayliss, and Romeis, who did not contribute significantly to their realization.

The elegant simplicity of the method and its implications should be viewed in relation to the problems facing the cytologist at the time. 1890 marked the zenith of devising and using complex fixatives and stains in cytology. At that time there was no theoretical basis in genetics or in general physiology for the fantastically complicated structures described

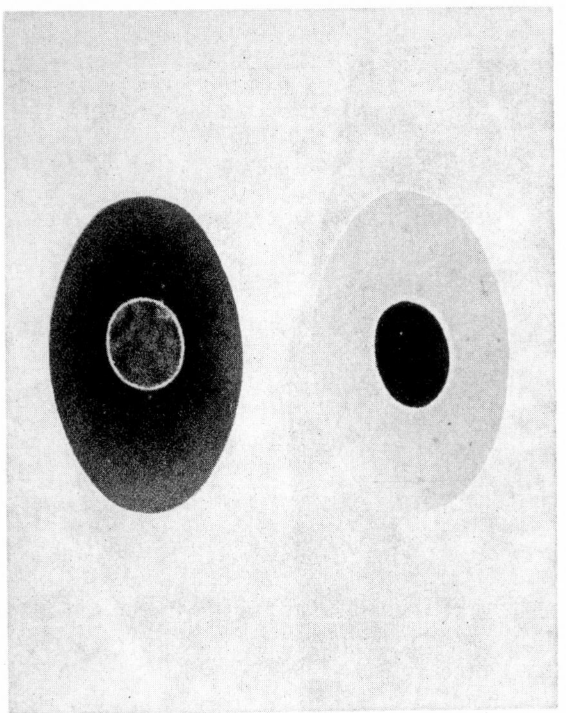

FIG. 1. Earliest illustration of frozen-dried material prepared for microscopic study. Blood cells of *Proteus anguineus*, frozen and dried, subsequently fixed with osmium. (Altmann, 1890, Plate VI, Figs. 3 and 4, and p. 24.)

by cytologists, and great skepticism of their reality was accordingly engendered. Cytological skeptics were encouraged by the notable contributions of such workers as Fischer (1899) and Hardy (1899), who were able to duplicate *in vitro* from simple protein preparations many of the morphological structures described as components of cells. In the re-evaluation of cellular findings, cytologists returned to the observation of fresh tissues and more varied experimental methods: the development of supravital and intravital staining, tissue culture, micromanipulation, histochemistry, the methods for the study of favorably thin organs and tissues in the living animal, fluorescence and polarization microscopy, and, more recently, the phase contrast microscope. It is as a part of this great movement toward a more functional interpretation of cellular activities that one must view the relatively recent development of the freezing-drying method.

The reintroduction and exploitation of the freezing-drying method owes much to Professor R. R. Bensley, whose fruitful scientific life has spanned the whole period described in the preceding paragraph. It was particularly appropriate that he—deeply planted in the achievements of the past, intimately aware of most of the deeper aspects and problems of classical morphology—should be the one at whose suggestion and with whose encouragement the method originally proposed by Altmann was first put on a practical basis.

Almost from the very beginning, some aspects of the method were the subject of controversy. The details of the method, the design of apparatus, and the analysis of the physical principles involved became subjects of numerous papers, many of which were based on "experience," dogmatic reiteration, and misapplication of formulae which are sound in their proper context. For example, as a result of constant reiteration, it now seems to be generally agreed that it is most desirable to dehydrate specimens at as close to −70°C. as feasible. Indeed, were it practicable, some would prefer a drying temperature of −170°C. As a matter of fact however, for many purposes there is little reason for preferring such low temperatures to one of, say, −30°C. The theoretical reason for drying at a very low temperature arises from data on eutectics of relatively simple salt solutions. Although it is true that it would be desirable to dry at a temperature at which *no* fluid water could exist in a specimen, no one knows what this temperature is. No one can say how much fluid water is present in a specimen at any specific temperature, or what the rate of diffusion of substances would be in the water. More important, no one knows the magnitude of the rate of diffusion as compared with the rate of drying of the tissue. If, for example, the rate of diffusion of a solute at a certain temperature were sufficiently small as compared with the rate of drying of a small sample of a specimen, the diffusion of the solute could be neglected. Only two observations in the literature bear on the subject. The first is that after microincineration the distribution of ash of material dried at −20°C. was reported to be different from that at −28° to −72°C. (Scott, 1934). The second is that the distribution of chloride in skeletal muscle dried at −30°C. is claimed to be different from that in muscle dried at −60°C. or lower (Gersh, 1938a). Both of these observations are only as good as the methods, and both have been criticized. It is obvious that a quantitative and mathematical analysis of the problem is long overdue.

A second example of dogma and misapplied, but otherwise sound, science is the effort, especially in the last three years, to build "the most efficient drying system." We believe that much misdirected effort continues to be expended in this direction and will consider the reasons for this belief in detail in Sections II–IX. Until recently, it has not been possible even to define the efficiency of a drying system. After an extended experimental and theoretical analysis of the problem, it seems most probable to us that *all* the systems so far described are of roughly the same order of efficiency under the usual conditions of laboratory use.

The key references on the freezing and drying of tissues and organs for microscopic studies have been brought together in this article. We intend to consider the basis of at least some of the dogmatism which pervades the field and to point out those aspects where quantitative studies underlying the principles of the method are desirable. An analysis of some of the theoretical and practical aspects of freezing and drying is presented in the second part of this review. It is also hoped that this review may help to direct the emphasis of research away from the purely mechanical aspects, which seem to us of little or no practical significance, towards the purposes for which the method is most fitted.

The method is most suitably used for the preservation of tissues and organs when an immersion fixative is not adequate or desirable. For any particular problem, fixation of a specimen by immersion may result in a number of artifacts: progressive *postmortem* autolysis in the inside of the specimen as compared with the outer shell; distortion, involving general or differential shrinkage or swelling of tissue or cellular components; oxidation or reduction of chemical substances; solution of some morphological entity or some chemical components resulting in their leaching out or diffusion (Sylvèn, 1951); denaturation of protein components. A more positive and extended statement of the uses of freezing and drying is given in the third part of this review.

## II. THEORY OF FREEZING

### 1. *Vitrification and Crystal Growth*

The basis of fixing specimens by freezing is that cooling reduces molecular motion. Presumably, cooling to a very low temperature rapidly enough would essentially stop the motion of the molecules and give an exact reproduction of their position at the start of freezing.

The physical principle underlying such *ideal* fixation is that crystallization of a liquid can occur only at the freezing temperature or within a certain range of temperatures below it. If this range is passed through rapidly enough, the molecules will not have time to arrange themselves in a crystalline pattern and the liquid will solidify in an amorphous state (called also vitreous or glass state). If the vitrified solid is warmed, the molecules will acquire enough mobility near the freezing point for transition to a crystalline state (devitrification) to take place.

Vitrification of biological materials by rapid cooling has been studied extensively by Luyet (1951), who in a recent paper ("Freezing and Drying," p. 79) states: "The only method of ultra-rapid cooling now available consists in immersing the object to be cooled in a liquefied gas, such as oxygen, nitrogen, hydrogen or helium, or in a fluid cooled by these liquefied gases, and in waiting until the heat content of the subject is transferred to the bath. On account of the slow transfer of heat from one body to another, it is impossible to reach the cooling velocity required for vitrification—which is of the order of several hundred degrees per second —with any object which measures more than about 0.1 mm. in one dimension, when the water content is between 70 and 80 per cent. With lower water contents, lower cooling velocities suffice and larger pieces can be treated." Again, Luyet (*ibid.*, p. 201) says: "The time for freezing a piece of tissue, say 1 mm. cube, is some 3 seconds in liquid nitrogen or in liquid air. This will be quite sufficient time for crystallization. By substituting *iso*pentane at −150°C. for liquid nitrogen at −195°C. the rate of cooling in some of our experiments was increased five-fold. With liquid air Meryman observed ice-crystallites of a size of 500 Å. If the size of the crystals is in proportion to the time given them to grow, one would expect to have in *iso*pentane, crystals measuring about 100 Å." It would seem that one cannot expect vitrification in histological work, as the specimens are too large in most cases. And the problem is in most cases to obtain the minimum size of crystal. So far the problem has not been solved, and even the underlying physics has not been completely developed.

In its general aspect crystallization is like any other phase transition and is initiated by the birth of crystalline "embryos" in the liquid phase. If these are larger than a certain critical size, they are stable and can grow by molecules from the surrounding liquid settling down on their surfaces. The rate at which this can occur is inversely proportional to the viscosity of the liquid, which increases as the temperature decreases. The rate of birth is inversely proportional to the temperature. [See Frenkel (1946) for further details.] Because of these opposed factors, at some temperature the rate of crystallization is a maximum. The detailed theory gives results of the correct order of magnitude for relatively simple substances such as salts and metals. Since the process is greatly modified by numerous factors, including the presence of colloidal particles, the theory does not apply quantitatively to such a complex physicochemical system as tissue. It merely indicates in a general way that the average size of the ice crystals should be inversely proportional to the rate of freezing. This subject has been extensively reviewed by Bell (1952).

### 2. *Factors Controlling the Rate of Freezing of Tissue*

During the freezing of a specimen, an amount of heat must be removed which equals the difference between the heat content of the tissue at the start of freezing and the heat content of the tissue at the temperature of the cooling bath (which includes the latent heat of fusion of ice). The time in which this can be accomplished depends on a number of factors: (1) the size and shape of the tissue, (2) its initial temperature, (3) the temperature of the cooling bath, (4) the heat constants of the tissue and of the cooling liquid, (5) the nature of the boundary between the tissue and the cooling liquid, and (6) the water content of the tissue. An exact theory of this cooling has not been developed and may be impossible. It would seem that the rate of freezing should decrease progressively toward the interior of the tissue with a corresponding increase in the size of the ice crystals.

## III. TISSUE OBSERVATIONS

The ice crystals which form during freezing separate from the organic matrix of the protoplasm. This organic matrix is compressed by the developing crystals and so forms a "wall" around each ice crystal. After the tissue is dried, embedded, and stained, the honeycomb formed by these walls can be observed and is called the ice-crystal artifact.

When tissues are frozen in liquid nitrogen, which was the initial method (Gersh, 1932), the surface fixation is relatively poor. This corresponds with poor initial heat transfer across the boundary between the liquid and the tissue, due to the insulating layer of gas bubbles which develops there. Toward the interior the fixation improves, probably because of the decrease in the thickness of the gas layer as cooling progresses. Deeper in the interior the size of the ice crystals again increases, possibly because of an increased insulating effect of the frozen shell. With the use of *iso*pentane chilled to about −150°C. with liquid nitrogen, the surface fixation is improved (Hoerr, 1936a). With *iso*pentane the cooling rate of small pieces is much more rapid than with liquid nitrogen (see above, p. 334). One important factor in this increased cooling is doubtless the better heat transfer across the boundary. In large pieces of tissue frozen in *iso*pentane three zones of fixation have been described: (1) an outer, well-fixed zone, (2) a middle, badly fixed zone, and (3) an interior, intermediately fixed zone, although fixation is always extremely irregular (Simpson, 1941a).

No quantitative data on the ice-crystal artifact have been reported in the literature. A limited number of measurements on the size of ice crystals in slices of guinea pig liver have been made, and these indicate:

1. On the average, surface fixation is better than fixation in the interior, but not always (Fig. 2). In some areas there is a regular gradation

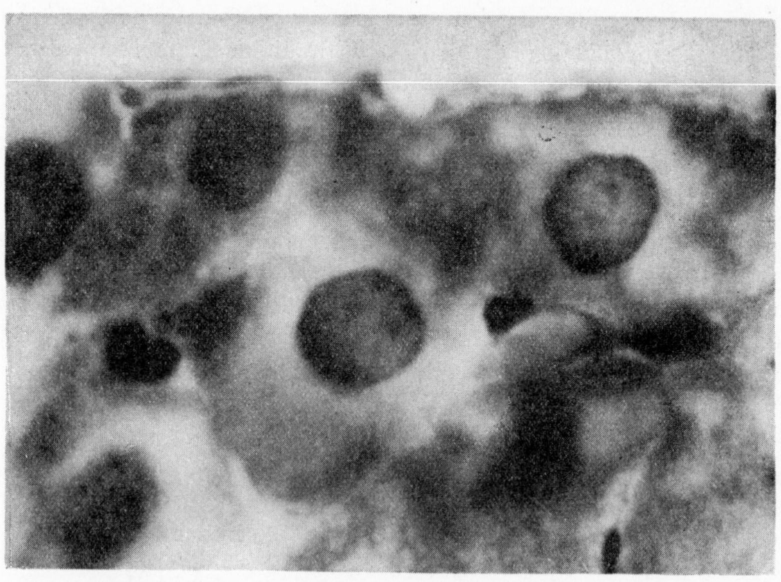

FIG. 2. A relatively broad zone of cells on the surface is optically homogeneous, and the cells below show evidence of minute ice-crystal artifact. Guinea pig liver, about 1 mm. thick, frozen at −120°C. in *iso*pentane and dried and stained with hematoxylin and eosin. 2350×. (Barr and Stephenson, unpublished.)

of ice crystal size from very small (less than 0.2 micron) at the surface to very large (1 to 2 microns) in the interior, but frequently there will be larger ice crystals at the surface and smaller ice crystals in the interior.

2. Fixation at low temperatures (below −100°C.) is usually better than at higher temperatures, but again the exceptions seem to be almost as numerous as the rule. More areas with ice crystals of 0.2 to 0.5 micron, extending to a depth of 100 microns or more, were observed below −100°C., but it was impossible to differentiate between the fixation obtained at −120°C. and that obtained at −140° or −160°C. (Fig. 3) (Barr and Stephenson, unpublished).

This study is being continued, and it may be that more extensive data will fall into a more regular pattern. It appears at present that for a given cooling bath its temperature is only one of many factors which affect the rate of cooling and the size of the ice crystals in so far as it is related to the rate of cooling.

Several cooling liquids other than *iso*pentane and liquid nitrogen have been used: ethyl alcohol at −100°C. (Scott, 1934); *iso*pentane with dry butane dissolved in it, melting point below −190°C. (Emmel, 1946);

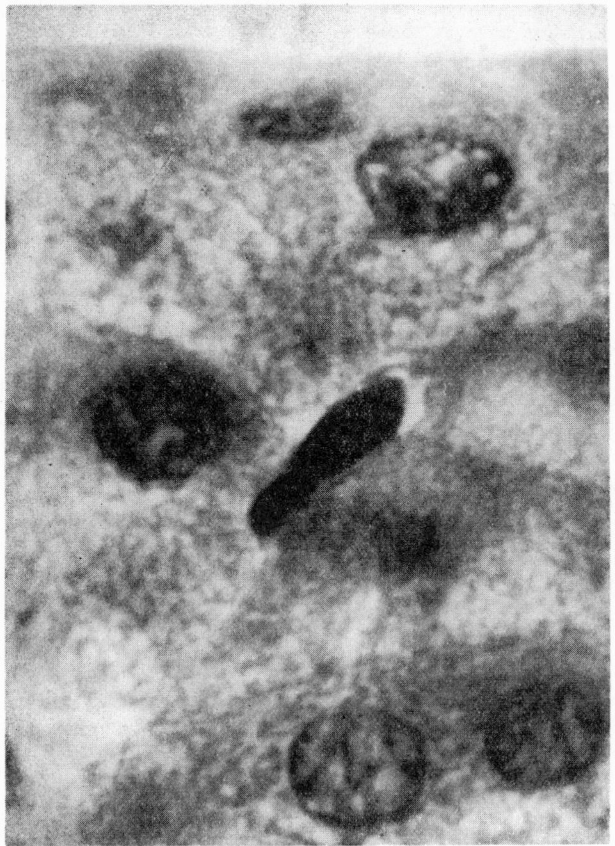

FIG. 3. A more common result, showing irregularities in the dimensions of the ice-crystal artifact, which may be of different size even in the same cell. In this particular specimen there is no regular increase in size of ice-crystal artifact towards the interior. Guinea pig liver prepared as above, freezing temperature at −160°C. 2350×. (Barr and Stephenson, unpublished.)

three volumes of propane with one volume of *iso*pentane, which is fluid at −190°C., propane melting point −185°C. (Bell, 1952). On none of these have quantitative data been published. Until this is done it is impossible to evaluate their relative merits.*

* The authors advise against the use of combustible cooling liquids below −183°C., the boiling point of oxygen, because of the possibility of condensing atmospheric oxygen into them.

## IV. DESCRIPTION OF THE DRYING PROCESS

### 1. *Present Standard Operating Procedure*

A glass beaker containing about 200 ml. of *iso*pentane or more is suspended in liquid nitrogen in a Dewar flask and cooled. The tissue is removed from the animal as rapidly as possible and placed on paper or aluminum which is held with forceps and plunged into the rapidly stirred *iso*pentane. As small a piece of tissue as possible is used. After freezing is complete, the tissue is transferred to a test tube filled with liquid nitrogen. The tube is stoppered with cotton and dropped into the Dewar flask filled with liquid nitrogen. When all the tissue specimens have been frozen, the drying chamber is opened and the tissue transferred to it, care being taken not to allow the tissue to warm up during the transference.

The frozen tissue is placed in a refrigerated drying chamber in which the partial pressure of water vapor is kept well below the vapor pressure of ice at the drying temperature. Ice sublimes; the dried tissue remains. This may be studied directly (Hoerr, 1936a) or infiltrated with some embedding medium and sectioned for staining or histochemical work.

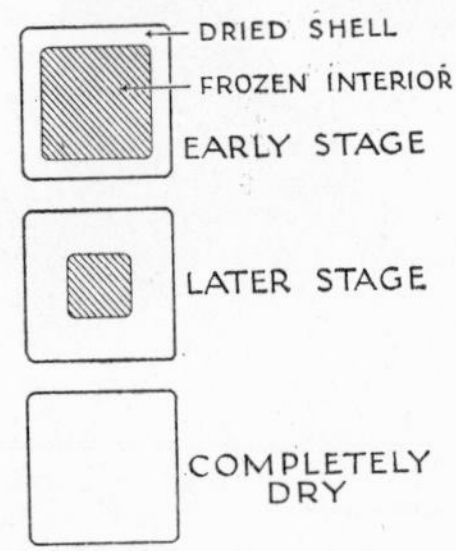


FIG. 4. Diagram showing progressive increase in thickness of dry shell as drying proceeds.

### 2. *General Observations on Drying*

If one removes a partly dried specimen from the drying chamber and cuts it in two with a razor, one sees a frozen and undried interior surrounded by a dry shell. As drying proceeds, the average thickness of the dry shell increases and that of the undried interior decreases until the tissue is completely dry (Fig. 4).

Examination with a dissecting microscope shows the dried shell to be pierced by cracks and blood vessels. On examination of tissues with an oil immersion objective one sees a still finer porous structure in the form of the ice-crystal artifact (see above, p. 337). The dimensions of the spaces originally formed by the ice crystals vary from several microns to 0.2

micron (the limit of optical resolution). Electron microscopy has shown even smaller spaces (Sjöstrand, 1951).

### 3. *Kinetic Details of the Flow of Water Vapor away from the Subliming Ice Crystals*

Heat supplied to the ice crystals lying at the interface between the dried shell and the frozen interior (Fig. 5) causes water molecules to sublime from the free surfaces of these crystals. After a water molecule sublimes, it either (1) passes through the dried shell into the drying

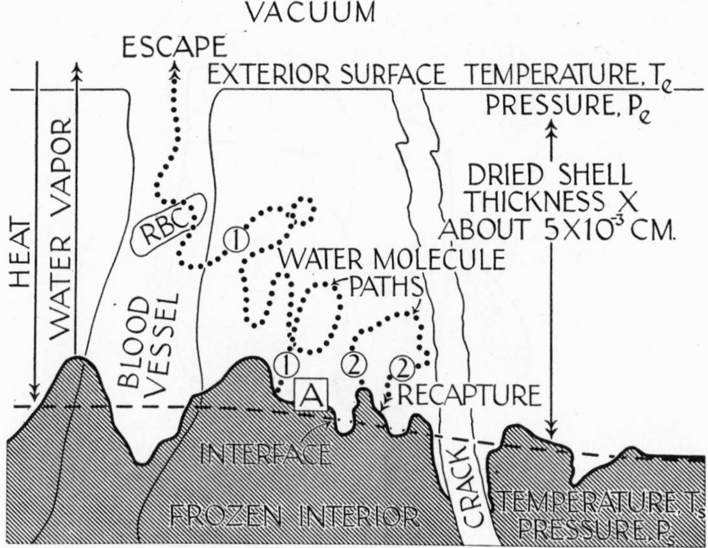


FIG. 5. Diagram to illustrate paths of water molecules after sublimation from ice crystals at the interface between the frozen interior and the dry shell. Solid line indicates the physical interface; dashed, that assumed for mathematical computations.

chamber (path 1, in Fig. 5) and eventually reaches the vapor trap or vacuum pump where it is permanently removed from the system or (2) returns to the interface to be recaptured by an ice crystal (path 2 in Fig. 5).

Both paths may have variations, some of which will be described. Initially a molecule which escapes from an ice crystal may enter the tissue space partially occupied by that ice crystal, such as space A in Fig. 6. After making an indeterminate number of collisions with the walls of this space, it is recaptured by the ice crystal or passes through one of the holes in the walls to a neighboring space. This space may be another at the interface such as D, or it may be one closer to the exterior surface of the tissue such as B. Only in the latter case has the molecule made any progress toward an escape from the system. A molecule in space B will eventually enter a neighboring space, which may be nearer to the exterior, C, nearer to the interface, A, or similarly located, E. A molecule which returns to A may be recaptured, may return to B, or may enter still another space. In general, a molecule which reaches the surface does so only after making a very large number of collisions within the dried shell. However, once a molecule reaches the exterior surface, although it may re-enter the dried shell, its chances of eventually being permanently removed from the system are greatly improved. As we shall show below,

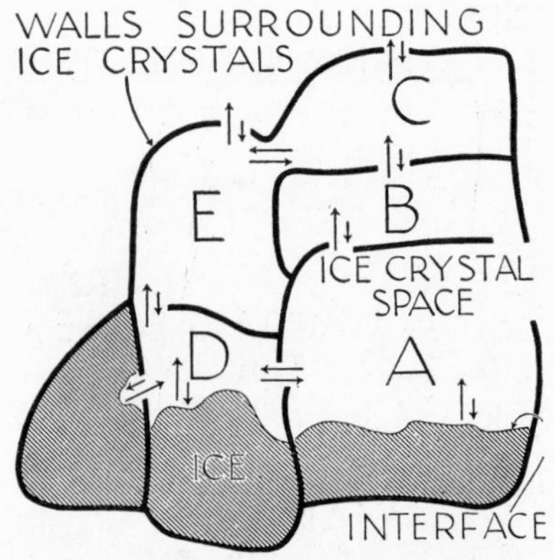


FIG. 6. Diagram of area A in Fig. 5, greatly magnified, to show relation of water vapor, ice, and ice-crystal spaces. Length of arrows indicate direction of flow of water vapor.

the dried shell is usually the principal obstruction to the flow of water vapor.

A net flow of water vapor between the interface and the vapor trap requires the establishment of a pressure gradient. Thus, in Fig. 6 for there to be a net flow from A to B, through the holes in the wall separating the two spaces, the average concentration and so the pressure of water molecules in B must be less than that in A. Likewise the pressure in C must be less than that in B. Since there is no net flow between D and A, the average pressure in these two spaces will be the same. It can be shown that the pressure, $P_s$, in tissue spaces contiguous with ice crystals is very nearly the saturated vapor pressure over ice at the temperature of the interface, $T_s$. The pressure at the surface of the tissue, $P_e$, must be large enough to maintain the flow of water vapor from the exterior surface of the specimen to the vapor trap, but it is usually small relative to the vapor pressure at the interface, $P_s$.

### 4. *Heat Flow to the Interface*

Between 600 and 700 calories are needed to sublime 1 gram of ice. This large latent heat of sublimation requires that heat be continuously supplied to the interface between the frozen interior and the dry shell. If the temperature of the interface remains constant, the rate of supply of heat divided by the latent heat of sublimation must equal the rate at which water vapor is flowing away from the interface. The heat transfer is partly by radiation from the walls of the drying chamber to the interface through the shell of dried tissue, by conduction and convection through the air and water vapor in the drying chamber, and by conduction through the dried shell. At present the exact details are unknown, but whatever the process, the temperature of the interface must be less than the average temperature of the surrounding environment if there is a net flow of heat to this surface.

## V. FACTORS CONTROLLING THE RATE OF DRYING

Anything which influences the supply of heat to the interface or the flow of water vapor away from the subliming ice crystals will affect the rate of drying. Various factors are conveniently separated for discussion, but they are all interrelated.

### 1. *Temperature of the Interface*

The temperature of the interface affects both the flow of water vapor away from it and the flow of heat to it. As the temperature of the interface decreases, the rate at which molecules are emitted from the ice crystals, and the flow of water vapor away from the interface, *decrease*. In contrast, if the temperature of the drying chamber remains fixed, as the temperature of the interface decreases, the flow of heat to it *increases*, because of the greater temperature drop of the interface relative to that of the drying chamber (Fig. 7). Therefore, a temperature of the interface somewhat lower than that of the drying chamber is reached such that the flow of heat to the interface and the flow of water vapor away from it are in equilibrium. As the drying proceeds, this equilibrium temperature may change slowly.

### 2. *Resistance of the Dried Shell of Tissue to the Flow of Water Vapor through It*

The probability that a molecule which is emitted from an ice crystal reaches the exterior surface of the tissue before it is recaptured is a very small fraction. The reciprocal of this probability can be defined as the "resistance" of the dried shell. This resistance depends on (1) the structure of the dried shell, (2) the thickness of the shell, (3) the shape of the tissue, and (4) the type of gas flow through the shell.

The structure of the shell includes the dimensions of the ice-crystal spaces, the size of the holes in their walls, and the number and size of cracks and blood vessels. The kind of tissue greatly influences the structure of the dried shell—dense connective tissue, bone, and cartilage give

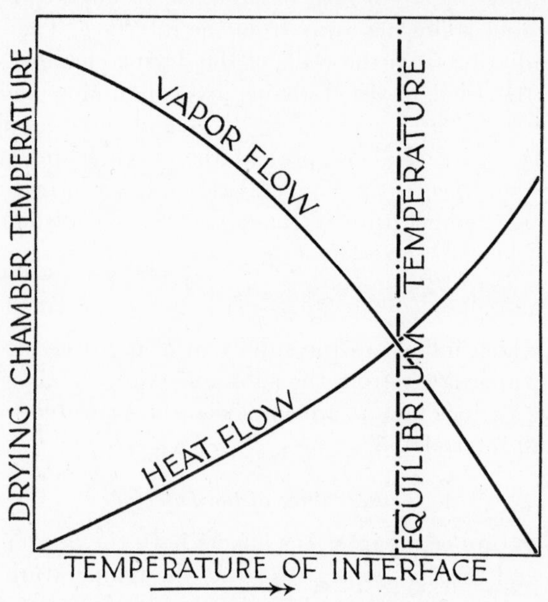


FIG. 7. Relation of heat flow to vapor flow at the interface between the frozen interior and the dry shell. The flow of water vapor depends only on the temperature of the interface for a given thickness of the dry shell. The heat flow is proportional to the temperature difference between the interface and the walls of the drying chamber. If the temperature of the drying chamber changes, the curve for heat flow must be translated along the temperature axis, while the curve for vapor flow remains fixed. The equilibrium temperature of the interface always occurs where the two curves intersect.

a less porous shell than tissues such as loose connective tissue or muscle, or organs such as liver and kidney with the capsule removed. The water content of a tissue influences the drying in two ways—by determining the amount of water which must be removed for drying and by affecting the structure of the dried shell. The latter is the more important, with the result that tissues with the largest water content usually dry the most rapidly.

As the thickness of the shell increases, so does its resistance. This follows theoretically from the above discussion and has been experimentally verified for guinea pig liver (Stephenson, 1953) (see p. 346). For shells of the same thickness, that of a sphere has the least resistance (see p. 349).

The gas flow through the shell is said to be *diffusive* if collisions of molecules with one another are numerous relative to collisions with the dried shell, that is, if the mean free path in the water vapor is short compared with the average dimensions of the tissue spaces. The flow is said to be *free molecular* if the collisions with the dried shell are numerous compared with collisions between water molecules. Calculations show that at the usual drying temperatures the flow is free molecular within the tissue spaces, whereas in the larger blood vessels and cracks it may be diffusive. In so far as the flow is free molecular, the resistance is independent of the pressure of the water vapor, that is, of the temperature of the interface.

### 3. *Resistance of Drying Apparatus to the Flow of Water Vapor from Exterior Surface of Tissue to the Vapor Trap*

This "resistance," which is defined as the reciprocal of the probability that a molecule which leaves the outside surface of the tissue reaches the vapor trap without re-entering the dried shell, depends on (1) the volume of gas flow between the exterior surface and the vapor trap, (2) the type of flow, (3) the geometrical design of the apparatus, and (4) the partial pressure of air in the drying chamber.

The volume of the water vapor flow through the apparatus must equal the volume of flow through the dried shell. It depends among other things on the kind of tissue being dried, the area of the interface, the temperature of the interface, and the resistance of the dried shell. The area of the interface excludes small irregularities (broken line in Fig. 5) according to the convention we have used in our computations, and the numerical values of the resistance of the dried shell, given below, refer to this area.

Flow through the apparatus may be diffusive when flow through the tissue is free molecular. If flow through the apparatus is of the free molecular type, the resistance of the apparatus is independent of the water vapor pressure.

The design of the drying apparatus involves the length and diameter of any tube which connects the drying chamber and vapor trap and any bends in such a tube.

### 4. *Partial Pressure of Air*

If the partial pressure of gases other than water vapor is large enough, the flow of water vapor will be hindered. Since in air at atmospheric pressure the mean free path of a water molecule is about 0.05 micron, collisions of water molecules with air molecules will be much more numerous than collisions with other water molecules, the walls of the tissue spaces, or the walls of the drying chamber. In contrast, if the partial pressure of air is $10^{-4}$ mm. Hg, which corresponds to a mean free path of 50 cm., the collisions of water molecules with air molecules are so relatively infrequent that the effect of the air can be completely neglected. At some intermediate pressure the effect of the air becomes significant. The exact pressure varies with the drying situation, but theory and experiment (Carman, 1948; Kramers and Stemerding, 1951; Stephenson, 1954) indicate that in most cases the critical pressure is around $10^{-3}$ mm. Hg.

### 5. *Heat Transfer to the Interface*

The parameters which control the transfer of heat to the tissue are the heat conductivities, emissivities, specific heats, and radiation absorption coefficients of the walls of the drying chamber, the dried shell, and the frozen interior. The rate of transfer also depends on the temperatures of the walls of the drying chamber and of the interface. An exact theoretical solution of a problem of this kind is virtually impossible, but by a combination of theory and experiment useful results have been obtained (see p. 347).

### 6. "*Limiting*" *Factors in the Rate of Drying*

Any factor which hinders the flow of heat or the flow of water vapor will reduce the rate of drying. If the resistance of the dried shell and of the apparatus to the flow of water vapor and the temperature of the drying chamber remain approximately the same and the transfer of heat is hindered, the temperature of the interface will decrease. This will reduce the vapor pressure at the interface and so the rate of drying. If the flow of vapor is obstructed, the conditions of heat transfer remaining constant, the flow of vapor and so its cooling effect on the interface will decrease; and the temperature of the interface will rise and decrease the temperature drop. This reduces the flow of heat to the interface and so the rate of drying. If the equilibrium temperature of the interface is only a fraction of a degree below the temperature of the drying chamber, the factors hindering the flow of water vapor are obviously relatively more important. On the other hand, if the temperature drop is very great, the limiting factors are those relating to the transfer of heat. However, in most cases both the factors controlling heat transfer and those controlling the rate of diffusion away from the interface are important, and it is improper to speak of a "limiting factor." (See general mathematical discussion, p. 348.)

## VI. QUANTITATIVE RELATIONS OF THE FACTORS CONTROLLING THE RATE OF DRYING*

*Fundamental equation for the diffusion of water vapor away from the interface:* We have:

$$\frac{dm}{dt} = \frac{\alpha P_s}{(2\pi RT_s)^{1/2}} \cdot \frac{1}{1/f_s + 1/f_e - 1} \tag{1}$$

Here, $dm/dt$ is the rate of evaporation in grams of water vapor per second per square centimeter of the interface. (As noted above, the area of the interface excludes small irregularities.) $\alpha$ is the coefficient of evaporation of ice. Its value is approximately unity (Kennard, 1938; Kramers and Stemerding, 1951). $P_s$ is the vapor pressure of water vapor at the interface in dynes per square centimeter. $R$ is the gas constant per gram of water vapor ($4.6 \times 10^6$ erg/deg.). $T_s$ is the absolute temperature of the interface. $\alpha P_s/(2\pi RT_s)^{1/2}$ is the maximum rate of sublimation of water vapor from ice at temperature $T_s$ in grams per square centimeter per second. Its computed value at different temperatures is plotted in Fig. 8. $1/f_s$ is the reciprocal of the probability that a water molecule emitted from the interface reaches the exterior surface of the dried shell without being recaptured by an ice crystal. It is the "resistance" of the dried shell to the flow of water vapor through it. $1/f_e$ is the reciprocal of the probability that a water molecule emitted from the exterior surface of the dried shell reaches the vapor trap without re-entering the dried shell. It is the "resistance" of the apparatus. Both $1/f_s$ and $1/f_e$ have a minimum value of 1 because of their definitions as reciprocal probabilities.

Equation 1 can be rewritten:

$$\frac{dm}{dt} = \frac{f_s \alpha P_s}{(2\pi RT_s)^{1/2}} \times \frac{1}{1 + f_s(1/f_e - 1)} \tag{2}$$

When the resistance of the apparatus is a minimum (i.e., when $f_e$ is 1), eq. (2) reduces to

$$\frac{dm}{dt} = \frac{\alpha f_s P_s}{(2\pi RT_s)^{1/2}} \tag{3}$$

Because of the way $f_s$ appears in eq. 3, the name "fractional drying factor" has been suggested for it. It will be seen that eq. 3 gives the maximum possible drying rate of a piece of tissue with a given thickness of the dried shell and at a given temperature of the interface. However, for eqs. 1, 2, or 3 to be of any use in computations, the numerical values of the resistance of the dried shell, $1/f_s$, the resistance of the apparatus,

* The derivations of formulae in this section are given elsewhere (Stephenson, 1953, 1954).

$1/f_e$, and the temperature of the interface, $T_s$, must be known. The computation and measurement of these are discussed in the following sections.

*Resistance of the dried shell to the flow of water vapor through it* ($1/f_s$): Because of the inhomogeneity of the shell, its resistance cannot be computed, but it can be measured. For guinea pig liver it has been found that the resistance of a dried shell 0.01 cm. thick is about 1000, of a shell 0.1 cm. thick about 3000. Extrapolation gives a value of 10,000 for a shell 1 cm. thick. For a shell thickness between 0.01 cm. and 0.1 cm. it was found that a maximum value of the fractional drying factor (reciprocal of the resistance) for a thin slab of tissue was given by

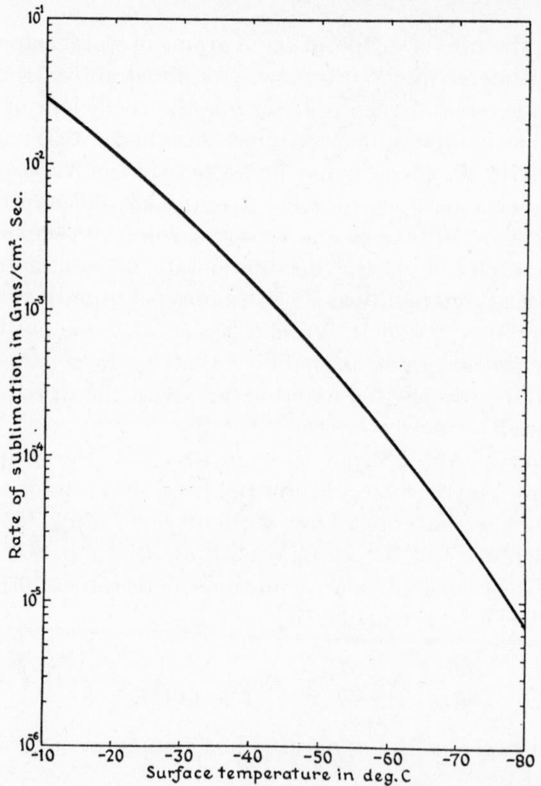


FIG. 8. Sublimation rate of ice as a function of temperature.

$$f_s = \frac{d}{x^n} \tag{4}$$

where $d$ is the "drying coefficient" ($1.2 \times 10^{-4}$ for guinea pig liver when $x$ is in cm.), $x$ is the thickness of the shell, and $n$ is the "drying exponent" (0.55 for guinea pig liver).

Doubtless slightly different values will be found for other tissues, and eq. 4 may not prove generally useful. However, nothing should obscure the central fact that a very thin shell of tissue reduces the maximum possible drying rate of the tissue to a very small fraction of that of ice at the temperature of the interface.

It should be noted that, because of limitations on the maximum rate of heat transfer, the above statement does not mean that if a piece of ice and tissue of similar size and shape are placed in a drying apparatus the time required for tissue to dry is several thousand times that needed for the ice to sublime. There is a much greater temperature drop of the ice relative to the walls of the drying chamber, which greatly reduces its rate of sublimation, although it still sublimes in less time than the tissue requires to dry.

*Resistance of the apparatus to the flow of water vapor* ($1/f_e$)*:* As this can be computed only in special cases, it must usually be measured. When the tissue and vapor trap are separated by a long straight tube through which the flow is diffusive and the resistance of the dried shell is large compared with the resistance of the tube, we have for the resistance of the tube:

$$\frac{1}{f_e} = \left[\frac{16\eta}{\pi P_s} \cdot \left(\frac{RT_s}{2\pi}\right)^{1/2} \cdot \frac{Al}{f_s a^4}\right]^{1/2} \tag{5}$$

where $\eta$ is the coefficient of viscosity of water vapor in the tube (approximately $10^{-4}$ dyne sec./cm.$^2$), $a$ is the radius of the tube, $A$ is the area of the interface between the dried shell and frozen interior, and $l$ is the length of the tube.

When the flow through the tube is free molecular, we have for its resistance:

$$\frac{1}{f_e} = \frac{3}{8\pi} \cdot \frac{Al}{a^3} \tag{6}$$

*Temperature of the interface:* We have:

$$(T_c - T_s) = \frac{\alpha P_s}{(2\pi RT_s)^{1/2}} \cdot \frac{L}{K} \cdot \frac{1}{1/f_s + 1/f_e - 1} \tag{7}$$

where $K$ is a general coefficient of heat transfer between the interface and its surroundings, $T_c$ is the average absolute temperature of the surroundings, usually the temperature of the wall of the drying chamber, $T_s$ is the temperature of the interface, and $L$ is the latent heat of sublimation of ice in calories per gram.

Equation 7 shows in a general way the dependence of the temperature drop, $T_c - T_s$, on the various factors discussed above. With an increase in the drying temperature the temperature drop must increase because of an increase in the maximum rate of sublimation of ice; with a decrease in the heat transfer coefficient the difference will increase; with an increase in the combined resistance of the apparatus and dried shell the temperature difference will decrease. For eq. 7 to be of general use, more data on heat transfer are needed. However, the temperature difference can be measured, and the value of $K$ so obtained can be used for calculations under similar conditions. We have found (Stephenson, 1953) that with the drying chamber at $-30$°C. the temperature of the tissue is between $-35$° and $-40$°C. with an appreciable shell thickness. The temperature difference gradually decreases until with the drying chamber at $-50$°C. it is less than a degree. In these measurements the tissue was not in contact with the wall of the drying chamber. To what extent the temperature drop can be decreased (i.e., $K$ increased by good thermal contact between the tissue and the walls of the drying chamber) has not been investigated.

*General mathematical relation of factors influencing the rate of drying:* From eqs. 1, 7, and the integrated form of the Clapeyron-Clausius equation for vapor pressure, we obtain an approximate formula for the rate of drying:

$$\frac{dm}{dt} = \frac{f\alpha P_c}{(2\pi RT_c)^{1/2}} \cdot \exp. \left[ - \frac{L}{RT_c^2} \cdot \frac{Lf}{K} \cdot \frac{\alpha P_c}{(2\pi RT_c)^{1/2}} \right] \tag{8}$$

Here, $dm/dt$ is the rate of drying in grams of water vapor per second per square centimeter of the interface; $\alpha P_c/(2\pi RT_c)^{1/2}$ is the maximum sublimation rate of ice at the temperature, $T_c$, of the drying chamber; $1/f$ is the compound resistance of the dried shell and apparatus and equals $1/f_e + 1/f_s - 1$; and $Lf/K$ can be interpreted as the ratio of the heat transfer "resistance" to the vapor flow resistance.

Equation 8 is not recommended for computing the rate of drying. This is better done by solving eqs. 1 and 7 by trial and error, with the help of vapor pressure tables. The chief interest of eq. 8 is that it shows the approximate functional relation of the various factors which influence the rate of drying: (1) the temperature of the drying chamber, (2) the combined resistance of the apparatus and the dried shell to the flow of vapor, and (3) the factors affecting heat transfer to the tissue.

## VII. EFFICIENCY OF DRYING APPARATUS

The efficiency of a drying apparatus for drying a given load of tissue may be defined as the ratio of the minimum possible drying time of the load to the actual drying time.

For the actual drying time of a piece of tissue we obtain

$$t = w \int_0^{x_t} \frac{(2\pi RT_s)^{1/2}}{P_s \alpha f_s} \left[ 1 + f_s \left( \frac{1}{f_e} - 1 \right) \right] dx \tag{9}$$

where $w$ is the water content of the frozen tissue in grams per cubic centimeter; $x$, the thickness of the dried shell, is the variable of integration; and $x_t$ is the thickness of the dried shell when drying is complete.

The minimum drying time is given by eq. 9 when the factor in brackets equals 1 (i.e., $1/f_e = 1$). For eq. 9 to be useful in computation, the temperature of the interface, $T_s$, the resistance of the dried shell, $1/f_s$, and the resistance of the apparatus, $1/f_e$, must be known.

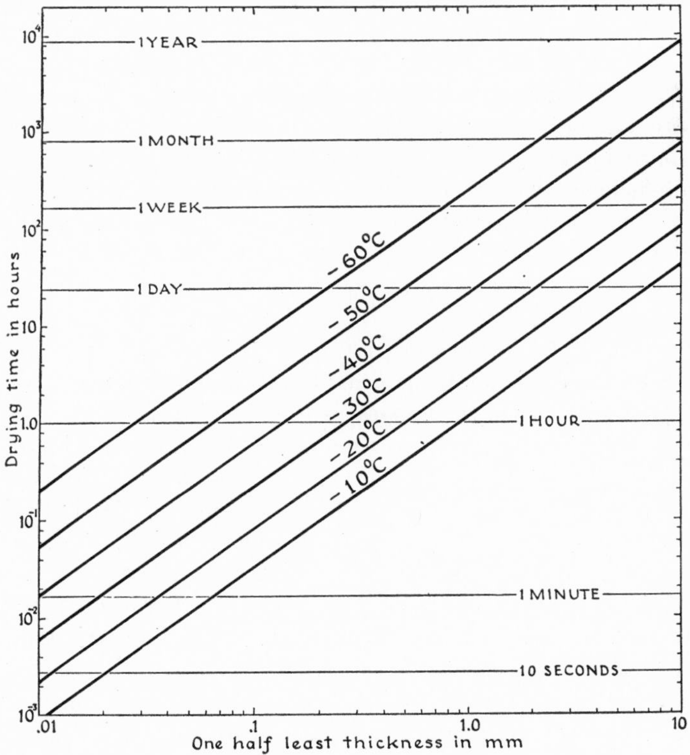


FIG. 9. Drying time of slices of guinea pig liver as a function of temperature and thickness. (Stephenson, 1953.)

Computed values of the minimum drying times of slices of guinea pig liver are shown in Fig. 9. In making the computations the temperature of the interface was assumed to remain constant and the value of the resistance of the dried shell to be given by eq. 4. Since the minimum value of the resistance is used and the temperature drop is ignored, these times are on the low side. This is partly offset by the decreased drying times of other shapes. For example a sphere will dry in about one-third the time of a slab of the same least thickness. The least thickness is defined to be the diameter of the largest sphere contained entirely within the piece of tissue. However, these computed times do show the great importance of drying temperature and of the thickness of the tissue pieces in determining drying time and give an idea as to whether a piece of tissue can be expected to dry in hours or weeks.

Experimentally the efficiency can be determined by measuring the temperature of the interior of the tissue and the partial pressure of water at its exterior surface. Approximately,

$$\text{Efficiency} = 1 - P_e/P_s \tag{10}$$

where $P_e$ is the pressure at the exterior surface and $P_s$ is the saturated vapor pressure of ice at the temperature of the interior (which is assumed to be approximately the temperature of the interface, $T_s$).

The efficiency can be computed if the average value of the ratio of the resistance of the dried shell to the resistance of the apparatus is known. Approximately,

$$\text{Efficiency} = 1/[1 + f_s(1/f_e - 1)] \tag{11}$$

From eq. 11 it can be seen that, since $f_s$ is always small, all that is required for the efficiency to be near its maximum value of 1 is that the ratio of the resistance of the apparatus to the resistance of the dried shell, $f_s/f_e$, be a small fraction, say less than 0.1. This statement disagrees with much of the literature on the design of laboratory drying apparatus (Bell, 1952; Glick and Malmstrom, 1952; Malmstrom, 1951; Packer and Scott, 1942; Scott and Hoerr, 1950), in which the importance of a low absolute value of the resistance of the drying apparatus has been emphasized. The difference in opinion arises from the fact that these authors have ignored the quantitative effect of the very large resistance of the dried shell. A source of confusion in discussing the efficiency of different designs of drying apparatus is failure to specify the operating conditions. Depending on the kind, amount, and surface area of the tissue, the drying temperature, and the partial pressure of air, the same apparatus might have an efficiency of 0.999 or 0.001.

Despite the complications of a precise analysis, the authors feel that under the usual conditions of laboratory operation, the resistance of the apparatus is negligible, relative to the resistance of the dry shell, unless some unusual obstruction, such as a small bore stopcock, is placed between the tissue and the vapor trap.

## VIII. DESIGN OF DRYING APPARATUS

On the basis of the preceding theory we will consider the various practical problems which arise in the design of a drying apparatus for the preparation of tissues. In order to demonstrate the many possible designs we have included in this review a fairly complete collection of simplified drawings of apparatus described in the literature* (see Fig. 10, A–T).

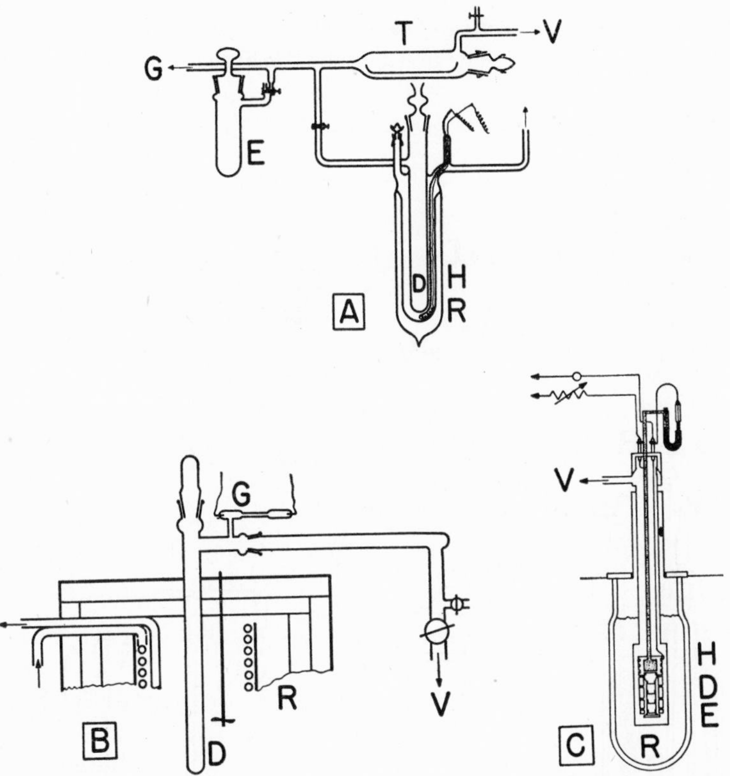


FIG. 10 (A–T). Simplified diagrams of essential elements in design of freezing-drying apparatus, 1932–1952. D, dehydrating chamber; V, to vacuum pump(s); T, vapor trap; R, refrigerating unit; E, embedding chamber; H, heating coil; G, vacuum gauge.

A. Gersh, 1932. Earliest published diagram.

B. Goodspeed and Uber, 1934. Fixed temperature control.

C. Scott and Williams, 1936. Variable temperature control, permitting embedding in dehydrating chamber.

We believe that all these apparatus will perform reasonably efficiently under the usual conditions of laboratory use and that the suitability of an

* Further useful descriptions of devices for freezing and drying are described in: K. Neumann, 1952, *Grundriss der Gefriertrocknung*, "Musterschmidt" Wissenschaftlicher Ver., Göttingen, and A. G. E. Pearse, 1953, *Histochemistry Theoretical and Applied*, Little, Brown and Co., Boston.

apparatus is determined mostly by convenience and economy of construction and operation.

### 1. *Temperature of the Drying Chamber*

*Recommended temperature of tissue:* Drying temperatures from −20° to −70°C. have been used. The first may be too high for many purposes, and

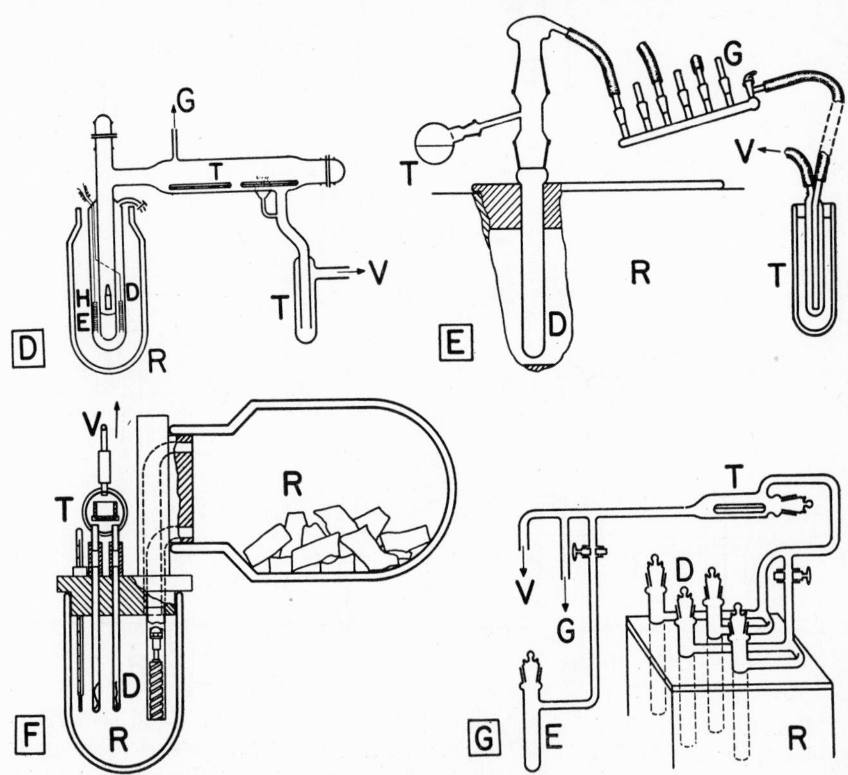


Fig. 10. *Continued.*

D. Packer and Scott, 1942. Variable temperature control, multiple gauges to determine time of complete drying, multiple vapor traps.

E. Sjöstrand, 1944. Battery of dehydrating chambers, fixed refrigeration.

F. Taylor, 1944. Multiple drying tubes, refrigerant-cool gas flow.

G. Gersh, 1948. Fixed refrigeration, multiple drying chamber.

the second probably unnecessarily low for most purposes. The choice of a proper temperature depends on several factors, on some of which fundamental data are lacking for a proper evaluation. Since the drying time increases as the temperature decreases (Fig. 9), the drying temperature should be as high as other factors permit. The preservation of cyto-

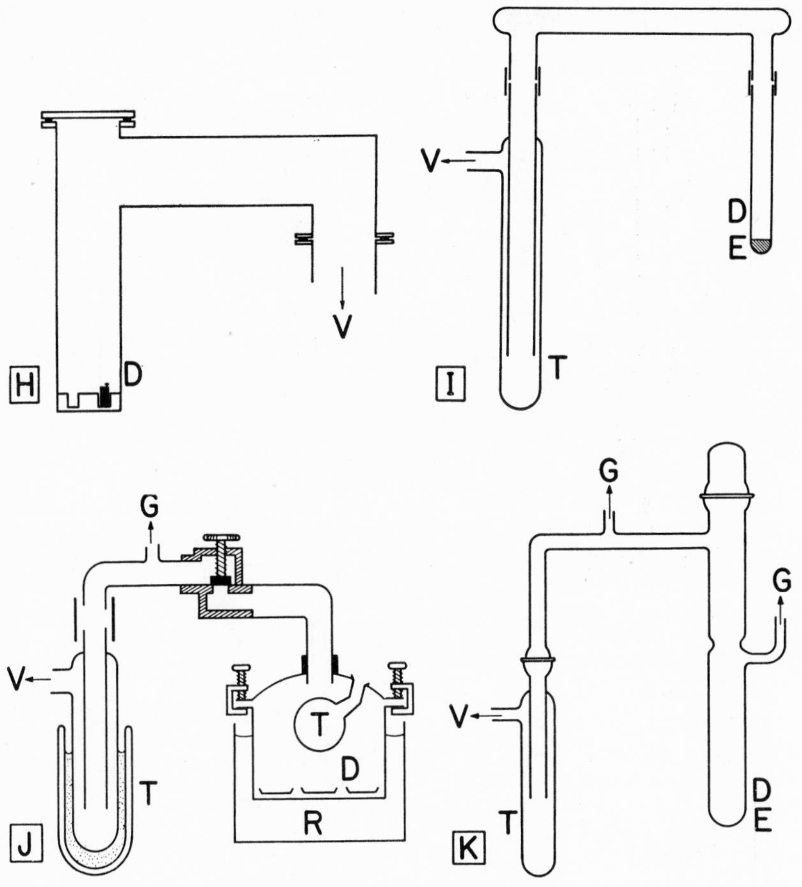


FIG. 10. *Continued.*

H. Pease and Baker, 1949b. Wide-bore metal vacuum line, no gauges, no vapor trap.

I. Wang and Grossman, 1949a. Tape joints.

J. Mendelow and Hamilton, 1950. Part metal and part glass, vapor trap close to tissue.

K. Scott and Hoerr, 1950. Multiple gauges, flat joints.

logical detail seems to be good provided that the drying temperature is below −30°C.; the exact temperature at which morphological detail is not well preserved has not been established. The temperature required for the preservation of various chemical components of the cell—proteins, enzymes, etc.—is not known. However, from data on various biological products (Flosdorf, 1949), −30°C. would appear to give adequate chemical preservation for most purposes. The movement of various cellular

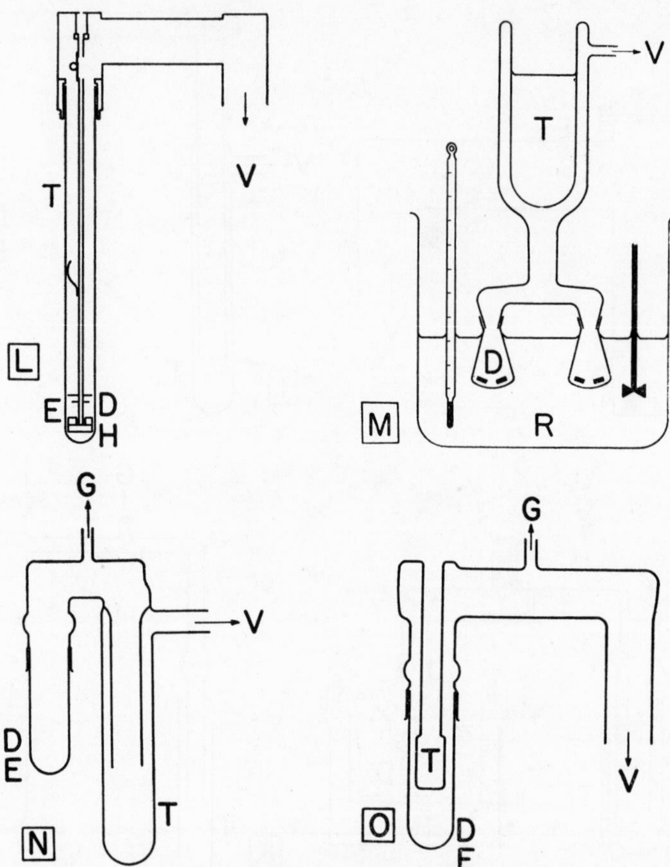


FIG. 10. *Continued.*

L. Stowell, 1951. Part metal and part glass, entire surface of dehydrating chamber cooled with liquid nitrogen, acting as a vapor trap and refrigerant.

M. Billingham and Medawar, 1951. Compact, efficient vapor trap.

N. Glick and Malmstrom, 1952. Large-bore tubing, large, close vapor trap.

O. Glick and Malmstrom, 1952. Large-bore tubing, small capacity, very close vapor trap.

components varies with the temperature and with the component. It is doubtful if the larger components move appreciably below −30°C., but some of the inorganic ions may do so. The total movement of any component will depend both on its mobility and on the drying time. These factors vary inversely with the drying temperature. Until the precise nature of this relationship has been experimentally determined, it is impossible to make a significant statement about the total movement of

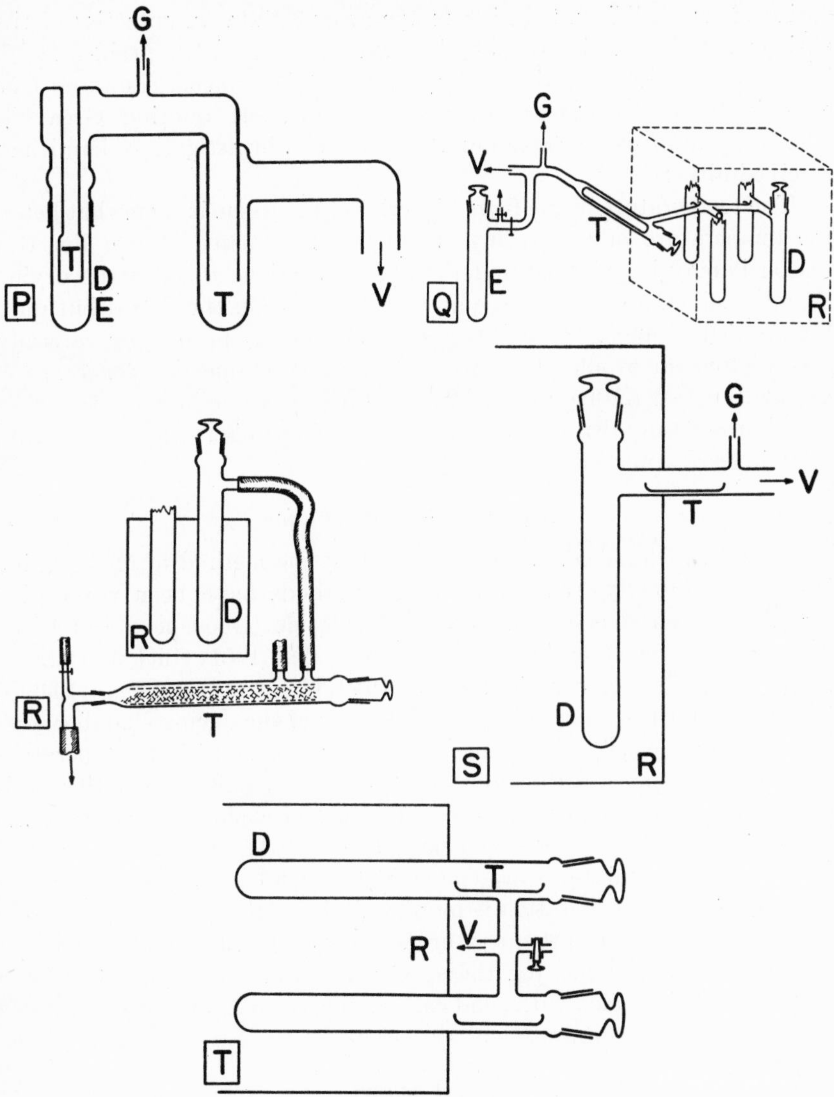


FIG. 10. *Continued.*

P. Glick and Malmstrom, 1952. Combined features of N and O.

Q. Gersh, 1952 (unpublished). All dehydrating tubes completely enclosed in refrigerator.

R. Hack, 1952 (unpublished). Small refrigerator, rubber tubing joining parts.

S. Doyle, 1952 (unpublished). Compact, standard deep-freeze used as refrigerator, which encloses dehydrating chamber.

T. Johnson, 1952 (unpublished). Compact, standard deep-freeze used as refrigerator.

various ions at different drying temperatures. Data on eutectics of the various salts in the tissue have almost no bearing on the problem. It is known that even a relatively simple system like plasma shows no true eutectic by conductance measurements (Flosdorf quoting Greaves). The entire problem deserves much more careful investigation than it has received hitherto.

The temperature of the frozen interior of the tissue is somewhat below the temperature of the drying chamber, as discussed above. For this reason it may be possible under certain conditions to have the drying chamber slightly above the required temperature of the tissue, but until the general problem of the temperature drop has been more carefully investigated this would seem hazardous. A related question concerns the extent to which the heat transfer to the tissue can be improved by contacting the tissue with the walls of the drying chamber. This too requires more investigation.

### 2. *Methods of Refrigeration*

There is at least general agreement that the method of refrigeration is not theoretically important. Many methods have been reported—liquid ammonia (Gersh, 1932), methyl chloride (Goodspeed and Uber, 1934; Harris *et al.*, 1950), eutectic mixtures (Bell, 1951; Glick and Malmstrom, 1952; Mendelow and Hamilton, 1950; Wang and Grossman, 1949a), mechanical refrigeration, cooling of the walls of the drying chamber with liquid air with electrical heating of the tissue to the proper temperature (Stowell, 1951), solid carbon dioxide and alcohol with heating of the specimen (Bell, 1951; Packer and Scott, 1942), and cool gas flowing around the drying chamber at the proper rate (Taylor, 1944). For a small amount of work eutectic mixtures are convenient, but for a permanent installation mechanical refrigeration is more desirable. Mechanical refrigeration is practically limited to temperatures above −50°C. Below this temperature the method of heating the specimen above the temperature of a drying chamber cooled with solid carbon dioxide or liquid nitrogen would seem particularly suitable.

### 3. *Vacuum*

The vacuum in the drying chamber is the sum of the partial pressures of air and of water vapor. These are best discussed separately.

#### a. Partial Pressure of Air

A rule we have found useful in determining the required partial pressure of air is that it should be about one-hundredth of the partial pressure of water vapor at the interface, that is, $0.01P_s$ (Carman, 1948; Kramers and Stemerding, 1951; Stephenson, 1954). If the partial pressure of air rises to above one-tenth of the partial pressure of water vapor at the interface, it may seriously interfere with the rate of drying. In practice this means that a partial pressure of water above $10^{-2}$ mm. Hg will almost always interfere with the drying; that $10^{-3}$ mm. Hg is adequate down to a drying temperature of about −40°C.; and that $10^{-4}$ mm. Hg is always adequate regardless of drying temperature. These results have considerable practical significance because under most circumstances the requisite vacuum can be obtained with a good mechanical pump and a diffusion pump is a needless complication and expense.

b. Partial Pressure of Water Vapor

Water vapor is usually removed from the system by a vapor trap between the drying chamber and the vacuum pump. The vapor trap serves as a pump for the water vapor and as protection for the vacuum pump. The residual vapor pressure over the vapor trap must be low enough to serve both purposes. For the first a vapor pressure over the vapor trap of one-hundredth that at the interface would seem low enough. For the second, pressure between $10^{-3}$ and $10^{-4}$ mm. Hg is required for mechanical pumps and between $10^{-4}$ and $10^{-5}$ mm. Hg for a diffusion pump.

The residual vapor pressure of alcohol–solid carbon dioxide (temperature −78°C., residual pressure 0.0005 mm. Hg), phosphorus pentoxide (used at room temperature, residual pressure 0.00002 mm. Hg), or liquid nitrogen (temperature −192°C., residual pressure $10^{-23}$ mm. Hg) is satisfactory. Each has certain practical advantages and disadvantages, and the choice is one based chiefly on design and convenience. In any case, the trap should be of reasonable size and conveniently constructed for removal of condensed water vapor and refilling.

c. Vacuum Gauges

The partial pressure of air can be measured with a Macleod gauge located between the vapor trap and the vacuum pump. This gauge does not give a true reading when condensable vapors such as water vapor are present. It is convenient for indicating the presence of small leaks in the vacuum system. The partial pressure of water vapor can be measured with a Pirani or an ionization gauge, located between the vapor trap and the tissue.* The use of such a gauge for determining efficiency of drying has been mentioned above. The use of two ionization gauges for determining when drying is complete has been described by Packer and Scott

* Actually such a gauge measures total pressure, but under ordinary drying conditions the partial pressure of air is relatively negligible.

(1942). Under ordinary circumstances the measurement of the pressure of water vapor is not particularly useful. The approximate load of tissue which a particular apparatus will dry efficiently and the time needed to dry different-sized pieces of different tissues is easily determined by experience. The appearance of a glow discharge gives a good enough indication of the vacuum; the glow appears at about 0.1 mm. Hg and disappears at about $10^{-3}$ mm. Hg. Hence, its disappearance or near disappearance indicates an adequate vacuum for most drying purposes. For further details on the design and operation of vacuum gauges and other aspects of vacuum technique the reader is referred to standard books on the subject (Dushman, 1949; Guthrie and Wakerling, 1949; Strong, 1938; Yarwood, 1945).

### 4. *Mechanical Design: Geometry*

There is infinite variety in the possible layout of a drying apparatus, and the choice of one in preference to another will depend on the type of refrigeration, the laboratory space, and even the available glassware one happens to have on hand.

According to the theory developed above, the length and radius of the tube connecting the tissue chamber and the vapor trap is not related to the efficiency of the apparatus in a simple way. However, the minimum radius necessary for a certain efficiency can be computed as a function of the drying temperature, the type of flow, and the composite "load factor," $f_sAl$, where $A$ is the area of the interface, $1/f_s$ is the resistance of the dried shell, and $l$ is the length of the tube. Some computed curves (Stephenson, 1954) are shown in Fig. 11. An example will illustrate their use. If we assume an interface area of 100 cm.$^2$, a resistance of the dried shell of 1000, corresponding to a thickness of 0.01 cm., and a tube length of 100 cm., a value of 10 cm. is obtained for $f_sAl$. If the drying temperature is $-30°$C., the minimum radius required, under these conditions, for an efficiency of 90%, is 2 cm. if the flow is diffusive and 2.3 cm. if it is free molecular. Using the formula

$$\lambda = 3 \times 10^{-3} \frac{f_e}{f_s P_s} \qquad (12)$$

where $P_s$ is in millimeters Hg, one finds 0.1 cm. for $\lambda$, the mean free path. Hence, the flow is diffusive in a tube with a radius of 2 cm.

The value of 10 cm.$^3$ for the load factor, $f_sAl$, is probably too high for the usual laboratory conditions. A value of 1.0 cm.$^3$ or less would probably be more typical, and there would be a corresponding decrease in the required radius. For a given load and drying temperature, the radius must be increased by a factor of 3.2 for diffusive flow and of 2.2 for free molecular flow, in order to increase the efficiency from 90 to 99%. Thus, the additional increase in efficiency, which does not significantly shorten the drying time, is dearly purchased. On the other hand, if the radius is reduced very much below that required for an efficiency of 90%, there is a significant increase in drying time. As long as the flow remains diffusive, the lower the drying temperature, the larger is the radius needed for a given efficiency and load. For some loads, however, there is a

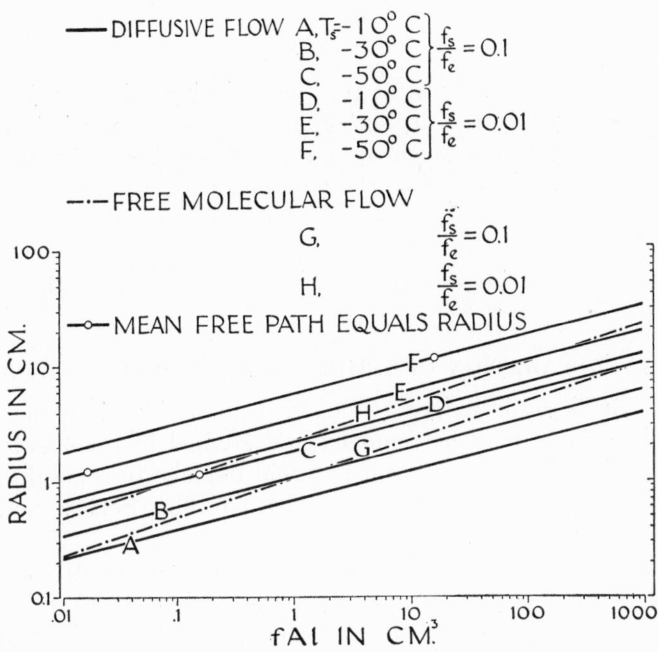


FIG. 11. Relationship between efficiency, radius of tube connecting drying chamber and vapor trap, temperature, and load factor, $f_sAl$. Efficiency equals $1 - f_s/f_e$. (Stephenson, 1954.)

transition to free molecular flow at low temperatures, and the radius required for a given efficiency becomes independent of temperature. Thus, for a value of $f_sAl$ of 1.0 cm.³, a drying temperature of −50°C., and an efficiency of 99%, one finds that a radius of 2 cm. is required, assuming free molecular flow, and a radius of 6 cm., assuming diffusive flow. Since for this efficiency and temperature the mean free path is about 10 cm., the assumption of free molecular flow is justified.

It is probably rash to try to oversimplify the problem, but on the basis of these computations it appears that, under the usual conditions of laboratory drying, design is not particularly critical. With the usual loads, tubing between 1 and 2 cm. in radius will give a good efficiency, provided that it is not over 100 cm. in length. (If it must be longer, the radius can be increased accordingly.) The flow is usually diffusive, so bends in the tubing do not affect the efficiency. There seems to be no theoretical advantage in a metal vacuum system, which has the disadvantage of being more difficult and expensive to construct. In locating stopcocks and valves, one should remember that stopcock grease solidifies when cold.

### 5. *Summary*

Despite the great interest of the theoretical problems which arise in the design of freezing and drying apparatus, the authors feel that these have much more relation to the design of large-scale freezing and drying equipment than to that used in the biology laboratory. In order to dry a few pieces of frozen tissue, vacuum and refrigeration equipment costing thousands of dollars is not necessary. Just as good results can be obtained by drying the tissues in a refrigerated test tube evacuated with a mechanical pump.

## IX. PREPARATION OF DRIED TISSUE FOR SECTIONING

After the tissue is judged to be dried, air is bled into the vacuum slowly. The tissue may be removed and studied in free-hand sections cleared in glycerin or mineral oil to avoid damage to some proteins by some process incident to infiltration with paraffin (Bensley and Hoerr, 1934; Hoerr, 1936, b, c).

Tissue can be embedded in paraffin in several ways. In one method degassed paraffin previously placed in the drying chamber is warmed and allowed to infiltrate the dried specimens *in vacuo*, the vacuum not being broken. When infiltrated, the specimen is embedded (Scott, 1934; Scott and Packer, 1939b). An alternative method is to warm the drying chamber above room temperature after the specimen is dried, break the vacuum, transfer the specimen to a tube containing melted paraffin, and place this in a vacuum. After a time the vacuum is broken and the specimen is removed and embedded. A third variant is to break the vacuum after drying is complete, remove the specimen to air, and infiltrate and embed as above. The time in the melted paraffin may be from 15 seconds to 15 minutes or more.

It is important that the sections be cut with few wrinkles and a minimum of compression, as these sources of difficulty are not easily removed without damage. The use of water or alcohol must be avoided, as this would cause solution or disintegration of the embedded material. Warming over clean mercury has been recommended (Bell, 1952); it remains to be seen what effect this may have on enzymes. The flat sections are mounted on albumenized or chemically clean slides by pressure with a finger, a fingernail, or a horn or ivory spatula. The slides are warmed until the paraffin is just melted, and the sections are then pressed down again. It would seem safest to prepare and study sections directly after embedding. Although it is very unlikely that embedding causes significant damage to many structures which are denatured only by drastic means (Catchpole, 1949; Engel, 1948), there is no doubt that it sometimes affects the extractability of some cell components, for example, mitochondria (Bensley and Hoerr, 1934). It is not clear how long is needed for such a change to occur or how general it is. In particular, how paraffin infiltration and embedding affects the extractability and other properties of proteins is not known, but it has been found that acid and alkaline phosphatase and peptidase activities may be preserved almost unaltered for appreciable times (Doyle, 1948, 1950).

Specimens may be infiltrated with celloidin very simply. They are removed from the drying chamber and dropped into a dish of absolute alcohol, equal parts of absolute alcohol and ether, or thin or thick nitrocellulose. The dish is placed in a vacuum desiccator which is evacuated briefly and then sealed. After a time the dish is removed from the vacuum desiccator. Specimens are then treated in the usual ways to thicken and harden celloidin. Tissue blocks are mounted, sectioned, and stained in the usual manner.

For the study of lipids, after the drying is completed, the tissue is infiltrated directly without breaking the vacuum with "200" polyethylene glycol at 0° to −20°C. The tissues are then transferred at atmospheric pressure to "400" polyethylene glycol and are cut with a freezing microtome. The sections are transferred to water or to the staining solution. The infiltrating medium (polyethylene glycol) has a very low water content, is relatively inert, is water- and alcohol-soluble, and is not capable of extracting lipids. These properties are extremely favorable for the preservation of lipids in sections of frozen-dried material (Hack, 1952).

## X. MORPHOLOGY AND HISTOCHEMISTRY OF FROZEN-DRIED TISSUES

Although it is often difficult to separate strictly morphological from histochemical data, nevertheless it seems advantageous to present the published material based on the use of the freezing-drying method under these two headings. In general, stains which do not involve impregnation with silver, osmium, or gold compounds color sections of frozen-dried material more readily than usual, and differentiation is slower. This may be attributed to the greater reactivity of the relatively undenatured protein constituents. Impregnation methods have not been successfully applied to frozen-dried material. As these methods depend to a great degree on adsorption of colloidal particles by suitable surfaces, one must conclude that the surfaces or state of the colloidal particles, especially the former, must be different in frozen-dried material.

Some general remarks on fixation may be pertinent here. Fixation is the process of preserving tissue components. When one (or more) cellular or tissue components is preserved very nearly in the state in which it occurs in life, or in an otherwise useful way (such as indicating a state of activity), then fixation of that component is satisfactory. When the component is destroyed or so altered as to result in error of interpretation bearing on its morphology or state of activity, fixation of that component is unsatisfactory. After freezing in such a way that ice crystals are small, and drying at a low temperature, many cellular and intercellular structures and components are well preserved and visible after staining of paraffin sections. (See below, Nissl bodies, nuclear structure, mitochondria, etc.) Some components may go into solution in the process of staining, unless some special effort is made to prevent this. (See below, enamel protein, gonadotrophic hormone(s), ground substance, etc.) Sometimes with the same treatment of the sections of the same organ or of different organs in the same animal, the structure may be visible in one but not in another cell type. This is particularly true of the Golgi apparatus. Many structures are much more easily demonstrated if the dried specimen is embedded directly in celloidin. (See below, blood vessels, lipid droplets, etc.)

It appears, then, that fixation by freezing and drying may be complete and satisfactory for some structures. However, for others freezing and drying must be followed by a second step, which consists of treatment of the section designed to complete its fixation. It is clear that from the point of view expressed above freezing and drying should be looked on as a method of fixation. The same viewpoint is also applicable to histochemical studies, including inorganic ions (such as chloride or phosphate), or states of proteins (such as in nerve cells or ground substance), lipids, and enzymes (see below).

## 1. *Morphology*

### a. Reality of Structures

(1) *Nissl Bodies.* There has long been a question whether the chromophilic substance of nerve cells pre-exists in the living cell as morphological aggregates (known as Nissl bodies). In motor nerve cells of the ventral horn, pyramidal cells of the motor cortex, cerebellar Purkinje neurones, spinal ganglion neurones, and sympathetic ganglion neurones,

the distribution of the Nissl substance in frozen-dried preparations is essentially the same as in those fixed by immersion in alcohol or formalin-alcohol (Bensley and Gersh, 1933b; Gersh, 1932; Hydén, 1943). Likewise in liver cells and in many other cell types studied (e.g., pancreas, salivary glands, uterine and intestinal epithelium, mucigen cells of the intestine, glands of Brunner, cervical epithelium) the chromophilic substance is similarly distributed after immersion fixation and after freezing and drying (Bensley and Gersh, 1933b). In these instances, the distribution of basophilic substance in cells as known to cytologists for many years is a good representation of their actual distribution in life. Sometimes, after common fixatives the amount of this material which is stained may be smaller than after freezing and drying. This may be attributed to shrinkage, decreased stainability following chemical immersion fixation, and leaching out of disaggregated material. The last factor may be illustrated from a study of ventral horn nerve cells of frog subjected to ultrasound. After fixation in formalin or alcohol with or without lanthanum directly after exposure to ultrasound, the Nissl substance is very weakly stained. After freezing and drying, the addition of lanthanum nitrate to all reagents results in the retention of chromophilic material (Gersh and Fry).

Basophilic substances of the cytoplasm have been studied with the ultraviolet microscope in a great variety of cells after fixation by freezing and drying because the sections have a smaller light scattering error than material fixed in other ways [summarized by Caspersson (1950)]. The swelling of protein in glycerin reduces light scattering, and this action is probably to be related to the relatively undenatured state of the protein in frozen-dried preparations.

(2) *Golgi Apparatus.* Despite the recent deplorable fashion of regarding the Golgi apparatus as an artifact [see critique by Bensley (1951)], there is no doubt that it can be preserved in frozen-dried material and that its pattern is essentially the same as after immersion and impregnation with osmium or silver solutions. The negative image was observed in spinal ganglion cells, in duodenal epithelial cells, in exocrine and some endocrine pancreatic cells, and in the epididymus. In spinal ganglion cells, a stainable component partly coextensive with the negative image was also observed (Simpson, 1941b). The Golgi apparatus of frozen-dried duodenal epithelium and glands of Lieberkühn was beautifully delineated with the Hotchkiss stain, which, it was deduced, probably stained the polysaccharide–protein complex in the structure (Gersh, 1949) (Fig. 12). The same methods have since shown the Golgi apparatus in liver cells (Aterman, 1952), kidney (E. Perl-Reaven, personal communication), thyroid gland (Gersh, 1950a), spinal ganglion cells, uterine

gland epithelium (J. G. Elchlepp, personal communication), and prostate gland epithelium (Arcadi, 1952). In all cases, the Golgi apparatus has a granular or reticulated structure which is exquisitely fine as compared with the well-known impregnation pictures. This is probably attributable to the deposition of osmium or silver oxides on the delicate filaments and nodal granules of the Golgi apparatus. It is difficult to avoid the conclusion that the Golgi apparatus pre-exists in living cells.

(3) *Neurofibrils and Myelin Sheath.* Neurofibrils can be observed in axones of free-hand sections of frozen-dried nerves mounted in glycerin

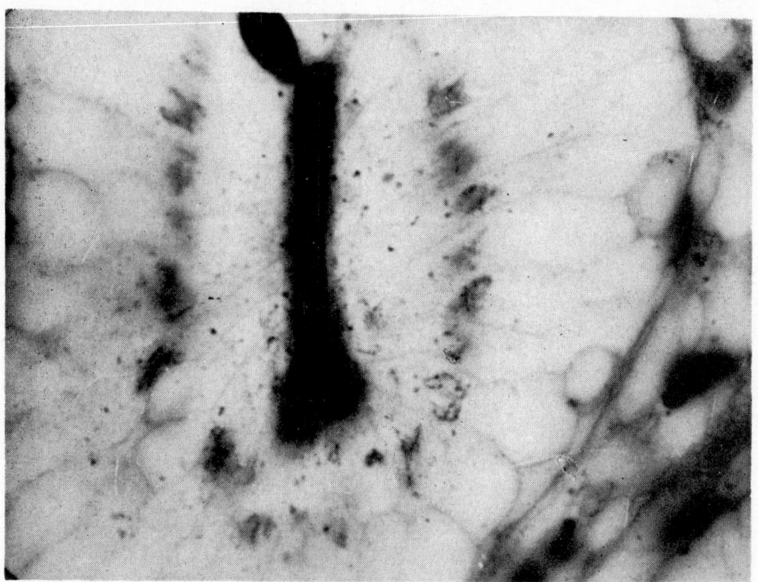

FIG. 12. Golgi apparatus in cells of glands of Lieberkühn of rabbit fixed by freezing and drying. (Gersh, 1949.)

or paraffin oil (Hoerr, 1936b). In the myelin sheath, the lipid and protein components are optically homogeneous—the "neurokeratin" nets observed after the use of fluid fixatives were not seen in frozen-dried material (Hoerr, 1936c).

b. Preservation of Structures Which Tend to Deteriorate When Fixed by Immersion

(1) *Mucigen Granules.* It is now well known that even with the best fluid fixatives mucigen granules tend to swell, fuse, and be reprecipitated as threads or as granules, with an accompanying distortion of the shape of the cell and a displacement of cellular organoids (Bensley, 1903). This series of artifacts is prevented by freezing and drying. Mucigen granules

have been found to be preserved when fixed by this method in all cells studied, notably goblet cells throughout the intestinal mucosa, and cells of the glands of Brunner, salivary glands, and cervix.

(2) *Functionally Active Blood Vessels.* It is extremely difficult to estimate the number of capillaries which are conducting circulating blood at any specific moment. The best method of fixation by fluids is the use of chilled alcohol or acetone (at −70°C.) until the specimen is frozen, with a subsequent prolonged immersion in the cold fixative. A far superior method is freezing of the desired part of the anesthetized animal with a fresh flow of *iso*pentane at about −150°C. When dried, the specimen is trimmed, immersed in absolute alcohol for several days, infiltrated with celloidin, embedded, and sectioned. The sections are mounted on slides without removing the celloidin and observed unstained. Camera lucida drawings of all capillaries give a measure, which is probably somewhat too high, of the ratio of surface area of capillaries per unit volume of specimen (S/V). This technique has been used to study S/V of adipose tissue (lean and fat) and the adrenal cortex. In the former, S/V for protoplasm of fat cells exceeds that of nearly all known organs (Gersh and Still, 1945). The ratio is even higher in adrenal cortex of rats. Here the values are increased during pregnancy in the fascicular and reticular zones, and depressed to below normal by treatment with cortisone (Davis *et al.*, 1953). A second method of demonstrating open capillaries involves the injection of a fluorescent dye. After 2 to 3 minutes the animal is killed and the structure prepared by freezing and drying. In paraffin sections, the endothelium of capillaries is fluorescent and may be photographed, even when collapsed (Schlegel, 1949). As the time when capillaries remain open is variable and in most cases unknown, the quantitative aspects are uncertain.

The response of cutaneous capillaries to physical and pharmacological specimens was studied in whole mounts of mouse skin prepared by freezing and drying (Deviks and Hanssen, 1951).

(3) *Preservation of Microscopic Gas Bubbles.* When gas bubbles are formed in animals decompressed rapidly, they may be intracellular or extracellular. Some of the latter may be intravascular, others in the tissue fluid spaces. These bubbles cannot be preserved by immersion in fluid fixatives as they may shift their position, fuse to form large pockets which cause artificial disruptions, or dissolve in the fixative. They are preserved in all sites by freezing and drying, followed by alcohol immersion, celloidin embedding, sectioning, and staining (Fig. 13) (Gersh *et al.*, 1944). Findings on the genesis of gas bubbles, their distribution in the body, and some of their pathological consequences are summarized in a recent review (Catchpole and Gersh, 1947).

(4) *Preservation of Lipid Droplets.* It is common knowledge that it is difficult by immersion fixation to preserve lipid droplets when they are tightly packed in the cytoplasm except in the superficial cells. In deeper parts, they tend to coalesce and disrupt the cytoplasm and nucleus. This does not occur when such specimens are fixed by freezing and drying. In early stages of regenerating liver, when the cytoplasm is laden with

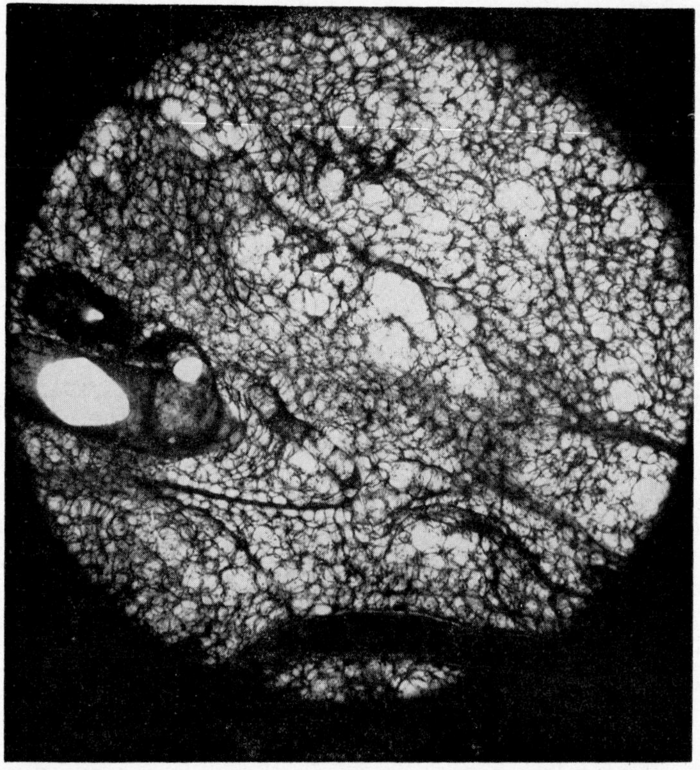

FIG. 13. Intravascular and extravascular gas bubbles in fat tissue of guinea pig decompressed from high-pressure atmosphere, fixed by freezing and drying. (Gersh, *et al.*, 1944.)

numerous lipid droplets, their size and shape are well preserved in paraffin sections (Aterman, 1952). In the lactating mammary gland, cytoplasmic structure is well preserved in the same way. In the adrenal cortex, the size and shape of the droplets are equally well preserved in paraffin or celloidin sections. They may be preserved in all their delicacy and stained after infiltrating the dried gland with polyethylene glycol of low melting point and sectioning with the freezing microtome (Hack, 1952).

(5) *Preservation of Vacuoles in Thyroid Gland Cells.* These are pre-

served in their entirety only in frozen-dried material (De Robertis, 1942; Gersh, 1950a; Gersh and Caspersson, 1940). In paraffin sections, they may be stained by aniline blue or by the periodate-leucofuchsin method (Fig. 14).

(6) *Nuclear Chromatin.* In frozen-dried preparations the space between the nuclear bodies has been found to contain homogeneously distributed material. In nerve cells, this homogeneously distributed nuclear plasm and the nucleolus are the only visible nuclear components (Bensley and Gersh, 1933b). After fixation by perfusion or immersion, the nuclear

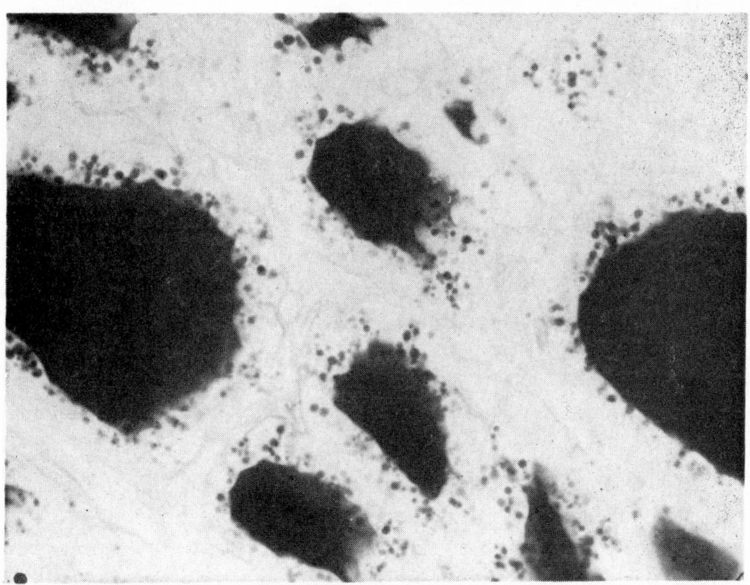

FIG. 14. Droplets in acinar cells of rat thyroid gland frozen and dried. Note that the colloid is relatively homogeneous and fills the whole lumen. (Gersh, 1950a.)

plasm in nerve cells appears as interconnected shreds and strands radiating from the nucleolus. In other cells, it seems highly probable that similar fixation results in a movement of the nuclear plasm to chromatin bodies, nucleolus, and nuclear membrane. The maintenance of the optically homogeneous component of the nucleus in that state is of crucial importance for quantitative studies on nucleoprotein either with the ultraviolet microscope or after Feulgen staining. From these studies using frozen-dried material Bensley (1933) concluded that the structure of the resting nuclei of well-fixed material reflects that of living cells. This conclusion is supported by recent observations on living cells with the phase contrast microscope.

Efforts have been made to study the structure of chromosomes during mitosis (Bell, 1951; Goodspeed *et al.*, 1935). It seems possible that the observations may represent results of ice-crystal artifact.

(7) *Preservation of Detailed Structure in the Inner Ear.* The preservation of this organ is more difficult than most because of the delay in penetration of the fixation fluid despite resort to perfusion. An attempt to prepare the organ by freezing and drying has been made, but it seems that, perhaps because of the large size, the ice-crystal artifact was so prominent as to obscure finer relations (Vilstrup, 1950). Preliminary observations on the bat inner ear, which is very small indeed, indicate that further progress in the study of the finer morphology of the inner ear is possible (H. B. Perlman, personal communication).

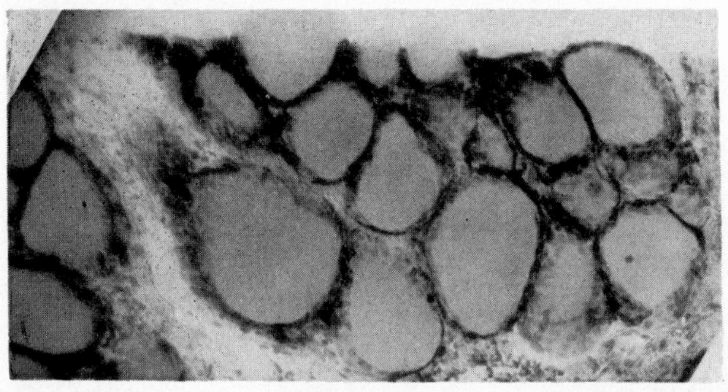

FIG. 15. Optically homogeneous colloid of follicles of thyroid gland of guinea pig fixed by freezing and drying. The colloid fills the acini. (Gersh and Caspersson, 1940.)

(8) *Preservation of Extravascular Protein.* In the thyroid gland, the follicular colloid is nearly always optically uniform when observed *in vivo*. After fixation by immersion or perfusion, the colloid may become granular or fibrillar or it may remain homogeneous. Depending on the state of activity of the follicle, peripheral vacuoles caused mostly by shrinkage frequently appear. In some follicles, the colloid may be absent. Although it is true that one may infer the density of the colloid from the extent of the artifacts, they interfere with quantitative studies. These artifacts do not occur after freezing and drying, and the material seems to be adequate for quantitative studies (Fig. 15) (Gersh, 1950a; Gersh and Baker, 1943; Gersh and Caspersson, 1940).

Similarly in the neural hypophysis, the extravascular stainable material appears to be uniformly distributed (Gersh and Tarr, 1935). There is no trace of the Herring bodies, which are interpreted as the coalesced remnants of extravascular protein material, the rest of which is dissolved out or hydrolyzed during fixation by immersion.

On fixation of edematous tissues by immersion in fluids, as in the nasal mucosa, the extravascular tissue appears to consist of cells and fibers, many of which are separated by wide spaces which seem empty. After freezing and drying, the specimens are not shrunken, and on sectioning they reveal no clear spaces. Instead, the intercellular material fills in the space not occupied by cells and fibers as a homogeneous stainable material (Rappaport *et al.*, 1953). In some abnormal veins, the similar shift of intercellular material in formalin-fixed vessels was not observed in frozen-dried specimens (Lev and Saphir, 1951).

These artifacts present in an exaggerated form the alterations of intercellular material which take place in normal connective tissues of numerous organs. In the regions between the fibers and cells of the connective tissues prepared by freezing and drying a homogeneous component, the ground substance, may be seen. In embryos, this material is extremely difficult to preserve by immersion methods. The ground substance of mesenchyme has been successfully preserved, however, after freezing-drying and embedding in paraffin (A. Moscona and H. Moscona, personal communication). The sections are treated with the reagent described by Cohn *et al.* (1950) as suitable for precipitating maximal blood proteins.

(9) *Prevention of Solution of Cellular and Extracellular Components.* The reader is referred to the preceding section and to pp. 365, 373 for comments on the preservation in frozen-dried material of ground substance and of gas bubbles, substances which are readily dissolved by fluid fixatives. Other examples which may be cited are: (a) the protein component of sites of early enamel formation in developing teeth, where vigorous fixation by an aqueous fixative was required after paraffin removal (Engel, 1948); (b) possibly gonadotrophic substance in the B cells of the anterior lobe of the hypophysis, where prolonged treatment of the section with alcohol was necessary (Catchpole, 1949); and (c) a disaggregated protein of bone matrix during bone resorption (Heller-Steinberg, 1951). In the last instance, fixation of minute spicules in chilled alcohol was also successful in preserving the soluble material, especially on the surface.

### c. Electron Microscopy

It is obvious that the numerous changes which cells may undergo during fixation may be so great as to mask the minute details of protoplasmic structure now capable of being photographed with the electron microscope. The greatest obstacle to the successful use of the method of freezing and drying for the preservation of specimens lies in the disturbances caused by ice crystals. How great can be the distortion caused by them, may be seen in an electron photomicrograph published by Fullam and Gessler (1946). Freezing in such a way as to produce vitrification would be most satisfactory. Despite assertions to the contrary (Pease and Baker, 1949a), optimal fixation for electron microscopy has not yet been achieved. (See comments on p. 335.) Very good results have been attained by Sjöstrand (1951) for the mouse pancreas and by Pease and Baker (1949b) for skeletal muscle. The most suitable material would seem to be that which can be smeared on a metal foil surface or collodion membrane for rapid freezing and drying.

#### d. General Comments

In the foregoing parts of this section the special situations where freezing and drying has been found to be useful in the preservation of some structure or component for morphological studies are somewhat artificially categorized. Freezing and drying, like every fluid or vapor fixative, is most suitably used only for certain problems, that is, when other methods are not so adequate for the purpose at hand. With freezing and drying, certain difficulties are introduced, the major ones being the ice-crystal artifacts which are difficultly, and only in part, controllable and the retention of at least some of the solubilities of some tissue components. After the tissue is dried, almost every technical problem originating in the nature of the material has to be met individually. No standard routine procedure following the drying will remove all difficulties. It is at this point that imaginative "tricks" and technical *tours de force* are necessary if the greatest use is to be made of the method of freezing and drying.

### 2. *Histochemistry*

#### a. Inorganic Components

The identification of inorganic components in the approximate sites of their occurrence in cells and intercellular substances is difficult. During fixation by immersion in fluid fixatives, these components frequently diffuse away from their original locations and into the fluid medium. These shifts (except for quite minor ones owing to ice-crystal formation) are avoided by freezing tissues at a low temperature and dehydrating them at some unspecified temperature lower than −33°C. (see p. 371). For identification of some of the elements, such as occur in calcium deposits, the specimen may be dehydrated at higher temperatures. The actual identification then requires special procedures designed to prevent diffusion or extraction. Some of these are described below.

(1) *Microincineration.* Superficially, microincineration would seem to be a satisfactory method of seeing how ash is distributed in and between cells, especially in view of the report that motion pictures at a magnification of 700 to 800 times show no movement of parts of the section during the incineration (Scott, 1943). Against this is the claim, also based on

photographic evidence, that, after a violent bubbling, intracellular displacements take place, with the formation of fissures, holes, masses, flakes, filaments, and granules (Godlewski, 1938). If such displacements occur, they may explain the failure after microincineration to detect physiological shifts in inorganic substances, the paucity of ash in the tissue fluid spaces, and the absence of ash in the glomerular space. It was found that the ash distribution in material dried at −20°C. is different from that dried at −28°, −33°, or −78.5°C. In muscle and nerve cells dehydrated at the lower temperatures, there was more ash than after fixation by immersion in formalin-alcohol, and the distribution of the ash was somewhat different (Scott, 1943; Scott and Packer, 1939a).

(2) *Electron Emission Induced by Calcium and Magnesium.* Apart from the identification of silicon by the double refraction of some of its compounds, no other elements could be identified in ashed preparations until recently. By a method in which sections of frozen-dried material were incinerated on the cathode of an electron microscope, the distribution of calcium plus magnesium was studied (Scott and Packer, 1939a, b). They were described in anisotropic bands of skeletal muscle and on the periphery of the fiber, in the nucleus and some cytoplasmic strands of smooth muscle cells, in the zymogen granules and basal portion of exocrine cells of the pancreas, and in the periphery of goblet cells (Scott, 1943). Whether the high temperature of the cathode (700° to 800°C.) induces shifts in the elements is not known.

(3) *X-Ray Absorption.* By their specific absorption of soft x-rays, many of the elements may be identified in sections of frozen-dried specimens (Engström, 1952). Except for the limits imposed by resolution and in some cases sensitivity, this method is most satisfactory as it avoids all possibilities of artifact arising from contact with dissolving agents.

(4) *Autoradiography.* The earlier efforts to demonstrate the sites where certain radioactive elements occur in sections of frozen-dried material apparently permitted some diffusion and extraction (Leblond, 1943). More precise localization was obtained with $I^{131}$ and $P^{32}$, with some sacrifice in resolution, by avoiding contact of section and photographic media altogether (Harris *et al.*, 1950; Holt *et al.*, 1952; Holt and Warren, 1951). The evidence that fixation by immersion results in a significant diffusion and extraction was particularly clear (Holt *et al.*, 1949; Holt *et al.*, 1952).

(5) *Chloride, Phosphate and Carbonate, and Potassium.* The distribution of chloride, and phosphate-carbonate in various organs has been found by a specific, sensitive method which avoids significant diffusion or extraction. In skeletal muscle, chloride was found only in the intercellular spaces, and phosphate and carbonate was visible there as well as intracellularly.

Potassium was present in both sites but was present in vastly greater amounts in the fibers (Gersh, 1938a). Colloidal calcium phosphate injected or otherwise introduced into the circulating plasma was phagocytosed by macrophages of the liver, spleen, and bone marrow, and later released (Fig. 16) (Gersh, 1938b). In addition, the method has been modified to expose the presence of a more and a less reactive state of calcium in developing and resorbing bone (Heller-Steinberg, 1951) (Fig. 17). In resorbing bone, as in carious dentine, there was a relationship between the more reactive calcium and the state of the ground substance of these structures (Engel, 1950). The method has been criticized by Scott and

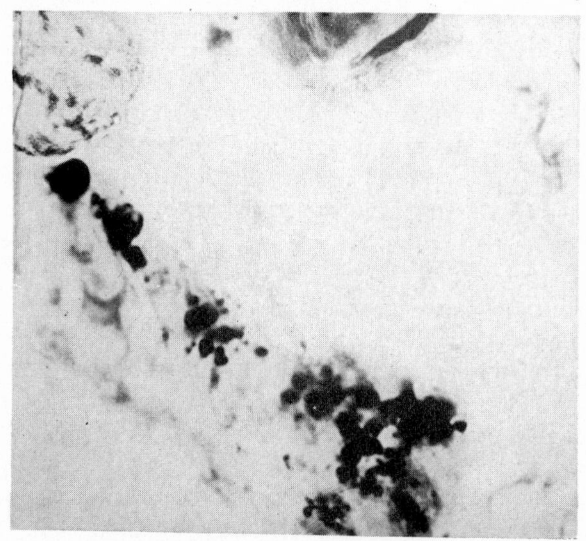

FIG. 16. Phagocytosis of colloidal calcium phosphate and carbonate by Kupffer cells of the rat liver demonstrated after freezing and drying. (Gersh, 1938b.)

Packer (1939a). Phosphate and carbonate in most sites where it occurs as visible granules has been used as an indication of the presence of calcium. The distribution of this element in Haversian systems has been studied by Engström (1952) by means of x-ray absorption.

(6) *Ferrocyanide.* When ferrocyanide is injected into animals it appears to be distributed like chloride, being confined to extracellular spaces in muscle, intestine, skin, etc. As the ion is dissolved in the aqueous phase of the connective tissues and reaches equilibrium with that in plasma rapidly, the amount visible in the microscope may be taken to represent the amount of water available in these sites (S. Permutt, personal communication). Ferrocyanide is readily demonstrated with great precision in sections of frozen-dried material. All other methods of fixation permit too much diffusion of the anion (Gersh and Stieglitz, 1934a).

A striking example which illustrates how freezing and drying prevents solution of substances may be seen in Fig. 18. The uric acid distribution after immersion fixation in alcohol (B) shows evidence of solution, *post-mortem* aggregation, and diffusion as compared with the discrete distribution after freezing and drying (A).

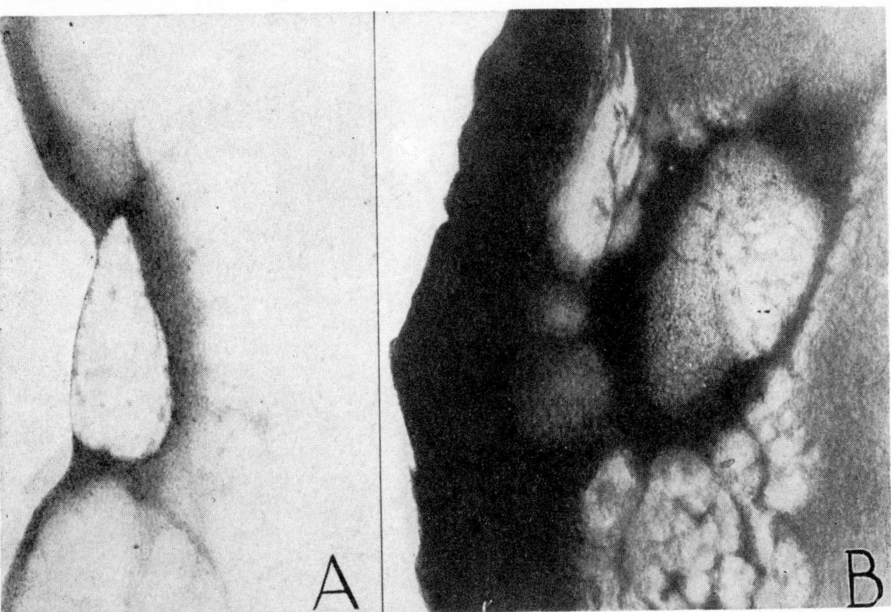


FIG. 17. Preservation of ground substance of bone spicule in experimental rats (A) and of "reactive" calcium phosphate and carbonate (B) after freezing and drying. (Heller-Steinberg, 1951.)

b. Water

The water concentration in microscopically circumscribed structures can be approximated only qualitatively by indirect methods. For example, ferrocyanide can be used to indicate regions with differing concentrations of water in the ground substance of connective tissues. In the kidney, sites of reabsorption of water may also be identified by the use of ferrocyanide (Gersh and Stieglitz, 1934a). Similarly under carefully controlled conditions the size of the ice crystals may be used as an indicator of water concentration in the ground substance of connective tissues (Gersh and Catchpole, 1949), as well as in cells. Examples of the latter are nerve cells during chromatolysis (Gersh and Bodian, 1943) and after exposure to ultrasound (Gersh and Fry). None of these deductions would be possible were the specimens fixed by immersion in fluid fixatives. On the other hand an example of where such a deduction based

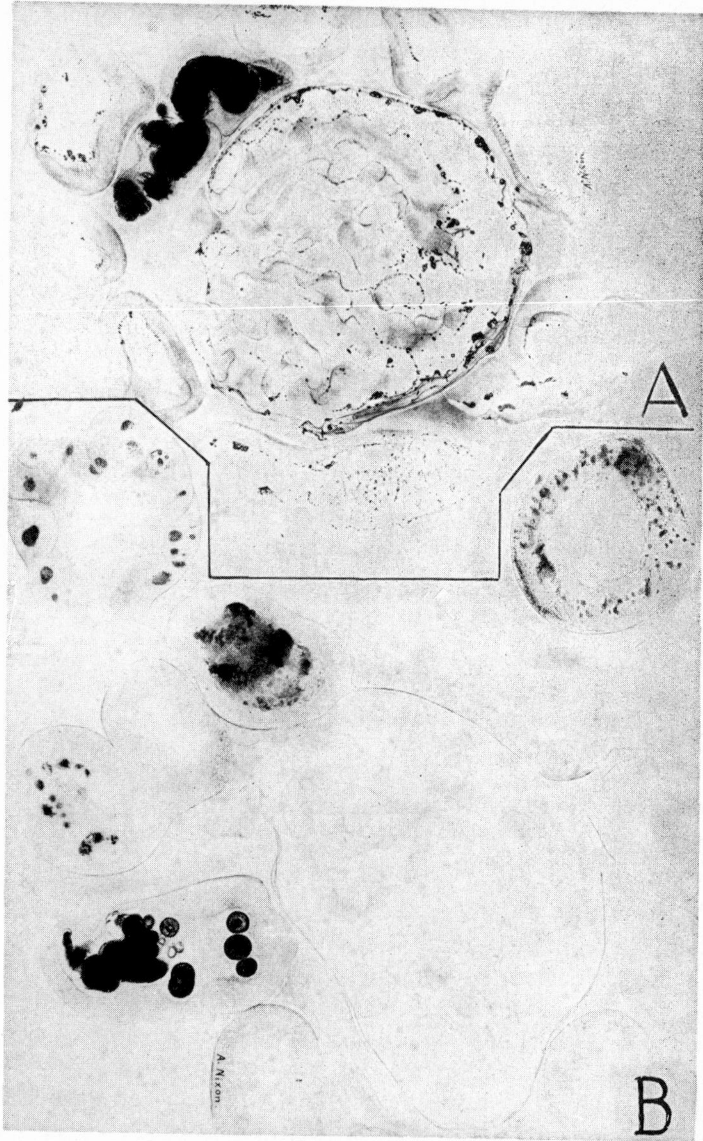


Fig. 18. Preservation of uric acid in the renal nephron by freezing and drying (A) as compared with its preservation after alcohol fixation (B). (Gersh and Stieglitz, 1934b.)

on material fixed by immersion was shown to be acceptable was the colloid of thyroid follicles, where peripheral shrinkage "vacuoles" and the appearance of granules and shreds indicate that the colloid is more dilute (Gersh and Caspersson, 1940).

c. Lipids

The method described above for preparing frozen and dried material without extracting the lipids has recently been used to make an extensive study of the distribution of plasmal (Hack, 1952).

d. Glycogen

It was found early that the losses and often marked redistribution of glycogen which take place after immersion fixation are avoided through fixation by freezing and drying. In the liver cell, for example, glycogen is more or less uniformly distributed in the cytoplasm (Gersh, 1932), in agreement with the finding by Lewis (1926) of a similar distribution of glycogen in certain tissue culture cells. When smaller amounts are present, glycogen may be present as irregularly distributed "flakes" or masses (Aterman, 1952). Glycogen was found in frozen-dried material to be uniformly distributed also in the cytoplasm of cells of cartilage, vaginal and cutaneous epithelium, endometrium, fatty tissue, placenta, kidney, and the glycogenic organ of chickens (Mancini, 1948). Mancini found that glycogen was distributed in granular form in the isotropic bands of muscle and in the cytoplasm of leucocytes. Glycogen has also been described in cartilage and bone cells (Bevelander and Johnson, 1950; Cobb, 1953; Heller-Steinberg, 1951), in the prostate gland (Arcadi, 1952), and in the ovary (Harter, 1948).

e. Dyes

The preservation by fluid fixatives of supra- or intravital dyes has been limited to those which are phagocytosed or bound to some cell component. The more water- or alcohol-diffusible dyes or dye components are not satisfactorily fixed by fluids as they diffuse and are extracted from the specimen. These difficulties do not occur after freezing and drying. The paraffin in the sections is replaced by mineral oil or Shillaber's oil and the sections are observed directly as was done by Mancini (1948) in his studies on glycogen. He used iodine dissolved in mineral oil to remove the paraffin from the section and color the glycogen simultaneously. Using frozen-dried material the distribution of indigo-carmine and a large series of carminic acid derivatives and indicators has been studied in the kidney. Phenol red was studied with another instructive method (Gersh, 1934). The yellow form was converted to the red form by a stream of anhydrous ethanolamine gas, this being a very satisfactory means of avoiding diffusion and extraction from the section. This simple method of handling the sections has made possible recent studies on the distribution of Evans blue. It was found that in a number of situations Evans blue is concentrated extravascularly in regions where the ground substance of the connective tissues has been altered in a particular way (Gersh, 1950b).

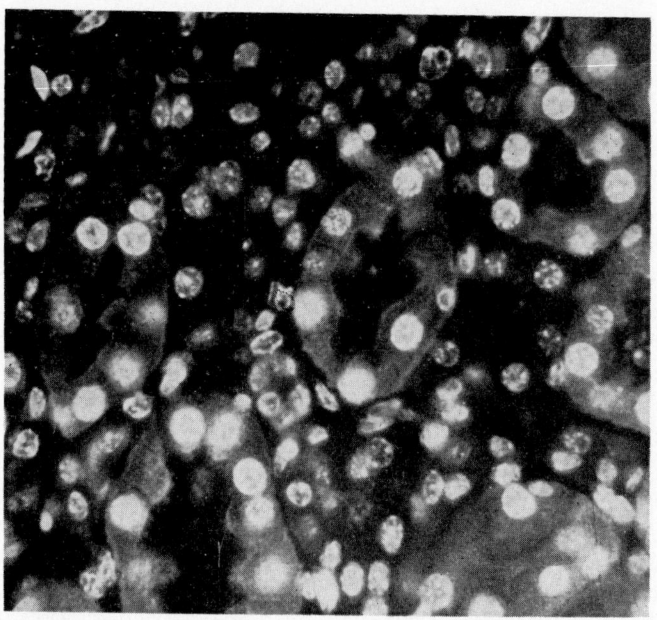

FIG. 19. Differential intravital staining of nuclei in guinea pig kidney with the fluorescent dye acriflavine hydrochloride after fixation by freezing and drying. (Courtesy of P. P. H. De Bruyn.)

Observation of frozen-dried sections in mineral oil is also quite suitable for the study of autofluorescence of cell components and the distribution of fluorescent dyes. An excellent and extensive report on the autofluorescence of numerous types of cells has been written by Sjöstrand (1944). His identification in renal tubular mitochondria of a flavin is particularly notable (Sjöstrand, 1951). The caution is given that the naturally occurring fluorescent substances may be extremely sensitive to storage. The use of an injected fluorescent compound for the identification of blood vessels has already been mentioned. Recently the distribution of a large series of intravital acridine dyes was reported on. Nuclei of the cells of all organs and tissues studied except those of the central nervous system were found to be nearly selectively stained (Fig. 19) (De Bruyn *et al.*,

1950). This property was adapted by Farr (1951), who studied the fate of lymphocytes injected into the blood stream and claimed that some of them were transformed into myeloid cells.

f. Hormones

As has been pointed out, fixation by freezing and drying makes it possible to make semiquantitative studies of homogeneous materials. In the thyroid gland, for example, it was possible to measure in sections of individual follicles the changes which take place in the organic, hormonally active, iodine-containing protein of the colloid in a variety of functional states (Gersh and Baker, 1943; Gersh and Caspersson, 1940). With less precision, radioactive iodine compounds were also localized with minimal shifts after freezing and drying (Holt and Warren, 1951). The polysaccharide protein(s) which were tentatively identified as gonadotrophin(s) were also identified in frozen-dried preparations of the rat adenohypophysis (Catchpole, 1949). Fixation by immersion results in their leaching out or destruction. Finally, by means of immunochemical methods and tagging with a fluorescent dye, it was possible to identify adrenocorticotrophin in the basophilic cells of sections of frozen-dried hog pituitary (Marshall, 1951).

g. Enzymes

That frozen-dried material should be useful for the study of enzymes in morphological components was seen early by Behrens (1932). The frozen-dried specimens were pulverized, sifted to remove large particles, and then separated by flotation in non-aqueous fluids into a number of fractions. From a variety of organs, nuclei or nuclear fragments were separated in a relatively pure state. They were found to contain arginase and lipase (Behrens, 1939). Dounce (1950), who modified the procedure somewhat, found that some enzymes were well preserved, whereas others were not. Arginase was undamaged, catalase was half-inactivated, and aldolase was nearly entirely inactivated. Mirsky (1951) also studied a great variety of organs and tissues and reported his findings in general terms. No consistent pattern was apparent. Arginase was present in liver nuclei of mammals, although not in renal nuclei. Esterases were found in most nuclei, with no relation to the total cellular content of the enzyme. Nucleoside phosphorylase was the one enzyme present generally in higher concentration in the nucleus than in the cytoplasm. Lipase occurs in pancreatic nuclei, phosphatases in the nuclei of most tissues.

The good qualities of fixation by freezing and drying and the application of quantitative methods to tissue analyses were ingeniously combined (Anfinsen *et al.*, 1942). Frozen tissue was sectioned at −20°C. and dehydrated at atmospheric pressure in the same cabinet. The section was stained (if staining did not affect the activity of the enzyme being studied) or observed unstained and then employed for chemical determination. Peptidase and diphosphopyridine nucleotidase of liver and cholinesterase of cerebral cortex were found to be stable. In this way, it was possible to study quantitative enzymic distribution in various layers of the retina.

These general principles have been extended by Lowry and his colleagues (Robins and Lowry, 1951; Strominger and Lowry, 1952), who have been making quantitative estimates of a variety of enzymes and other substances in sections, or parts thereof, of various portions of the central nervous system. These are: phosphatases, adenosine triphosphatase, cholinesterase, aldolase, fumarase, malic, lactic and glutamic dehydrogenase, chloride, various phosphorus fractions, and certain lipids (Lowry).

The preservation of phosphatases by freezing and drying of organs and by other methods of dehydration was studied quantitatively by Doyle (1948). Alkaline phosphatase was found to be preserved somewhat better, and acid phosphatase markedly better, by freezing and drying as compared with chilled acetone. Phosphatases were stable in the paraffin block even at room temperature for several days but deteriorated rapidly after sectioning. In sections kept at −20°C., phosphatases were stable. Peptidase was also well preserved and stable in paraffin and in sections, and Doyle (1950) suggests, "The method has promise for other enzymes usually considered too labile to permit embedding in paraffin."

Phosphatases have been studied qualitatively in several sites after fixation by freezing and drying: intestine, kidney, liver, stomach, pancreas, and uterine epithelium (Deane and Dempsey, 1945; Emmel, 1946; Wang and Grossman, 1949b). Only Wang and Grossman could discern an improvement in the amount of enzyme demonstrable in certain sites. As the method was not quantitatively controlled, their conclusion is not altogether justified. The site of phosphorylase activity has been identified in certain cells of cartilage and bone (Cobb, 1953).

### h. Glycoproteins

The distribution of polysaccharide protein complexes has been studied in numerous structures. Of particular interest for this review are: (1) The identification of glycoprotein granules and rods, probably gonadotrophic in nature, in B cells of the anterior lobe of the hypophysis, which show cyclic changes during estrus. This identification was made possible only by reason of the virtual insolubility of the stainable component after prolonged treatment with alcohol (Catchpole, 1949). (2) The separation of at least two components in the colloid of the thyroid follicles, with quantitative assay of the probably active and probably inactive portions of the colloid. These observations were made possible for the same reason as above, and because of the relatively homogeneous state of the colloid after freezing and drying (Gersh, 1950a; Gersh and Caspersson, 1940). (3) The identification of at least one component of the Golgi apparatus, which because of the nature of the method of fixation must be conceded to be a true organoid and not an artifact (see p. 363). (4) The preservation of the optically homogeneous component (ground substance) of the connective tissues. This was feasible after freezing and drying, whereas after immersion in fluid fixatives the shifts which commonly take place result in such great distortion or extraction as to obscure its identification in many sites (see p. 369).

### i. Ultraviolet and X-Ray Microspectrometry

Some of the advantages of the preparation of tissues by freezing and drying for absorption spectrometry are: (1) the maintenance of protoplasmic constituents very nearly in the sites occupied during life through avoidance of solution, extraction, and spatial shifts; (2) the absence of significant shrinkage or swelling in frozen-dried material; and (3) the reduced light scattering of the sections referrable at least in part to the retention of the swelling properties in sections of the frozen-dried specimens. It is no wonder, then, that most of the measurements of nucleic acids, of proteins, and of total mass with ultraviolet and x-ray absorption (Engström, 1952) were made on material prepared by freezing and drying. Whether the data are strictly quantitative or only relatively so has not yet been agreed (Faraday Society, 1950). The theoretical basis of these methods and the concepts and results have been summarized in a recent review by Caspersson (1950). For identical reasons, frozen-dried material is well suited for quantitative studies after the Feulgen stain.

### j. Solubility of Proteins

The solubility of certain cell components in sections of frozen-dried material has afforded the possibility of the identification, however crude, of some of their chemical constituents (see pp. 375, 377, 378). Such identification must agree with the properties of purified biochemical preparations. Solubilities have also made it possible to analyze the state of aggregation of some tissue components, particularly the state of polymerization of the ground substances of connective tissues, including dentine, cartilage, and bone. A comprehensive theory of the role of changes in consistency and state of the ground substance was evolved which encompasses some aspects of growth in mass, cyclic phenomena in endocrine organs, capillary permeability, immunological phenomena, endocrine target effects, and calcification processes of cartilage, bone, and teeth

(Gersh, 1950a). The use of solubilities in sections of frozen-dried material to ascertain at least gross differences of state of aggregation of protoplasm has only just begun (see p. 373). The extension of this approach awaits chiefly the exercise of ingenuity.

## REFERENCES


Altmann, R. 1890. *Die Elementarorganismen und ihre Beziehungen zu den Zellen.* Veit and Co., Leipzig.

Anfinsen, C. B., Lowry, O. H., and Hastings, A. B. 1942. The Application of the Freezing-Drying Technique to Retinal Histochemistry. *J. Cellular Comp. Physiol.* **20,** 231–237.

Arcadi, J. A. 1952. Some Polysaccharide Components of the Prostate Gland of the Dog. *Anat. Record* **112,** 593–607.

Aterman, K. 1952. Some Local Factors in the Restoration of the Rat's Liver after Partial Hepatectomy. I. Glycogen; the Golgi Apparatus; Sinusoidal Cells; the Basement Membrane of the Sinusoids. *Arch. Pathol.* **53,** 197–208.

Behrens, M. 1932. Untersuchungen an isolierten Zell- und Gewebsbestandteilen. I. Mitteilung: Isolierung von Zellkernen des Kalbsherzmuskels. *Z. physiol. Chem.* **209,** 59–74.

Behrens, M. 1939. Über die Verteilung der Lipase und Arginase zwischen Zellkern und Protoplasma der Leber. *Z. physiol. Chem.* **258,** 27–32.

Bell, L. G. E. 1951. Some Applications of Freezing and Drying in Cytochemistry, in *Freezing and Drying.* Edited by R. J. C. Harris. The Institute of Biology, London. Pp. 35–63.

Bell, L. G. E. 1952. The Application of Freezing and Drying Techniques in Cytology. *Intern. Rev. Cytol.* **1,** 35–63.

Bensley, R. R. 1903. The Structure of the Glands of Brunner. *Decennial Publs., Univ. Chicago* **10,** 279–326.

Bensley, R. R. 1933. Studies on Cell Structure by the Freezing-Drying Method. IV. The Structure of the Interkinetic and Resting Nuclei. *Anat. Record* **58,** 1–13.

Bensley, R. R. 1951. Fact *vs.* Artifact in Cytology: the Golgi Apparatus. *Exptl. Cell Research* **2,** 1–9.

Bensley, R. R., and Gersh, I. 1933a. Studies on Cell Structure by the Freezing-Drying Method. II. The Nature of the Mitochondria in the Hepatic Cell of Amblystoma. *Anat. Record* **57,** 217–237.

Bensley, R. R., and Gersh, I. 1933b. Studies on Cell Structure by the Freezing-Drying Method. III. The Distribution in Cells of the Basophil Substances, in Particular the Nissl Substance of the Nerve Cell. *Anat. Record* **57,** 369–385.

Bensley, R. R., and Hoerr, N. L. 1934. Studies on Cell Structure by the Freezing-Drying Method. V. The Chemical Basis of the Organization of the Cell. *Anat. Record* **60,** 251–266.

Bevelander, G., and Johnson, P. L. 1950. A Histochemical Study of the Development of Membrane Bone. *Anat. Record* **108,** 1–21.

Billingham, R. E., and Medawar, P. B. 1951. The Viability of Mammalian Skin after Freezing, Thawing and Freeze-Drying, in *Freezing and Drying.* Edited by R. J. C. Harris. The Institute of Biology, London. Pp. 55–62.

Carman, P. C. 1948. Molecular Distillation and Sublimation. *Trans. Faraday Soc.* **44,** 529–536.

Caspersson, T. O. 1950. *Cell Growth and Cell Function.* W. W. Norton and Co., New York.

Catchpole, H. R. 1949. Distribution of Glycoprotein Hormones in the Anterior Pituitary Gland of the Rat. *J. Endocrinol.* **6,** 218–225.

Catchpole, H. R., and Gersh, I. 1947. Pathogenetic Factors and Pathological Consequences of Decompression Sickness. *Physiol. Revs.* **27,** 360–397.

Cobb, J. D. 1953. Relation of Glycogen, Phosphorylase and Ground Substance to Calcification of Bone. *Arch. Pathol.* **55,** 496–502.

Cohn, E. J., Gurd, F. R. N., Surgenor, D. M., Barnes, B. A., Brown, R. K., Derouaux, G., Gillespie, J. M., Kahnt, F. W., Lever, W. F., Liu, C. H., Mittelman, D., Mouton, R. F., Schmid, K., and Uroma, E. 1950. A System for the Separation of the Components of Human Blood: Quantitative Procedures for the Separation of the Protein Components of Human Plasma. *J. Am. Chem. Soc.* **72,** 465–474.

Davis, M. E., Plotz, E. J., and Plotz, E. 1953. A Quantitative Study of the Vascularity of the Adrenal Gland of the Rat during Pregnancy and after Cortisone Treatment. *Endocrinology.* **52,** 164–172.

Deane, H. W., and Dempsey, E. W. 1945. The Localization of Phosphatases in the Golgi Region of Intestinal and Other Epithelial Cells. *Anat. Record* **93,** 401–417.

De Bruyn, P. P. H., Robertson, R. C., and Farr, R. S. 1950. *In vivo* Affinity of Diaminoacridines for Nuclei. *Anat. Record* **108,** 279–308.

De Robertis, E. 1942. Intracellular Colloid in the Initial Stages of Thyroid Activation. *Anat. Record* **84,** 125–135.

Deviks, F., and Hanssen, O. E. 1951. The Freezing-Drying Technique Applied to Investigation of Vascular Reactions in the Skin of Mice. *Acta Pathol.* **29,** 357–362.

Dounce, A. L. 1950. Cytochemical Foundations of Enzyme Chemistry, in *The Enzymes.* Edited by J. B. Sumner and K. Myrbäck. Academic Press, New York. Pp. 187–266.

Doyle, W. L. 1948. Effects of Dehydrating Agents on Phosphatases in the Lymphatic Nodules of the Rabbit Appendix. *Proc. Soc. Exptl. Biol. Med.* **69,** 43–44.

Doyle, W. L. 1950. Peptidase Activity of Paraffin-Embedded Tissue. *Federation Proc.* **9,** 34.

Dushman, S. 1949. *Scientific Foundations of Vacuum Technique.* John Wiley and Sons, New York.

Emmel, V. M. 1946. The Intracellular Distribution of Alkaline Phosphatase Activity Following Various Methods of Histologic Fixation. *Anat. Record* **95,** 159–175.

Engel, M. B. 1948. Glycogen and Carbohydrate-Protein Complex in the Developing Teeth of the Rat. *J. Dental Research* **27,** 681–692.

Engel, M. B. 1950. The Softening and Solution of the Dentin in Caries. *J. Am. Dental Assoc.* **40,** 284–294.

Engström, A. 1952. X-Ray Absorption Methods in Histochemistry. *Lab. Invest.* **1,** 278–282.

Faraday Society 1950. *Spectroscopy and Molecular Structure and Optical Methods of Investigating Cell Structure.* Aberdeen University Press, Aberdeen, Scotland.

Farr, R. S. 1951. Experiments on the Fate of the Lymphocyte. *Anat. Record* **109,** 515–533.

Fischer, A. 1899. *Fixierung, Färbung und Bau des Protoplasmas.* Gustav Fischer, Jena.

Flosdorf, E. W. 1949. *Freeze-Drying.* Reinhold Publishing Corp., New York.

Frenkel, J. 1946. *Kinetic Theory of Liquids.* Oxford University Press, London.

Fullam, E. F., and Gessler, A. E. 1946. A High Speed Microtome for the Electron Microscope. *Rev. Sci. Instr.* **17,** 23–35.

Gersh, I. 1932. The Altmann Technique for Fixation by Drying while Freezing. *Anat. Record* **53,** 309–337.

Gersh, I. 1934. The Tubular Elimination of Phenol Red in the Rabbit Kidney. *Am. J. Physiol.* **108,** 355–359.

Gersh, I. 1938a. Improved Histochemical Methods for Chloride, Phosphate-Carbonate and Potassium Applied to Skeletal Muscle. *Anat. Record* **70,** 311–329.

Gersh, I. 1938b. Histochemical Studies on the Fate of Colloidal Calcium Phosphate in the Rat. *Anat. Record* **70,** 331–349.

Gersh, I. 1948. Application in Pathology of the Method of Fixation by Freezing and Drying of Tissues. *Bull. Intern. Assoc. Med. Museums* **28,** 179–185.

Gersh, I. 1949. A Protein Component of the Golgi Apparatus. *Arch. Pathol.* **47,** 99–109.

Gersh, I. 1950a. Glycoproteins in the Thyroid Gland of Rats. *J. Endocrinol.* **6,** 282–287.

Gersh, I. 1950b. Ground Substance and the Plasticity of Connective Tissues. *Harvey Lectures, Ser.* **45,** 211–241.

Gersh, I., and Baker, R. F. 1943. Total Protein and Organic Iodine in the Colloid of Individual Follicles of the Thyroid Gland of the Rat. *J. Cellular Comp. Physiol.* **21,** 213–227.

Gersh, I., and Bodian, D. 1943. Some Chemical Mechanisms in Chromatolysis. *J. Cellular Comp. Physiol.* **21,** 253–279.

Gersh, I., and Caspersson, T. 1940. Total Protein and Organic Iodine in the Colloid and Cells of Single Follicles of the Thyroid Gland. *Anat. Record* **78,** 303–319.

Gersh, I., and Catchpole, H. R. 1949. The Organization of Ground Substance and Basement Membrane and Its Significance in Tissue Injury, Disease and Growth. *Am. J. Anat.* **85,** 457–521.

Gersh, I., and Fry, W. Action of Ultrasonics on Nerve Cells. In preparation.

Gersh, I., Hawkinson, G. E., and Rathbun, E. N. 1944. Tissue and Vascular Bubbles after Decompression from High Pressure Atmospheres—Correlation of Specific Gravity with Morphological Changes. *J. Cellular Comp. Physiol.* **24,** 35–70.

Gersh, I., and Stieglitz, E. J. 1934a. Histochemical Studies on the Mammalian Kidney. I. The Glomerular Elimination of Ferrocyanide in the Rabbit, and Some Related Problems. *Anat. Record* **58,** 349–367.

Gersh, I., and Stieglitz, E. J. 1934b. II. The Glomerular Elimination of Uric Acid in the Rabbit. *Anat. Record* **58,** 349–367.

Gersh, I., and Still, M. A. 1945. Blood Vessels in Fat Tissue. Relation to Problems of Gas Exchange. *J. Exptl. Med.* **81,** 219–232.

Gersh, I., and Tarr, A. De L. 1935. The So-Called Hyaline Bodies of Herring in the Posterior Lobe of the Hypophysis. *Anat. Record* **63,** 231–238.

Glick, D., and Malmstrom, B. G. 1952. Simple and Efficient Freezing-Drying Apparatus for the Preparation of Embedded Tissue. *Exptl. Cell Research* **3,** 125–135.

Godlewski, H. 1938. Quelques observations concernant la microincinération effectuée à l'aide d'un dispositif nouveau permettant le contrôle direct de ce processus. *Bull. histol. appl.* **15,** 245–264.

Goodspeed, T. H., and Uber, F. M. 1934. Application of the Altmann Freezing-Drying Technique to Plant Cytology. *Proc. Natl. Acad. Sci.* **20,** 495–501.

Goodspeed, T. H., Uber, F. M., and Avery, P. 1935. Application of the Altmann Freezing-Drying Technique to Plant Cytology. III. Chromosome Structure in *Lillium longiflorum. Univ. Calif. (Berkeley) Publs. Botany* **18,** 33–43.

Guthrie, A., and Wakerling, R. K. 1949. *Vacuum Equipment and Techniques.* McGraw-Hill Book Co., New York.

Hack, M. H. 1952. A New Histochemical Technique for Lipides Applied to Plasmal. *Anat. Record* **112,** 275–302.

Hardy, W. B. 1899. On the Structure of Cell Protoplasm. *J. Physiol. (London)* **24,** 158–210.

Harris, J. E., Sloane, J. F., and King, D. T. 1950. New Technique in Autoradiography. *Nature* **166,** 25–26.

Harter, B. T. 1948. Glycogen and Carbohydrate-Protein Complexes in the Ovary of the White Rat during the Oestrus Cycle. *Anat. Record* **102,** 349–367.

Heller-Steinberg, M. 1951. Ground Substance, Bone Salts, and Cellular Activity in Bone Formation and Destruction. *Am. J. Anat.* **89,** 347–379.

Hoerr, N. L. 1936a. Cytological Studies by the Altmann-Gersh Freezing-Drying Method. *Anat. Record* **65,** 293–313.

Hoerr, N. L. 1936b. Cytological Studies by the Altmann-Gersh Freezing-Drying Method. III. The Preexistence of Neurofibrillae and Their Disposition in the Nerve Fiber. *Anat. Record* **66,** 81–90.

Hoerr, N. L. 1936c. Cytological Studies by the Altmann-Gersh Freezing-Drying Method. IV. The Structure of the Myelin Sheath of Nerve Fibers. *Anat. Record* **66,** 91–95.

Holt, M. W., Cowing, R. F., and Warren, S. 1949. Preparation of Radioautographs of Tissues without Loss of Water-Soluble $P^{32}$. *Science* **110,** 328–329.

Holt, M. W., Sommers, S. C., and Warren, S. 1952. Preparation of Tissue Sections for Quantitative Histochemical Studies. *Anat. Record* **112,** 177–186.

Holt, M. W., and Warren, S. 1951. Radioautographic Solubility Studies of $I^{131}$ and $P^{32}$ in Frozen-Dehydrated Tissues. *Proc. Soc. Exptl. Biol. Med.* **76,** 4–9.

Hydén, H. 1943. Protein Metabolism in the Nerve Cell during Growth and Function. *Acta Physiol. Scand.* **6,** *Suppl.* 17.

Kennard, E. H. 1938. *Kinetic Theory of Gases.* McGraw-Hill Book Co., New York.

Kramers, H., and Stemerding, S. 1951. The Sublimation of Ice in Vacuum. *Appl. Sci. Research* **3,** 73–82.

Leblond, C. P. 1943. Locating Iodine in Tissues Autographically, Especially after Fixation by Freezing and Drying. *Stain Technology* **18,** 159–164.

Lev, M., and Saphir, O. 1951. Endophlebohypertrophy and Phlebosclerosis. *Arch. Pathol.* **51,** 154–178.

Lewis, W. H. 1926. Cultivation of Embryonic Heart Muscle. *Contribs. Embryol.* **18,** No. **90,** 1–21.

Luyet, B. J. 1951. Survival of Cells, Tissues and Organisms after Ultra-Rapid Freezing, in *Freezing and Drying.* Edited by R. J. C. Harris. The Institute of Biology, London. Pp. 77–98.

Malmstrom, B. G. 1951. Theoretical Considerations of the Rate of Dehydration by Histological Freezing-Drying. *Exptl. Cell Research* **2,** 688–692.

Mancini, R. E. 1948. Histochemical Study of Glycogen in Tissues. *Anat. Record* **101,** 149–159.

Marshall, J. M. 1951. Localization of Adrenocorticotrophic Hormone by Histochemical and Immunochemical Methods. *J. Exptl. Med.* **94,** 21–30.

Mendelow, H., and Hamilton, J. B. 1950. A New Technique for Rapid Freezing and Dehydration of Tissues for Histology and Histochemistry. *Anat. Record* **107,** 443–451.

Mirsky, A. E. 1951. Some Enzymes of Isolated Nuclei. *Cold Spring Harbor Symposia* **16,** 481–482.

Packer, D. M., and Scott, G. H. 1942. A Cryostat of New Design for Low Temperature Tissue Dehydration. *J. Tech. Methods* **22,** 85–96.

Pease, D. C., and Baker, R. F. 1949a. Preliminary Investigations of Chromosomes and Genes with the Electron Microscope. *Science* **109,** 8–10.

Pease, D. C., and Baker, R. F. 1949b. The Fine Structure of Mammalian Skeletal Muscle. *Am. J. Anat.* **84,** 175–200.

Rappaport, B. Z., Samter, M., Catchpole, H. R., and Schiller, F. 1953. The Mucoproteins of the Nasal Mucosa of Allergic Patients before and after Treatment with Corticotropin. *J. Allergy.* **24,** 35–51.

Robins, E., and Lowry, O. H. 1951. Microdetermination of Phospholipids and Sphingolipids in Brain. *Federation Proc.* **10,** 238.

Schlegel, J. V. 1949. Demonstration of Blood Vessels and Lymphatics with a Fluorescent Dye in Ultraviolet Light. *Anat. Record* **105,** 433–443.

Scott, G. H. 1934. A Critical Study and Review of the Method of Microincineration. *Protoplasma* **20,** 133–151.

Scott, G. H. 1943. Mineral Distribution in the Cytoplasm. *Biol. Symposia* **10,** 277–289.

Scott, G. H., and Hoerr, N. L. 1950. Drying: Frozen-Dehydration Method for Histologic Fixation, in *Medical Physics,* Vol. II. Edited by O. Glasser. The Year Book Publishers, Chicago. Pp. 292–296.

Scott, G. H., and Packer, D. M. 1939a. The Electron Microscope as an Analytical Tool for the Localization of Minerals in Biological Tissues. *Anat. Record* **74,** 17–29.

Scott, G. H., and Packer, D. M. 1939b. An Electron Microscope Study of Magnesium and Calcium in Striated Muscle. *Anat. Record* **74,** 31–45.

Scott, G. H., and Williams, P. S. 1936. A Simplified Cryostat for the Dehydration of Frozen Tissues. *Anat. Record* **66,** 475–481.

Simpson, W. L. 1941a. An Experimental Analysis of the Altmann Technique of Freezing-Drying. *Anat. Record* **80,** 173–189.

Simpson, W. L. 1941b. The Application of the Altmann Method to the Study of the Golgi Apparatus. *Anat. Record* **80,** 329–345.

Sjöstrand, F. 1944. Über die Eigenfluoreszenz tierischer Gewebe mit besonderer Berücksichtigung der Säugetierniere. *Acta Anat. Suppl.* 1.

Sjöstrand, F. 1951. Freeze-Drying of Tissues for Cell Analysis by Light and Electron Microscopy, in *Freezing and Drying.* Edited by R. J. C. Harris. The Institute of Biology, London. Pp. 177–188.

Stephenson, J. L. 1953. Theory of the Vacuum Drying of Frozen Tissue. *Bull. Math. Biophys.* **15:** 411–429.

Stephenson, J. L. 1954. Theory for the Design of Apparatus for Drying Frozen Tissues. *Bull. Math. Biophys.* **16:** 23–43.

Stowell, R. E. 1951. A Modified Freezing-Drying Apparatus for Tissues. *Stain Technol.* **26,** 105–108.

Strominger, J. L., and Lowry, O. H. 1952. Microchemical Determination of Several Dehydrogenase Enzymes in Rabbit Brain. *Federation Proc.* **11,** 295.

Strong, J. S. 1938. *Procedures in Experimental Physics.* Prentice-Hall, New York.

Sylvèn, B. 1951. Effects of Freezing and Drying Compared with Common Fixation Procedures, in *Freezing and Drying.* Edited by R. J. C. Harris. The Institute of Biology, London. Pp. 169–176.

Taylor, A. C. 1944. Apparatus for the Freezing-Drying of Tissues for Storage. *J. Lab. Clin. Med.* **29,** 657–663.

Vilstrup, T. 1950. *Studies on the Structure and Function of the Semicircular Canals.* Hansens, Copenhagen.

Wang, K. J., and Grossman, M. I. 1949a. A Simplified Vacuum Dehydration Technique for the Preparation of Sections by Freezing-Drying. *J. Lab. Clin. Med.* **34,** 292–296.

Wang, K. J., and Grossman, M. I. 1949b. Histochemical Study of Alkaline Phosphatase in Tissue Prepared by the Freezing-Drying Method. *Anat. Record* **104,** 79–87.

Yarwood, J. 1945. *High Vacuum Technique.* John Wiley and Sons, New York.

# Author Index

Numbers in italics indicate the page on which the reference is listed at the end of the article.

# Subject Index

## A

## E

F

G

O



P

T

U



V